CHEMISTRY:
a search for understanding

laboratory manual

Holt, Rinehart and Winston of Canada, Limited
Toronto   Montreal

H. D. Webber, M.Sc., F.C.I.C
Associate Professor Curriculum and
Instruction (Chemistry)
Science Department
Althouse College of Education
University of Western Ontario
London, Ontario

G. R. Billings, B.Sc., M.C.I.C.
Head of The Science Department
Oakridge Secondary School
London, Ontario

R. A. Hill, B.A.Sc., M.C.I.C.
Vice-Principal
Sir Frederick Banting Secondary School
London, Ontario

Cover Design: Ralph Campbell

Art Work: Loates Visual Arts

ISBN 0-03-922241-1

Printed in Canada
2 3 4 5   74 73

PREFACE

It is our firm contention that any introductory course in chemistry is meaningless if practical laboratory experience does not form an integral part of the course.

The purpose of this laboratory program is fourfold:

1. to have students recognize the fundamental fact that chemistry is an experimental science
2. to encourage students to acquire an understanding of chemistry by involving themselves directly in experimental work
3. to illustrate the difference between observation and interpretation
4. to develop some facility in handling basic laboratory techniques and apparatus.

The laboratory manual is divided into four parts:

I The Laboratory Program

A The Student in the Laboratory

In this section are contained a brief discussion of the correct scientific approach and suggestions for laboratory sessions and record keeping.

B Safety in the Laboratory

The standard basic precautions exercised in any elementary chemistry laboratory are outlined. A few first aid procedures are also included.

C Working in the Laboratory

Basic laboratory techniques are described in this section, including the operation of the gas burner, the handling of chemicals, gravimetric and volumetric operations and glass manipulation.

II Experiments

These experiments have been selected to develop the important principles of general chemistry.

III Guide to the Laboratory Sessions

This section is intended to aid the teacher in preparing for the laboratory periods.

IV The Appendix

The appendices provide general reference materials of use to students following the laboratory program.

The order of the experiments follows the organization of the textbook—Chemistry: A Search For Understanding. The laboratory manual should, nonetheless, be suitable for use with *any* high school chemistry text. Experiments have been selected, designed and tested for a course that allows generously for student laboratory work. Many of the experiments have been designed to precede the class discussion of the concept being investigated. This provides an element of discovery for the students. In the process of discovering regularities, making generalizations which lead to the development of concepts and principles and seeking explanations, students learn many of the facts of descriptive chemistry. These facts provide important background information and give more meaning to classroom discussion.

Numerous experiments have been included which are related to the work on atomic structure and periodic classification. Such experiments provide a basis for the development of ideas, and facilitate the understanding of difficult concepts. They also provide a means of testing the validity of the concepts developed. Some of these laboratory experiences are not "chemical experiments" in the strict sense of the term. They are designed to follow the class discussion of a concept and to clarify the students' understanding of that concept. The majority of the experiments are quantitative in nature. The emphasis is on the importance of careful observation and accurate measurement. As a result, students are provided with an opportunity to evaluate the quality of their laboratory technique by comparing their experimental results with the accepted values. A number of experiments also involve work with unknowns. This work with unknowns is intended to increase the students' interest and enthusiasm and will to some extent foster a spirit of the excitement of scientific discovery.

Many more experiments have been included than can possibly be performed in one year. This, we hope, will permit some variation in the laboratory program from year to year. A few of the experiments have sections that are repeated two or more times in different contexts in the laboratory manual. This was done so that the teacher might choose for himself at what stage in the course these procedures would be most useful in the students' development.

Wherever it is appropriate, experiments are characterized by the following approach:

1. A general discussion which provides some background information and introduces the students to the experiment.

2. Explicit procedures with an emphasis on safety.

3. Clear, simple diagrams of experimental apparatus.

4. Data tables listing the data to be recorded and the calculations to be made.

5. Questions for discussion which are designed to help students (a) interpret experimental results, (b) further develop a concept, (c) apply a concept and (d) evaluate their understanding of the experimental work by applying principles associated with the experiments in new situations.

We have attempted to provide clear, concise instructions for the experiments which emphasize the importance of safety in the laboratory. At the same time we have tried to avoid being overly pedantic in order to provide some opportunity for the students to exercise themselves mentally as well as physically in the laboratory. With a few exceptions, all of the experiments have been designed to be performed in a forty-five to fifty minute laboratory period using inexpensive equipment. Where more than 45 minutes is required, the experiment can easily be broken and continued in a later laboratory period. Chemicals, other required materials and complete instructions for the preparation of all solutions are given in the guide to the laboratory sessions.

The material in this laboratory manual is presented in terms of oxidation state, mole and molarity.

H.D.W.
G.R.B.
R.A.H.

Table of Contents

Preface

I The Laboratory Program

II Experiments

Introduction to Experimental Work in Chapter 5

PHOTOGRAPH CREDITS

The authors and the publisher would like to thank the following companies and people for their co-operation in supplying the photographs which appear in this manual:

Fisher Scientific Company Limited
O. H. Johns Scientific
Sargent-Welch Scientific Company of Canada Limited
Scarborough College (University of Toronto)

I The Laboratory Program

A THE STUDENT IN THE LABORATORY

The experiments in this laboratory manual have been designed to actively involve you in the study of chemistry. In following this laboratory program you will learn, by observation, how matter behaves under different conditions. Each experiment has been selected to lead you to at least one fundamental of modern chemistry. It follows that you will obtain maximum benefit from your laboratory experience if you follow the directions carefully, observe what actually happens and accurately and objectively record these observations. *Objectively* is a key word in all these exercises. It is important to forget all preconceived notions of what is "supposed to happen". What *does* happen in a particular experiment, when you do it, *is* what is supposed to happen. Never consider observed behaviour as being wrong. If an observation seems unreasonable, look for an explanation for its behaviour. Discuss the problem with your fellow students and with your teacher. If there is any doubt about the accuracy of your results, repeat the experiment to justify your findings. A great deal can be learned from such an approach. You will not only develop your ability for critical scientific observation but also for analysis and interpretation of results. This is a most important phase of experimental chemistry.

One of the main purposes of the laboratory program will be to distinguish between experimental observations and theoretical concepts based upon these observations. Emphasis is placed upon the fact that there is a degree of uncertainty associated with all scientific measurements. All concepts and principles are, therefore, valid only within the limits placed on them by the experimental observations upon which they are based.

Every laboratory experience, if it is to have maximum effectiveness, should involve three steps: (1) a pre-laboratory session, (2) a laboratory session and (3) a post-laboratory session.

The Pre-Laboratory Session

The purpose of the pre-laboratory session is to prepare for the experiment prior to the actual laboratory period. This preparation includes reading the experiment to determine what is involved, preparing appropriate data tables in your notebook for recording results during the laboratory session and discussing the experiment. This discussion, directed by your teacher, will vary considerably, depending on the nature of the experiment, but will probably include some background information, references to difficult parts of the procedure, cautions and an open question period.

The Laboratory Session

As soon as the pre-laboratory session is complete you are ready to begin the laboratory investigation. Make a conscientious effort to *think about the overall experiment in broad general terms as you carry out each individual step of the procedure.* That is, think about what you are doing as you procede and consider the significance of the results you obtain. Avoid reaching the end of the laboratory session having mechanically "completed" the experiment and having not the slightest idea of the significance of the whole exercise. This will only be possible if your pre-laboratory preparation was adequate.

The work to be covered during the laboratory session may be assigned in a number of ways. Members of the class may work in groups where (1) different members of a group work on different parts of the experiment (2) different groups work on different parts of the experiment. In either of these cases, students exchange data to compile a complete set of results for the experiment. In some situations you may work individually on experiments. Frequently it will be necessary to work in pairs and share equipment with a partner. In the latter case the data obtained will also be shared.

Regardless of the manner in which the experimental work is apportioned you must assume an active role in the laboratory work. Whether you are working in groups or pairs the work responsibilities should be divided to give each person an opportunity to become proficient in all laboratory operations used in the experiment. Work carefully and safely with laboratory equipment and chemicals. Observations and measurements should be recorded directly in your notebook. From the experimental results you may be able to observe regularities and arrive at a logical explanation for what you have observed.

The Post-Laboratory Session

Having completed the laboratory work, prior to any post-laboratory discussion you are expected to process and interpret your experimental data using the instructions and questions in the laboratory manual as a guide. Sometimes the observations recorded in your notebook will have little apparent meaning until they are transformed to secondary data by mathematical calculations, graphing or some other means. Often, both the initial observations and secondary data will be reported in tabular or graphical form. Through the study of this processed data and a consideration of its meaning, you may be led to the discovery of a regularity which in turn may suggest a generalization. The generalization may be tested by further experimentation. As you process and interpret data, search continually for explanations of the regularities that you are discovering. Keep asking yourself the question "why?"

Classroom discussion should now provide an opportunity for individuals or groups to compare processed data, interpretations and conclusions. This discussion should provide additional information about the procedure you carried out or about a related procedure. In light of this additional information you may review your own work and decide on changes in your interpretation. Your data may not always agree with that of your classmates who have performed the same experiment. The reasons for these differences are not always easy to determine. Discuss these differences with your teacher and with other members of the class. Do not hesitate to repeat the experiment in order to justify your work.

The results of your experiment and those of other members of the class may suggest additional investigations that could assist you in answering the original question. Other questions may have arisen during the experiment. Feel free to design and carry out further experiments of your own but always prepare an outline and present it to your teacher for checking, approval and advice before you proceed.

We hope that you will find the work in the laboratory both interesting and instructive. The value that you obtain from this laboratory program will depend largely upon your attitude.

The Laboratory Record Book

You should use a laboratory record book to keep a permanent day by day record of all information obtained in the laboratory investigations. All information associated with each experiment should appear in this notebook. The record should be concise but at the same time complete enough to be understood by the teacher and your fellow students. All entries must be neat, legible and orderly. If it is necessary to delete or change anything, a single line should be neatly drawn through the entry in order that the original writing can still be read. *Never erase initial observations.* A comment in the margin concerning an error or change may be very valuable if the experiment is to be repeated. Where neatness and accuracy conflict, neatness must be sacrificed.

In order to use your time in the laboratory most effectively, you should prepare the laboratory record book to some extent, before the laboratory session. Listed below are some of the entries that might be made prior to the laboratory period.

1. Your name and the date.

2. The title of the experiment.

3. Notes and information requested from the pre-laboratory assignments and discussion.

4. Code numbers or letters of assigned unknowns.

5. Names and quantities of chemicals used.

6. Details of the procedure used.

7. Any necessary data tables for recording results.

While doing the experiment a detailed record of observations, including a precise record of the measurements taken, should be kept in your record book. Never keep these records on loose scraps of paper. Following the experiment entries will be made to interpret the data. Many of these will emerge from the post-laboratory session. These post-laboratory entries may include:

1. A tabular summary of the data collected.

2. A graphical representation of the data.

3. The information gained from processing the data.

4. All calculations; sample calculations only need be included—one for each calculated item. Long hand arithmetic need not be shown.

5. Treatment of errors; sources and magnitudes.

6. The significance of the experimental results.

7. The theoretical and experimental factors that affect the precision of the results.

8. Generalizations or conclusions based upon actual laboratory observations or upon calculations made using the experimental data.

All of these entires will not be made in every experiment. Your teacher will offer guidance in this regard.

When writing your reports, always consult your textbook and other references to obtain additional information related to laboratory problems.

B SAFETY IN THE LABORATORY

Chemistry is an experimental science. Much of your time will be spent performing experiments in the laboratory. The experimental work will be different from any you have done before. The equipment and supplies used in many instances will be unfamiliar to you. Much of the equipment is expensive and many of the chemicals are potentially hazardous in inexperienced hands; therefore they must be treated with care and respect. This is not to imply that chemistry is dangerous and that the chemistry laboratory is a dangerous place. It simply means that the laboratory is a place to be serious and business-like. Safety, your safety and the safety of all persons with whom you are associated in the laboratory is of the utmost importance. The possibility of injury in the laboratory will be minimized if attention is paid to the suggestions listed below. These suggestions, if followed, will lead to the development of safe working habits in the laboratory.

1. Always protect your **clothing** with a laboratory coat or apron.

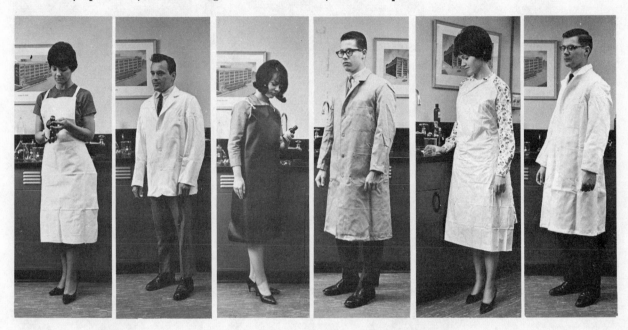

2. Always protect your arms, hands and fingers against heat, chemical action and other potential hazards with rubberized sleeves and gloves. Asbestos gloves used for protection against heat and rubber gloves for protection against chemicals are available.

Rubberized sleeves give $14\frac{1}{2}$ inches of arm protection

3. Your eyes are one of the your most prized possessions. They are particularly susceptible to permanent damage by corrosive chemicals and by flying fragments. When working in the laboratory, always protect your eyes and your face by wearing safety glasses or a face shield.

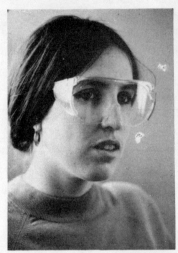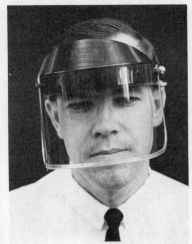

Safety visor covers entire face, lifts out of the way easily

4. Know the location and proper use of the fire extinguishers, fire blanket, safety shower and eye bath in the laboratory. Know the location of the first-aid station. Most accidents in the laboratory are minor but one should always be prepared for serious trouble.

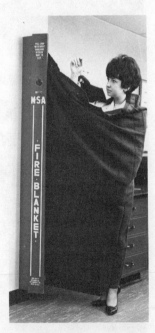

SAFETY IN THE LABORATORY

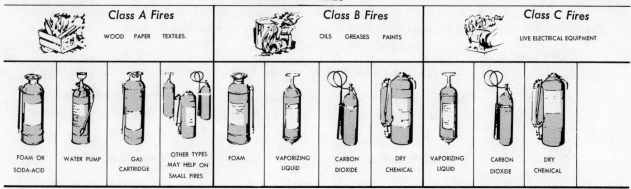

CLASSES OF FIRES

Class A Fires				Class B Fires				Class C Fires		
WOOD PAPER TEXTILES.				OILS GREASES PAINTS				LIVE ELECTRICAL EQUIPMENT		
FOAM OR SODA-ACID	WATER PUMP	GAS CARTRIDGE	OTHER TYPES MAY HELP ON SMALL FIRES	FOAM	VAPORIZING LIQUID	CARBON DIOXIDE	DRY CHEMICAL	VAPORIZING LIQUID	CARBON DIOXIDE	DRY CHEMICAL

Use of proper extinguisher stops fires early

The following is a tentative list of first-aid supplies that should be available in any laboratory first-aid cabinet:

adhesive tape ½″ and 1″

band aids ¾″

gauze bandages 1″ and 2″

gauze pads, sterile

cotton pickers

cotton buds

tongue applicators

stick applicators

safety pins

sodium hydrogen carbonate
    solution 5%

tincture of green soap

alcohol

hydrogen peroxide 3%

olive oil

boric acid solution, saturated

boric acid powder

boric acid ointment

aqueous ammonia 1%

aromatic spirits of ammonia

acetic acid 2%

amyl nitrate capsules

castor oil

cold compress

copper (II) sulphate solution (5%)

scissors and tweezers

eye cup

washaway bottle

tourniquet

tincture of merthiolate

furacin solution

vaseline

Unguentine

sodium hydrogen carbonate powder

egg albumen

magnesium sulphate powder

milk of magnesia

mouth to mouth airway

sodium thiosulphate solution
    (hypo) 5%

sodium sulphate

stainless steel spoon

tannic acid

sodium hydrogen phosphate

soluble starch

butescin picrate ointment

Universal Antidote

2 parts activated charcoal

1 part magnesium oxide

1 part tannic acid

Keep dry until used

5. All chemicals are potentially dangerous. The improper handling of chemicals may lead to serious injury to you and to your classmates. In order to minimize this possibility:

(a) Give full attention to the teacher's discussions and demonstrations.

(b) Read the laboratory instructions carefully and thoughtfully before starting an experiment and determine what precautions must be observed.

(c) No experiment should be carried out in the absence of the teacher.

(d) Unauthorized experiments must never be performed.

(e) Always work quietly, thoughtfully and carefully with as much speed as safety will permit.

(f) Always double check the label on the reagent bottle before using a chemical. If you use the wrong chemical you may cause a serious accident.

(g) Always use only the amounts of chemicals specified in the instructions.

(h) Never taste chemicals or solutions unless you are specifically directed to do so. Assume that all are toxic until proven harmless.

(i) To test the odour of a substance sniff, cautiously; *do not inhale*. Gently waft fumes toward you, keeping your face a safe distance away. If an experiment generates an objectionable gas, conduct the experiment under the fume hood.

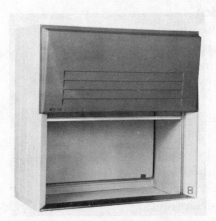

When smelling a substance, use a gentle fanning motion to waft the vapours toward your face. Wear protective glasses when working with potentially dangerous chemicals.

(j) When diluting concentrated acids and preparing solutions where heat is evolved as the solution forms, one should add the solute slowly, with constant stirring, to the solvent. When diluting concentrated acids, always add the concentrated acid to the water. *Never* add water to the concentrated acid.

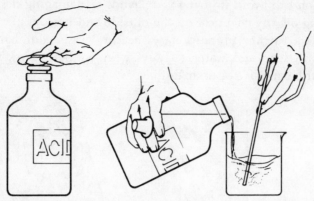

(k) When pouring a solution or removing a chemical from a reagent bottle, hold the stopper between two fingers, as above. If it is a flat-topped stopper, place it on the table beside the appropriate bottle with the stopper up, as shown in the diagram. This avoids mixing the stoppers and consequently the chemicals. Furthermore, it avoids contaminating the chemicals with substances from the table surface on which the stopper may be placed.

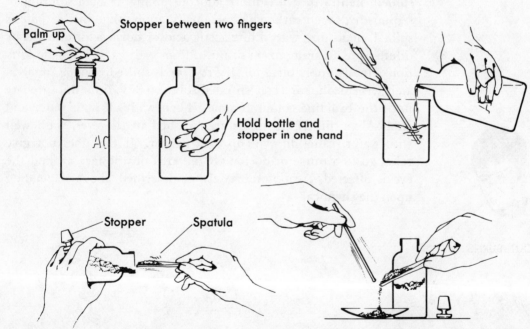

Techniques for removing a sample from a stock bottle. Be sure to close the reagent bottle tightly with the correct lid or stopper.

(l) Always cap or stopper reagent bottles securely before returning them to their proper places in the laboratory.

(m) To prevent contamination, never return unused chemicals to stock bottles.

(n) You can avoid injuring your hands or damaging desk tops by rinsing off any chemical on the outside and bottom of reagent bottles. As a further precautionary measure wash your hands frequently with soap and water. Always wear rubber gloves when working with corrosive or toxic liquids.

(o) If you spill or splash any corrosive chemical on your skin or in your eyes, immediately flood the splashed area with water. If *acid* is spilled, neutralize with dilute aqueous ammonia or a solution of sodium hydrogen carbonate and finally apply olive oil. If *base* is spilled, neutralize with dilute acetic acid or boric acid followed by dilute aqueous ammonia or dilute sodium hydrogen carbonate solution. Finally apply olive oil. If *bromine* is spilled, sponge immediately with alcohol or a concentrated solution of sodium thiosulphate until the bromine colour is gone. Then wash off with water and apply olive oil. If chemicals are splashed in the eyes, wash well with water, using an eye cup or a beaker. If this does not give relief go to a nurse or doctor. If the area on the face around the eye is affected, treat immediately as described above depending upon the chemical.

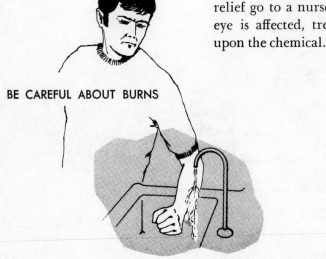

BE CAREFUL ABOUT BURNS

IF CHEMICAL GETS IN YOUR EYES

NOTIFY YOUR TEACHER OF ANY ACCIDENT NO MATTER HOW MINOR

(p) Clean up mercury spills and any other chemical spills immediately in order to avoid injury from toxic vapours or chemical burns. Use a small aspirator bottle with a capillary tube and a suction pump to recover spills of mercury.

If small drops of mercury spill into inaccessible cracks, cover the area with a polysulphide solution to form mercury sulphide or with zinc to form an amalgam. Store mercury in strong stoppered bottles. Vapourization can be controlled by keeping a layer of dilute sulphuric acid over the mercury.

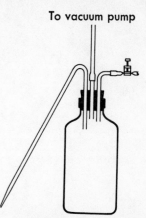

To vacuum pump

Aspirator bottle to recover mercury spills

(q) Many other chemicals are poisonous and potentially hazardous. Keep these materials in tightly stoppered bottles and handle them with care. Avoid bringing such materials into contact with the skin and do not inhale their vapours. Whenever possible, work with these materials in a fume hood. Some of the more common of these substances are carbon disulphide, carbon tetrachloride, benzene, phenol, aniline, white phosphorus, sodium, potassium and arsenic.

TOXIC FUMES

(r) When heating a solid or a liquid in a test tube, keep the tube in constant motion and *do not* point the mouth of the tube toward anyone. Never look down into the mouth of a test tube while heating it. Always hold the tube at an angle and heat the sides of the tube as well as the bottom. If only the bottom of the tube containing a liquid is heated, bubbles of vapour are often produced at that point. The bubbles form and suddenly expand near the bottom of the tube causing the liquid to *bump*. That is, the liquid spatters or spurts out of the tube. This problem is minimized by placing boiling chips in the liquid being heated.

(s) To avoid fire and possible asphyxiation, always be certain that your burner tubing is tightly attached and does not leak gas.

(t) Never use a gas flame for heating flammable liquids. Always use a heating mantle or a hot plate.

Heat liquids cautiously to avoid bumping.

(u) Never allow strong oxidizing agents (nitrates, chlorates, perchlorates, permanganates, iodates, etc.) to come in contact with organic materials. When disposing of such chemicals dissolve and dilute them with water and then flush them down the drain with a continuous flow of cold tap water.

(v) Dry ice (solid carbon dioxide) can be a serious hazard. It can produce serious *frost burn* or *suffocation*. Always handle dry ice with heavy gloves or tongs.

(w) Always discard liquids or solids found in *unlabelled* bottles. Never guess at the nature of the substance.

Throw away the contents of unlabelled containers

Don't drink from beakers

Never taste any chemical

Smell a chemical only when necessary

6. Improper or careless handling of glass containers, and in particular glass tubing and glass rods, may also result in serious injury. In order to minimize the possibility of serious injury remember:

(a) Hot glass looks like cold glass and can cause severe burns. Be cautious when handling glass that has just been heated. Always give it time to cool. If in doubt as to the temperature of any glass use tongs to move it. If you forget and burn yourself, sponge the area with picric acid solution and immediately apply burn ointment. If it is a serious burn, see a doctor.

(b) Always fire polish a piece of glass tubing or rod before using it. First remove any jagged edges by stroking the cut end of the tubing or rod with a wire screen. Now hold the glass in a hot flame until the sharp edges have fused into rounded surfaces. Fire polishing takes only a few seconds and may prevent serious cuts.

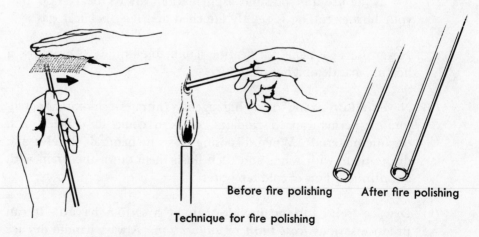

Before fire polishing   After fire polishing

Technique for fire polishing

Remove jagged edges by stroking the cut end of the glass tubing with a wire screen.

(c) When inserting glass tubing into cork or rubber stoppers always (i) lubricate the tube and stopper with water, soap solution, glycerine or vaseline; (ii) wrap the stopper and tubing in a towel; (iii) grasp the tubing close to the stopper to reduce leverage on the glass and, with a *twisting motion*, guide the tubing into the stopper. Never force glass tubing into a stopper.

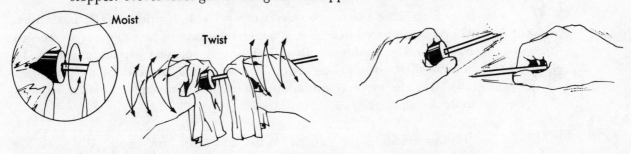

When inserting a piece of glass tubing, funnel or thermometer into a stopper, keep your hands close together and work the glass using a gentle twisting motion. Never force glass tubing into a stopper.

or

(i) use a metal tube; for example, a cork borer; (ii) slide the stopper onto the end of the metal tube; (iii) slide the glass tubing inside the metal tube to the correct depth; (iv) grasp the glass tube and stopper in one hand and pull the metal tube out with the other; the stopper will be left on the glass tube; (v) to readjust the position of the stopper, simply insert the metal tube over the glass through the stopper again, adjust the glass and remove the metal tube as before; (vi) to remove glass tubing, use the metal tube in the same manner.

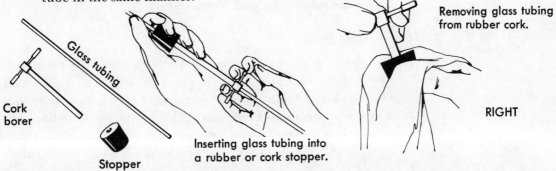

Inserting glass tubing into a rubber or cork stopper.

Removing glass tubing from rubber cork.

RIGHT

(d) Never work with glass equipment that is cracked or broken. Throw it away.

(e) If a glass stopper sticks in a bottle, gently tap the stopper with a wooden object. If it still sticks, consult your teacher.

(f) To remove glass tubing from a stopper or some rubber or plastic fitting, lubricate the tubing by prying a bit of rubber or plastic away from the glass and dropping in a bit of water or glycerine.

WRONG

Don't twist or pull
glass tubing.

Now twist off the stopper or fitting. Relubrication may be necessary. Never try to force glass tubing. If it is really stuck, cut the stopper off with a razor blade in a holder or a knife.

ACCIDENTS AND FIRST AID IN THE LABORATORY

No matter how careful we are, accidents will happen in the laboratory. Always be prepared to act when a mishap occurs. The following treatments are first-aid procedures only. Professional medical attention should be summoned at once for any serious injury. These suggestions are concerned only with the more common situations that you may encounter in your study of chemistry.

1. *Shock*: Make the patient lie flat and keep him warm. When he has sufficiently recovered, give him a mild stimulant such as hot coffee or tea.

2. *Cuts due to broken glass*: Wash the cut with warm water and soap *after making sure that no glass remains in the wound.* Apply a prepared sterilized dressing or boracic ointment on lint. Bandage the wound firmly.

3. (a) *Caustic alkali in the mouth: for example, sodium or potassium hydroxide*: Rinse the mouth immediately with dilute acetic acid.

   (b) *Acid in the mouth: for example, hydrochloric, sulphuric or nitric acids*: Rinse the mouth immediately with dilute sodium hydrogen carbonate solution or with limewater.

4. *Heat or Scald Burns*:

   (a) *Heat*: Clean the burned area gently with cool soap solution then apply three percent hydrogen peroxide solution with a pad of cotton. Rinse the burn with cool water, dry it and cover it with a layer of furacin solution, vaseline or a mixture of sodium hydrogen carbonate and an ointment (such as Unguentine). Take the patient to a physician for observation and further treatment.

   (b) *Scald*: This type of burn should be treated by a physician as soon as possible.

5. *Substances on the skin*: Many substances on contact with skin cause serious burns or very unpleasant sores which heal very slowly. If any one of these substances contact the skin, immediate action is necessary. Three substances which behave this way on contact with skin are white phosphorus, phenol (carbolic acid) and hydrofluoric acid.

(a) *White phosphorus*: Keep the affected area very wet and, if possible, under water. Pick out any small pieces of phosphorus with tweezers. Sponge the wound, first with sodium hydrogen carbonate solution, and then with dilute copper (II) sulphate solution. Finally treat the wound as outlined above for burns.

(b) *Phenol (carbolic acid)*: Wash the chemical off immediately with water. Treat the burned area with very dilute bromine water. Finally, wash the burned area with water and cover it with glycerine.

(c) *Hydrofluoric Acid*: Treat the affected area immediately with calcium hydroxide solution (limewater).

6. *Inhalation of Noxious Gases*: Discomfort from this cause should be relieved by sniffing solid ammonium carbonate or dilute aqueous ammonia. This treatment is effective for bromine vapour, chlorine gas, halogen hydrides, nitric acid vapour, nitrogen dioxide, sulphur dioxide and hydrogen sulphide.

7. *Poisons Swallowed*: The patient should either be given an emetic (commonly a tablespoonful of common salt in a tumbler of water), or a substance which will convert the poison to a harmless compound. The universal antidote previously described is often administered. An emetic should never be given when a corrosive substance has been swallowed because the damage done on the way down will be intensified on the way up.

Antidotes for poisons.

(a) *Acids (strong mineral)*: Administer a suspension of magnesium oxide or limewater to neutralize the acid without producing a gas.

(b) *Alkalis*: Administer a very dilute acetic acid solution.

(c) *Arsenic*: Administer iron (III) hydroxide in any form as quickly as possible. The hydroxide must be freshly precipitated.

(d) *Barium and Lead (soluble compounds)*: Administer sodium sulphate decahydrate (Glauber's salt) or magnesium sulphate heptahydrate (Epsom salt) in order to convert the barium and lead to their insoluble sulphates.

(e) *Cyanide*: Administer freshly precipitated iron (II) hydroxide as quickly as possible.

(f) *Iodine*: Administer a thin starch paste, a sodium hydrogen carbonate solution or a suspension of magnesium oxide.

(g) *Mercury (II) Chloride (Corrosive sublimate)*: Administer raw white of egg or sodium thiosulphate (hypo) solution.

(h) *Oxalic Acid (or soluble oxalates)*: Administer slaked lime (lime-water) or precipitated chalk to form insoluble calcium oxalate.

(i) *Phenol (Carbolic acid)*: Administer magnesium sulphate hepta-hydrate or limewater followed by olive oil.

(j) *Silver nitrate*: Administer a dilute solution of sodium chloride to form the very insoluble compound, silver chloride.

8. *Burning Clothing or Hair*: Smother the fire with a towel, coat, or something similar. Use what is at hand. A few seconds delay in searching for something more suitable may result in an extremely serious if not a fatal injury.

C WORKING IN THE LABORATORY

You are embarking upon a search for understanding. The laboratory is the place where all chemical discovery is initiated. It is here that you will do experiments, gather data, organize, classify, seek regularities, attempt to explain the regularities and develop the basic concepts and principles which constitute the foundations of modern chemistry. Your experimental study of chemistry should provide the necessary basis for a successful search.

Effective laboratory work requires good working habits, an alertness to possible hazards, and the development of skill in performing a variety of laboratory techniques. All of these require careful training. One of the purposes of any laboratory program is to train you in these important aspects of laboratory work.

Safe Work Habits

The following general suggestions may help to develop safe working habits in the laboratory:

1. Keep the laboratory clean and orderly.

2. Place only the apparatus and chemicals necessary for the experiment on your desk.

3. Avoid breakage, loss of time and possible injury by keeping all equipment as far back from the table edge as possible. Place cylindrical apparatus like thermometers or pipettes on the table at right angles to the edge to prevent them from rolling onto the floor.

4. Give your full attention to the experiment until it is completed. The laboratory is a dangerous place to play the fool.

5. If you are in doubt about any part of the procedure, ask your teacher.

6. When attaching apparatus to a retort stand make sure the centre of gravity is within the base area. For example, a flask should be attached to a retort stand so that it is above the base and not to one side.

7. When lifting or carrying a bottle containing a chemical, always grasp the body of the bottle. Never carry a bottle by its neck or top. A large bottle should be given added support by placing the other hand underneath it.

8. Never leave an experiment that is in progress unattended.

9. *Always* allow sufficient time at the end of a laboratory period for cleaning up and putting clean apparatus back into the locker in an orderly arrangement. Leave desks clean and dry and sinks clean.

10. Lockers should not be crammed with glass equipment. Return all equipment that is not part of the regular locker equipment as soon as it is no longer needed. Before closing a locker or drawer make sure that no glass equipment is sticking out.

11. Flush soluble waste materials down the sink with plenty of water. Deposit other waste materials, except broken glass, in a waste jar provided for this purpose. Deposit broken glass in a separate waste container provided.

12. Remove at once any liquids or solids spilled on the floor or table workspace. Ice cubes, glass beads, glass rods or stoppers left on the floor can be the cause of falls and result in serious injury.

13. Make sure that the gas and the water are turned off before you leave your working area.

14. Wash your hands thoroughly after a laboratory period.

Laboratory Techniques

Facility in performing the laboratory techniques listed below is essential for effective experimental work in the laboratory.

(1.) Measuring Masses of Substances, (2.) Measuring Volumes of Liquids, (3.) Transferring Solids and Liquids, (4.) Operating a Gas Burner, (5.) Glassworking, (6.) Separating a Liquid from a Solid, (7.) Drying of Residues.

1. Measuring of Masses of Substances

This is one of the most common operations in experimental chemistry. It is usually done by comparing the weight of an object with the weight of a known mass. Four types of balances are commonly used for making this comparison. These are the platform balance (Figure I-1), the triple beam balance (Figure I-2), the two-pan analytical balance (Figure I-3) and the open-pan semi-automatic balance (Figure I-4). Although specific instructions must be followed when operating each type of balance, certain general instructions apply to the operation of balances.

(a) Laboratory balances must be protected from abuse and kept clean if they are to operate properly. They are sensitive instruments. Moisture and volatile corrosive chemicals should be kept away from laboratory balances in order to protect them from fumes. Ideally, balances should be kept in a room separate from the laboratory proper where

Figure I-1. *A platform balance.*

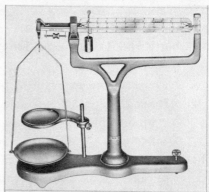

Figure I-2. *A triple beam balance.*

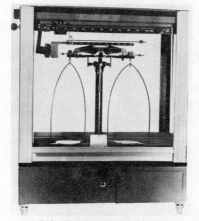

(a) Analytical balance

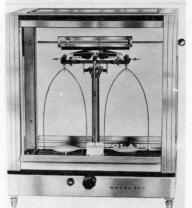

(b) Chainomatic balance

Figure I-3. *Two-pan analytical balances.*

(a) Mettler H-15   (b) Oertling RP20

Figure I-4. *One-pan semi-automatic balances.*

a reasonably constant temperature can be maintained. They should not be placed near a window or radiator and should not be exposed either to direct sunlight or drafts.

(b) Before using any balance, place all masses at the zero position and check to see that the balance pans swing freely. Make sure that the balance is level.

MEASUREMENT OF MASS

(c) Determine the zero point of the balance. The zero point of any balance with a pointer is the estimated rest point of the pointer as it moves back and forth on the scale when there is no load on the balance. This point will not necessarily be located at the centre of the pointer scale (Figure I-5). There is no need to wait for the balance to come to rest before taking the zero point reading.

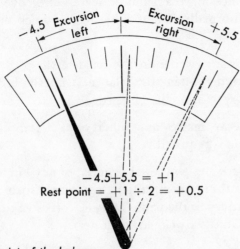

$$-4.5 + 5.5 = +1$$
$$\text{Rest point} = +1 \div 2 = +0.5$$

Figure I-5. *The zero point of the balance.*

(d) When determining the mass of any object using a balance with a pointer, the pointer should oscillate about the same zero point as when there was no load on the balance.

(e) When using a *platform balance,* place the unknown mass on the left-hand pan. Now balance this mass by placing large masses on the right-hand pan and then sliding the masses attached to the cross-beam until the pointer makes equidistant swings to the right and left of the zero point of the balance.

When using a *triple beam* balance, equilibrium is achieved by sliding masses along the three beams until the pointer makes equal swings above and below the zero point of the balance. Always raise the beam and, if possible, support the pan before any substantial mass is placed on the pan, removed from the pan or moved along the beams. Fractional masses can be added to or removed from this beam with the beam released.

Follow a similar procedure when using a two-pan analytical balance. The one-pan semi-automatic balance should be treated the same way when adding or removing masses. However, this balance operates on a different principle from the others. Masses equivalent to the mass of the object are removed from instead of added to the beam. All masses are therefore determined under constant load and the sensitivity of the balance remains constant over the whole range.

Platform balances are capable of measuring mass to a precision of ± 0.1 g. The triple beam balance is capable of measuring mass to a precision of ± 0.01 g. The two-pan analytical balance is capable of measuring mass to a precision of ± 1 mg and ± 0.1 mg depending upon the type. The one-pan semi-automatic balance is capable of measuring mass to a precision of ± 0.1 mg.

(f) Most balances have a metal or agate knife edge. The balance cannot function normally if it is subjected to shock or if the knife edge is dirty.

(g) Use the beam release on the balances to prevent the balance pans from swinging when the balance is not in use. This will prevent unnecessary wear on the knife edge.

(h) Do not leave masses and other objects standing on the pans any longer than is required.

(i) Do not place any powdered material of any kind directly on the pans. Place all substances in suitable containers such as beakers or vials to prevent injury to the pans. Volatile, corrosive liquids and solids must be placed in tightly closed containers.

(j) Never place hot objects on a balance. Anything placed on a balance pan must be at room temperature. Pans may be damaged by hot objects and these objects may also cause convection currents of air around the pans which will interfere with the operation of the balance and produce grossly inaccurate results.

(k) Never overload the balance.

(l) Masses should be handled only with bone or plastic-tipped forceps. In counter-balancing an object the large masses are first tried, and the smaller masses are added in a systematic order. Always use the smallest number of masses possible. Avoid dropping these standard masses. Always double check each determination and record the result in your notebook immediately.

(m) If the balance is not behaving properly or if adjustments are required seek the assistance of your teacher.

2. *Measuring Volumes of Liquids*

The glassware used in measuring volumes of liquids is referred to as volumetric glassware. There are four articles of volumetric glassware that are commonly used: graduated cylinders, volumetric flasks, pipettes and burettes. Some of this glassware is calibrated to *contain* a certain volume of liquid while some is calibrated to *deliver* a certain volume of liquid. Usually this glassware is calibrated at a specific given temperature, 20°C.

The volume in question must be correctly read on a scale which is usually etched into the glass. The surface of most liquids when viewed in any glass vessel is curved. The curved surface is called the *meniscus*. When reading the meniscus in a graduated glass vessel, your eye must be on a line of sight level with the bottom of the curved surface (Figure I-6).

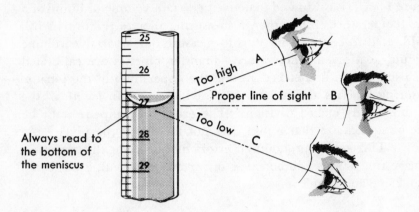

Figure I-6. *Errors due to parallax in reading the level of a liquid in a graduated tube.*

(a) GRADUATED CYLINDERS (GRADUATE)

These vessels are usually calibrated to contain 1 ml, 5 ml, 10 ml, 25 ml, 100 ml, 250 ml, 500 ml, 1000 ml and 2000 ml. They are used for measuring volumes of pure liquids and solutions (Figure I-7).

Figure I-7. *A graduated cylinder.*

(b) VOLUMETRIC FLASKS (Figure I-8)

Volumetric flasks are usually calibrated to contain a certain volume of liquid at a given temperature. The common sizes of volumetric flasks are 50ml, 100 ml, 250 ml, 500 ml, 1000 ml and 2000 ml. Each flask is fitted with a suitable ground glass or plastic stopper and is calibrated with a single line etched on the neck of the flask. This line extends completely around the neck of the flask to avoid errors due to parallax when filling the flask up to the mark. Since the neck of the volumetric flask is comparatively narrow, a small change in volume of the liquid will cause a considerable difference in the height of the meniscus. Thus any error made in adjusting the meniscus to the mark will be very small. The distance from the mark to the stopper is relatively large. This provides sufficient room for mixing a solution after the volume has been brought up to the mark.

A volumetric flask is used to prepare a certain volume of a solution of a known concentration. The required amount of

Figure I-8. *A volumetric flask.*

substance (solute) is measured out and transferred to the flask. Water is added, ideally at the temperature for which the flask is calibrated, until the solution fills the flask up to the mark.

(c)   PIPETTES

There are two common types of pipette. One type, a transfer pipette [Figure I-9(a)], is calibrated to deliver a certain volume of liquid at a given temperature. The other, a measuring pipette [Figure I-9(b)], is calibrated to contain and thus to measure out a variable volume of liquid at a given temperature. Transfer pipettes are calibrated with a single thin line etched around the upper limb of the pipette. Measuring pipettes are calibrated by dividing a given length of the tube into many etched divisions. The orifice of a pipette must be made of such a size that liquid does not flow from the pipette too rapidly. This avoids pronounced errors due to slight differences in drainage time. The common sizes of pipettes are 1 ml, 2 ml, 5 ml, 10 ml, 25 ml and 50 ml.

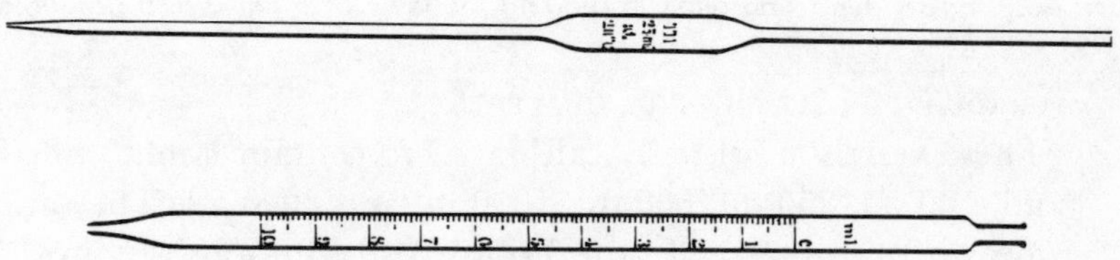

Figure I-9.   *Pipettes.*

(a)   A transfer pipette

(b)   A measuring pipette

Using a pipette
  (i) Clean the pipette with a warm detergent solution.
 (ii) Rinse it thoroughly with tap water followed by distilled water and allow it to drain out as much as possible.
(iii) Before dipping the pipette into a solution, blow out the drop of water remaining in the tip and dry the tip with a piece of filter paper. This will avoid diluting the solution that is to be pipetted.
 (iv) Rinse the pipette thoroughly with two or three small portions of the solution.
  (v) Immerse the stem of the pipette in the liquid. Draw up the liquid carefully into the pipette with a gentle suction action using your mouth or a suction bulb [Figure I-10(a)]. Continue this gentle suction action until the level of the liquid is just above the calibration mark. Hold the liquid at this level by placing your forefinger over the top of the pipette [Figure I-10(b)].

MEASURING OF LIQUIDS

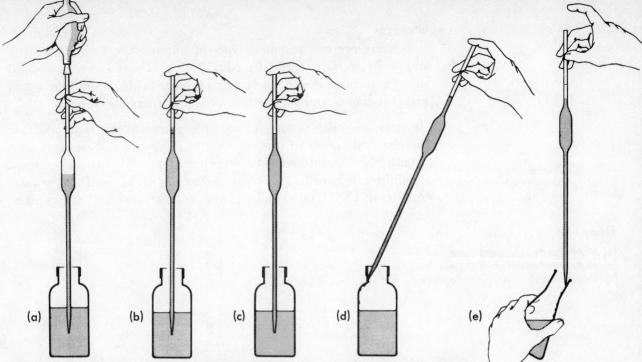

Figure I-10. *The Technique used in pipetting a liquid. Allow 15-20 seconds for drainage after the liquid has stopped flowing. Touch the tip of the pipette against the side of the receiving vessel for a few seconds. Do not blow out the liquid remaining in the tip of the pipette into the receiving vessel.*

Strong suction should never be used. Do not immerse the stem of the pipette unnecessarily far into the solution but be sure that the tip of the pipette is always covered by the solution. If the tip does come out of the solution, the liquid may be drawn up into your mouth with unpleasant results if it is caustic or poisonous. Pipetting by mouth can be extremely dangerous. *Always* use a safety-pipette filler or suction bulb, *not your mouth*, when filling a pipette with poisonous, corrosive or volatile liquids (Figure I-11).

Never measure out the following volatile liquids with a pipette: ether, carbon tetrachloride, chloroform, benzene and aqueous ammonia solution.

(vi) Lower the level of the liquid to the etched mark by carefully admitting air to the top of the tube [Figure I-10 (c)]. Do this by rotating the pipette with your fingers and thumb.

(vii) Transfer the liquid to the receiving vessel [Figure I-10(d)].

(viii) After use, rinse the pipette with distilled water and set in a rack to drain until it is to be used again.

(ix) Practise this pipetting technique using water before using the pipette with any other solution.

Figure I-11. *A suction bulb or safety-pipette filler should always be used to fill a pipette with a corrosive, poisonous or volatile liquid. Never use your mouth.*

(d) BURETTES

There are two common types of burette; the Geissler burette and the Mohr burette (Figure I-12). Both consist of a long, graduated tube of uniform bore with an arrangement at the lower end which makes it easy to control the flow of liquid from the burette.

Burettes are used to deliver variable amounts of liquid and are therefore calibrated with many small divisions. They are used most extensively in titrations. The 50 ml burette, calibrated in tenths of a millilitre, is most frequently used. For micro and semi-micro work, burettes of 1 to 10 ml capacity graduated to 0.01 or 0.02 ml are used.

Figure I-12.

(a) *Mohr burette with glass bead;*
(b) *Mohr burette with pinch clamp;*
(c) *Geissler burette with glass stopcock.*

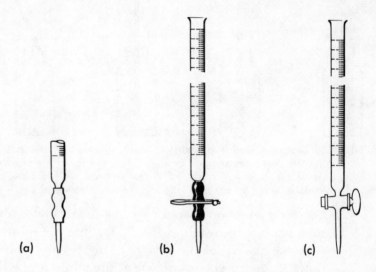

(a)   (b)   (c)

Figure I-13.
Lubricating the stopcock.

Using a burette

(i) Lightly lubricate the glass stopcock** of the burette with silicone stopcock grease until it turns easily (Figure I-13). Avoid using too much grease as it is likely to plug the stopcock or the tip.

(ii) Clean the burette using a warm detergent solution and a burette brush.

(iii) Rinse the burette thoroughly with tap water followed by distilled water and allow it to drain out as much as possible.

(iv) Rinse the burette thoroughly with two or three 5 ml portions of the solution with which it is to be filled and allow each portion to drain out thoroughly.

**Burettes with a Teflon stopcock do not require lubrication.

(v) Support the burette in a burette clamp (Figure I-14).

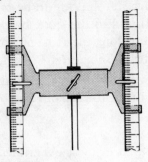

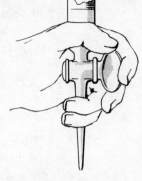

Figure I-14. *Student burette clamp.*

Figure I-15. (a)
The stopcock of a burette is regulated with the left hand.

(vi) Fill the burette slightly above the zero mark using a burette funnel. Then remove the funnel.

(vii) Open the stopcock [Figure I-15(a)] to expel air from the tip of the burette and to fill the tip with liquid [Figure I-15 (b)]. Adjust the level of the liquid as closely as possible to the zero mark on the scale. If this level falls below the zero mark, read and record this level as described in (ix) below.

(viii) Transfer the liquid from the burette slowly, that is, at a rate of about 10 ml min^{-1}. This slow transfer is necessary to avoid drainage errors. When transferring a liquid from a burette, regulate the stopcock with the left hand and hold the receiving vessel in the right hand [Figure I-15(b)]. Do not place the tip of the burette so far above the receiving vessel that splashing results when the solution from the burette strikes the liquid below.

(ix) Read the volume of the liquid transferred to the nearest 0.02 ml. You will be forced to estimate when the burette is calibrated with 0.1 ml divisions. When reading the position of the meniscus, errors due to parallax can be avoided by using a reading device (Figure I-16). This device causes the bottom of the meniscus to be darkened and sharply outlined against the white background, so that the level of the liquid can be read very precisely.

Figure I-15. (b)
Filling the tip of the burette with liquid.

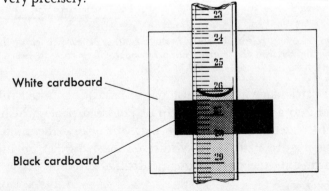

White cardboard

Black cardboard

Figure I-16.
Card for reading meniscus in a graduated tube; the upper edge of the dark portion should be placed approximately 1 mm below the meniscus.

(x) After the transfer, run off any liquid remaining in the burette into the sink unless other transfers are to be made shortly. *Do not* return any of this liquid to the stock bottle. Do not leave solutions in burettes for long periods of time, particularly those that are alkaline (basic) in nature.

(xi) Rinse the burette out with distilled water and cover the open end with an inverted test tube to keep out dust.

3. Transferring Solids and Liquids

Solid and liquid chemicals are used in most experiments in chemistry. They are stored in bottles referred to as *stock bottles* or *reagent bottles*. As chemicals are required for experiments they must be removed from these bottles without contaminating any of the material that remains in the bottle.

(a) SOLIDS

Solid chemicals are usually kept in wide-mouth stock bottles. Use a spatula or a scoopula to lift out the solid [Figure I-17(a)]. When removing solid from a stock bottle be careful not to contaminate the bottle cap [Figure I-17(b)]. Remove large quantities of solid from a stock bottle by tilting and rolling the bottle (Figure I-18). Frequently you will find it necessary to transfer a solid to a container with a relatively narrow mouth. A piece of paper is often used to facilitate this operation. The exact method that is suitable depends upon the quantity of solid to be transferred. If the quantity of solid is large, roll a clean unglazed piece of paper into a cone. Insert the smaller end of the cone into the mouth of the receiving vessel and then pour the solid chemical into the larger end of the cone (Figure I-19). If the quantity of solid to be transferred is small

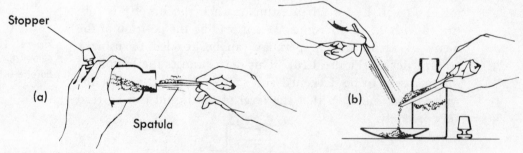

Stopper

(a)

Spatula

(b)

Figure I-17. *Technique for removing a sample from a stock bottle. Be sure to close the reagent bottle tightly with the correct lid or stopper. Take care to prevent contamination of the bottle cap.*

and particularly if the transfer is to be made to a test tube, pour the solid into a clean narrow strip of unglazed paper which has already been creased to form a trough that will fit into the mouth of the test tube (Figure I-20). With the test tube lying flat on the laboratory bench, slide the paper trough into the test tube. Now lift the test

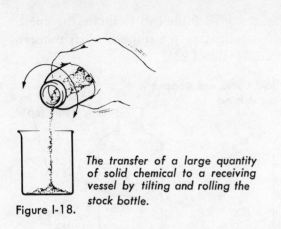

The transfer of a large quantity of solid chemical to a receiving vessel by tilting and rolling the stock bottle.

Figure I-18.

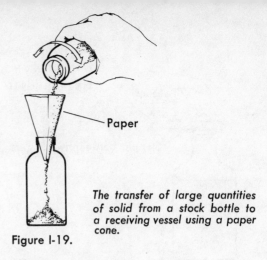

Paper

The transfer of large quantities of solid from a stock bottle to a receiving vessel using a paper cone.

Figure I-19.

tube to a vertical position and tap the paper gently to encourage the chemical to slide down into the tube. Never pour solid chemicals directly from a stock bottle into a test tube.

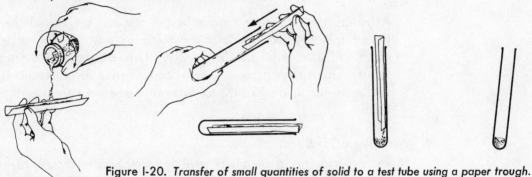

Figure I-20. *Transfer of small quantities of solid to a test tube using a paper trough.*

(b) LIQUIDS

Liquids are generally poured directly from one container into another. Since splashing must be avoided when making a transfer, hold a stirring rod against the lip or pouring spout of one container and pour the liquid down the stirring rod into the receiving vessel (Figure I-21). If the liquid is to be poured into a small mouthed

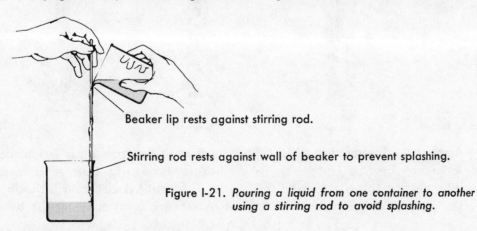

Beaker lip rests against stirring rod.

Stirring rod rests against wall of beaker to prevent splashing.

Figure I-21. *Pouring a liquid from one container to another using a stirring rod to avoid splashing.*

TRANSFERRING SOLIDS AND LIQUIDS

27

receiving vessel, use a clean dry glass funnel to facilitate the operation. Take care to avoid contaminating the stopper when transferring liquids from a stock bottle (Figure I-22).

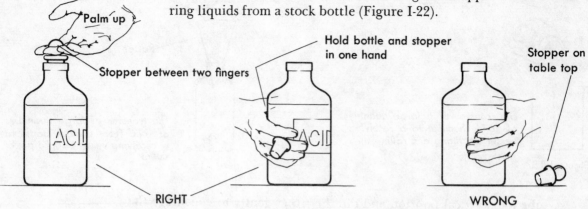

RIGHT

Palm up

Stopper between two fingers

Hold bottle and stopper in one hand

Stopper on table top

WRONG

Figure I-22. *Care must be taken to avoid the contamination of the stopper when transferring liquids from stock bottles.*

After the transfer from a stock bottle, remove any liquid that may have run down the outside of the bottle by washing the bottle with water. Finally, wipe the bottle dry. This rinsing and drying procedure is particularly important when corrosive or poisonous liquids are being handled. Failure to do so may result in serious injury or burns.

4. Operating a Gas Burner

Many experiments in chemistry require a simply constructed, adjustable source of heat. The gas burner is most frequently used for this purpose. The most commonly used are the Bunsen, Meker, and Tirrill burners (Figure I-23). The operation of these three burners is essentially the same. The gas

Figure I-23. *Common types of burner.*   Bunsen   Meker   Tirrill

flows to the burner through a rubber or plastic tube from a gas jet on the laboratory bench. The gas enters the burner through an inlet at its base. The quantity of gas entering the burner is controlled either by adjusting the gas jet on the laboratory bench or by making adjustments at the base of the burner. Air enters the burner through the air-inlet holes in the barrel usually situated just above the base. The amount of air entering the burner is regulated by moving a rotating collar which fits over the air-inlet holes in the barrel. The air and the gas mix in the barrel of the burner and this mixture is ignited at the top of the barrel (Figure I-24).

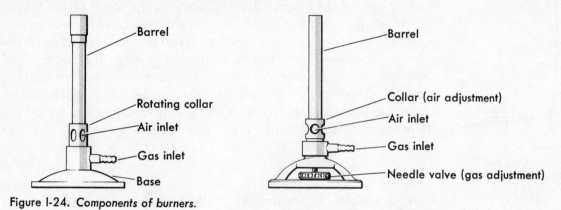

Figure I-24. *Components of burners.*

Follow these steps when lighting a gas burner:

(a) Close off the air supply by rotating the collar.

(b) Turn on the gas and light the burner using a flint lighter (Figure I-25). The resulting flame will be large and yellow coloured.

(c) Rotate the collar and gradually open the air-inlets until the flame changes to a blue colour and two distinct zones appear. The inner

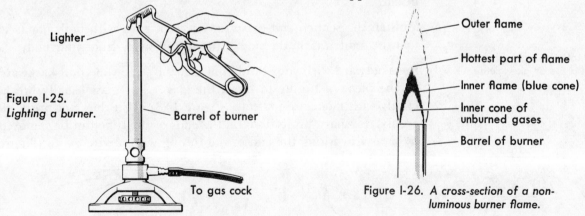

Figure I-25. *Lighting a burner.*

Figure I-26. *A cross-section of a non-luminous burner flame.*

cone (Figure I-26) is bright blue and the flame surrounding this cone forms a lighter, almost invisible outer cone. The temperature of the flame varies from region to region. The hottest part of the flame is just above the bright blue cone. The area of the flame just above the barrel of the burner is relatively cool because there is no combustion occurring in that region. If there is a gap between the flame

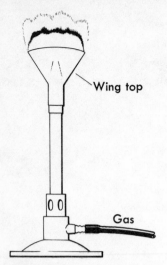

Figure I-27. A wing top is used to spread out the flame.

and the top of the burner, too much air is being admitted. If the flame is burning at the jet inside the barrel of the burner or if the flame is originating from the jet at the base of the burner, the burner is said to be *striking back*. This occurs either when the quantity of gas and air being introduced is reduced to such an extent that the inner cone of the flame is drawn down into the barrel of the burner or when the amount of air in the air-gas mixture is increased so that the burning takes place too rapidly. When this happens, turn off the gas flame to avoid overheating of the barrel, close the air vent and relight. Never touch the barrel of a burner that has been burning from a strikeback since it may become very hot. In some laboratory operations, such as in glass working, it is advantageous to spread the flame out. This is done by placing a wing top (flame spreader) over the barrel top (Figure I-27).

5. Glassworking

Four basic skills in glassworking should be acquired to facilitate your work in the laboratory: cutting, fire-polishing, bending, and constructing fine bore tubes.

Figure I-28.

Breaking glass tubing.

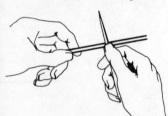

1. Make a single scratch with a file or glass cutter

CUTTING GLASS

(a) Lay the tubing flat on the laboratory bench and hold it down firmly with one hand.

(b) With the edge of a triangular file or a glass-tubing cutter, make a single scratch across the tubing at the point at which the glass is to be cut.

(c) Moisten the scratch and grasp the piece of glass with both hands so that the scratch is on the side of the tubing away from your body.

(d) Press outward with your thumbs and at the same time pull backward on the piece of tubing to break the glass. The glass usually breaks evenly with moderate pressure (Figure I-28). If it does not break off evenly, the sharp projections on the ends of the tube can be removed by lightly brushing the end of the tubing with a wire gauze (Figure I-29).

Scratch

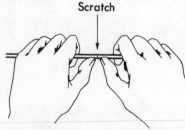

3. Press outward and pull backward

2. Place thumbs together opposite the scratch

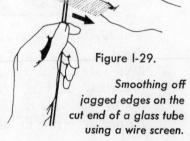

Figure I-29.

Smoothing off jagged edges on the cut end of a glass tube using a wire screen.

CUTTING GLASS

FIRE-POLISHING

The ends of a freshly cut piece of glass tubing have very sharp edges that are dangerous to handle. These cut edges are generally sharp enough to damage stoppers and make it difficult to insert tubing through rubber stoppers and corks. The ends of glass tubing or glass rods should always be fire-polished before being used.

Follow these steps when fire-polishing:

(a) Hold the glass tube in an almost vertical position with the end of the glass in the hottest part of a burner flame (Figure I-30).

(b) Rotate the glass tube in the flame to insure uniform heating. As the end of the glass tube is heated, the glass softens and flows slowly producing a smooth edge which is safe to handle and easy to insert into rubber tubing, rubber stoppers and corks.

(c) Place the hot portion of the glass on an asbestos pad or wire gauze— *not on the painted desk top.* Do not handle the glass until it has cooled. Do not hold the end of a piece of glass tubing in the flame too long. This may result in the end of the tube being constricted or completely closed (Figure I-31).

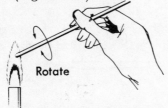

Figure I-30. *The technique of fire-polishing.*

Rotate

Constricted because it was heated too long

Figure I-31. *Constricted tube.*

BENDING GLASS

The following steps should be carried out when bending glass:

(a) Place the wing top on the gas burner (Figure I-32) to distribute heat over a greater length of glass.

(b) Hold a piece of glass tubing in a horizontal position over the hottest region of the flame.

(c) Rotate the tubing continuously with both hands as it is heated in the flame in order to uniformly soften the glass in the region where it is to be bent (Figure I-33).

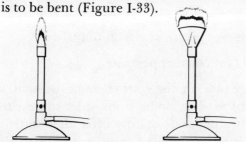

Figure I-32. *Wing top fitted on a gas burner to distribute heat over a greater area of the glass.*

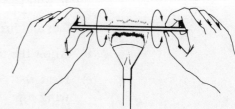

Figure I-33. *Heating glass tubing to soften it so that it can be bent into the desired shape.*

(d) When the glass is soft enough to sag slightly under its own weight, it is sufficiently soft to be worked. At this point, remove the tubing from the flame (Figure I-34), allow it to cool for a few seconds, and then rapidly bend the tube to the desired angle. While bending the tubing, gently press the glass against an asbestos pad. This is done to ensure that the entire bend is in one plane (Figure I-35). The bend should be smooth and should have the same diameter throughout to be considered acceptable (Figure I-36).

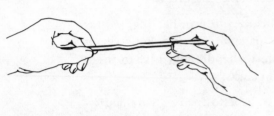

Figure I-34. *Glass tubing is allowed to cool a few seconds when removed from the flame before it is bent into the desired shape.*

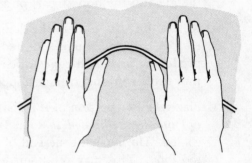

Figure I-35. *Bending glass tubing.*

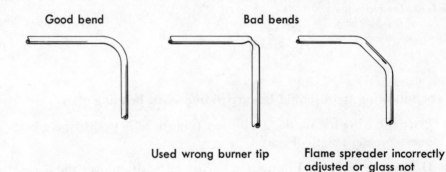

Good bend   Bad bends

Figure I-36. *Glass bends.*

Used wrong burner tip   Flame spreader incorrectly adjusted or glass not hot enough

CONSTRUCTION OF FINE BORE TUBES, JET TIPS, AND SMALL TEST TUBES

The following steps are common to each of these operations:

(a) Cut and fire-polish a one foot length of glass tubing.

(b) Allow the tubing to cool to room temperature.

(c) Heat the centre of this tube in the burner flame without using a wing top. Rotate the tube while doing so in order to heat the glass uniformly. Continue heating and rotating even after softening has occurred. While still heating the glass, push the ends of the tube together to thicken the molten glass. *Do not pull the ends apart while the tube is in the flame* (Figure I-37).

GLASS CONSTRUCTION

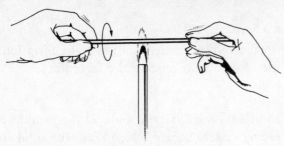

Figure I-37. *Heating glass tubing.*

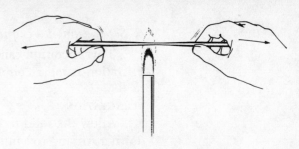

Figure I-38. *Drawing out glass tubing.*

(d) Remove the tube from the flame and continue rotating for a few seconds.

(e) Slowly pull the ends apart until the diameter of the hot portion is reduced to the dimension required (Figure I-38).

(f) Allow the tubing to cool to room temperature on a wire gauze or an asbestos pad.

(g) To make:

> i) *a fine bore tube*: Make the scratches on each end of the fine bore portion of the tubing at such points that this piece of tubing has a uniform bore throughout its length (Figure I-39). Break the tubing gently at these points. Now cut the fine bore tube into suitable lengths and fire-polish all cut ends. Be careful not to seal the ends of the tubes. If these tubes are to be used as melting point tubes, carefully seal one end in the flame.

> ii) *a jet tip*: Make a file scratch at the point chosen for the tip end of the jet and break the tubing gently (Figure I-40). Cut off the other end to give a jet tip of the desired length. Fire-polish both ends, being careful not to seal the jet tip.

> iii) *a small test tube*: Heat a shoulder of the constriction strongly and pull off the excess glass to the right, sealing the tube you hold in your left hand (Figure I-41). Round off the sealed end of the tube by returning it to the flame, heating it strongly with rotation until it is soft, removing it from the flame and blowing gently into the cool end. This operation will have to be repeated several times to be successful.

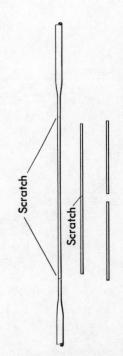

Figure I-39. *Construction of fine-bore tubes.*

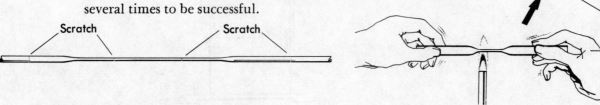

Figure I-40. *Construction of jet tips.*

Figure I-41. *Construction of a small test tube.*

6. *Separation of a Liquid From a Solid*

This operation can be performed either by decantation or by filtration. Filtration is more commonly used for this purpose in the laboratory.

DECANTATION

Allow the solid to settle, and then carefully pour most of the liquid off down a stirring rod into a receiving vessel (Figure I-42). Wash the solid in the containing vessel free of any remaining liquid by adding suitable solvent and decantating again. Repeat this procedure several times.

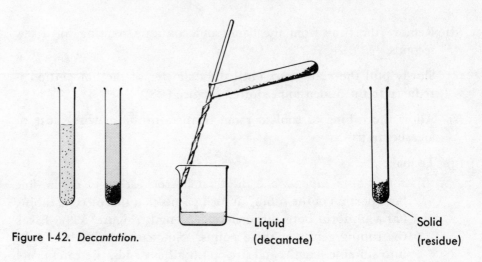

Figure I-42. *Decantation.* Liquid (decantate) Solid (residue)

FILTRATION

The following equipment is required for any filtration procedure: funnel, filter paper, funnel support, retort stand and receiving vessel. The funnel and the filter paper are usually referred to collectively as the *filter* (Figure I-43.)

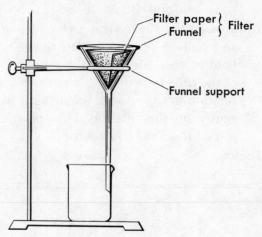

Figure I-43. *Equipment required for filtering.*

DECANTATION AND FILTRATION

The steps involved in filtration are listed below.

(a) Place the funnel in the funnel holder.

(b) Fold a piece of filter paper as follows: (i) fold the paper in half along one diameter, crease it slightly, and then fold it into quarters (Figure I-44); (ii) tear the corner off two thicknesses of the paper; (iii) open the paper out into a cone; (iv) use a squeeze bottle to wet the funnel;

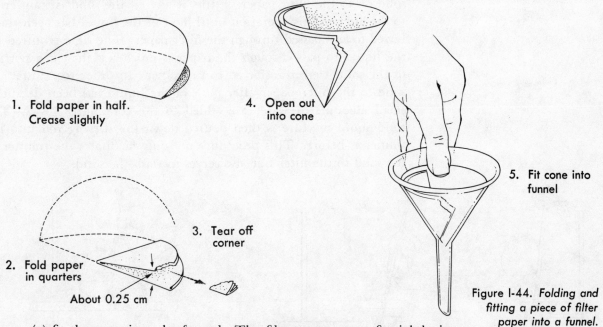

1. Fold paper in half.
   Crease slightly

4. Open out
   into cone

2. Fold paper
   in quarters

About 0.25 cm

3. Tear off
   corner

5. Fit cone into
   funnel

Figure I-44. *Folding and fitting a piece of filter paper into a funnel.*

(v) fit the cone into the funnel. The filter paper must fit tightly in the funnel so that air cannot be drawn down between the paper and the funnel wall. The corner is torn off the paper to prevent air from leaking into the fold.

(c) Pour some water through the filter paper to moisten it and fill the pores of the filter paper with liquid. If this is not done, the solid tends to clog the pores of the paper thus reducing the efficiency of the operation. The filter should not be wet with water when the liquid to be filtered is immiscible with water.

(d) Press the paper gently against the funnel wall. If the funnel is properly sealed, liquid will be retained in the funnel stem, and this liquid will help pull through the liquid from above the filter paper. If the paper is not sealed or if the stem of the funnel is dirty, the liquid will not be retained in the stem and bubbles will form in it. If the stem of the funnel is dirty, it should be cleaned with a pipe cleaner or twisted strip of cheesecloth.

(e) Place a receiving vessel under the funnel so that the tip of the funnel touches the side of the vessel. This will avoid splashing.

(f) Pour the solid-liquid mixture down a stirring rod into the filter. Be careful not to punch a hole in the filter paper with the glass rod (Figure I-45). Never let the level of the liquid in the funnel go above the top of the filter paper. Keep the liquid level at least 3 mm below the top of the paper. This prevents any liquid or solid getting between the filter paper and the wall of the funnel.

Filtration will be more rapid if the liquid is decanted from the solid on to the filter paper. Little, if any, of the solid is transferred to the filter in this operation until most of the liquid has been transferred to and passed through the filter paper. The time required for the liquid to pass through the paper is much less than if a portion of the solid were transferred to the paper. In order to transfer the solid to the filter paper after most of the liquid has been decanted, small amounts of water are added to the containing vessel. The solid-liquid mixture is then poured down the stirring rod into the funnel as before. This procedure not only facilitates the transfer of the solid to the filter but also serves to wash the solid.

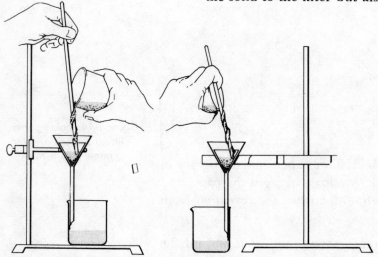

Figure I-45. *Filtration technique.*

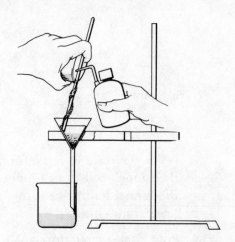

Figure I-46. *Using a plastic squeeze bottle, the last bits of solid residue are washed from the containing vessel onto the filter paper.*

(g) Wash out the last remaining particles of the solid from the containing vessel using a suitable solvent in a plastic squeeze bottle (Figure I-46).

(h) Thoroughly wash the solid collected in the funnel with distilled water or some other suitable solvent to remove as completely as possible the liquid from the solid. Wash the solid down into the apex of the filter paper (Figure I-47). Do this by carefully adding some of the wash liquid to the upper edge of the filter paper. Exces-

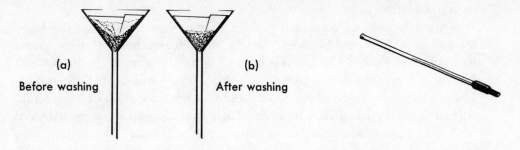

(a)   (b)

Before washing   **After washing**

Figure I-47. *Washing a solid in paper.*   Figure I-48. *Stirring rod fitted with rubber policeman.*

sive quantities of solvent should not be used for washing if the solid being filtered is soluble to any extent in the solvent. If this is the case, wash with a cold solvent, because most substances are less soluble in cold solvents than in hot solvents.

Sometime particles of solids adhere to the beaker even after attempts to wash them from the container. If this happens, use a stirring rod equipped with a rubber policeman to scrape the last portion of the solid from the containing vessel (Figure I-48).

The solid that collects on a filter paper during a filtration procedure is called the *residue*. The liquid or solution that passes through the filter paper is called the *filtrate*. In some cases the solid may pass through the filter paper. If this happens heat and then cool the mixture before refiltering. This will cause the finely-divided particles to aggregate and form particles large enough that they can be separated from the liquid by filtration.

Filtration can be speeded by using suction. Suction is commonly applied using a *water aspirator*, a piece of equipment that is attached to a water faucet. A fast stream of water running through an aspirator sucks air through the side arm. Thus an aspirator acts as a weak vacuum pump. A special funnel is used to support the filter paper whenever suction is applied. Without this support the filter paper breaks quite easily (Figure I-49).

Figure I-49. *Vacuum filtration.*

CENTRIFUGATION

Another piece of equipment called a *centrifuge* is used for the rapid separation of solids and liquids (Figure I-50). Your teacher will demonstrate its use if it is available in the laboratory. While in motion the mixture in the centrifuge tube is subjected to a force many times that of gravity. Usually the time required for separation does not exceed 15 or 20 seconds. Any tube of solution placed in a centrifuge must always be counterbalanced by a second tube containing an equal amount of liquid. This second tube is placed diametrically opposite the first. This is necessary to prevent vibration as the centrifuge rotates. The liquid standing above the solid in the tube can be removed by decantation or using a pipette or medicine dropper. The solid can be washed by adding a suitable solvent, stirring the mixture with a glass rod and centrifuging again.

Figure I-50. A centrifuge.

7. *Drying of Residues*

Following filtration and washing, the filter paper containing the residue is often removed from the funnel and carefully unfolded so that the residue can be spread out to dry. The time required for drying depends upon the amount and the nature of the residue. Residues are commonly dried in three ways: air drying, drying over a hot water bath and oven drying.

(a) AIR DRYING

Air drying is perhaps the easiest method of drying a residue provided time is not an important factor. Drying time can be reduced by placing the wet filter paper on several thicknesses of paper towelling immediately after it is removed from the filter funnel. This will remove much of the solvent from the filter paper and residue by absorption. It is usually sufficient to allow the paper and residue to stand on fresh paper towelling for 24 hours in the *open air*. The paper and residue are considered to be dry when they are observed to have a constant mass.

(b) DRYING OVER A HOT WATER BATH

Less time is required to dry residues using this method. This procedure is limited to residues that are not hygroscopic and that are not decomposed at 100°C. The method involves the following steps:

(i) Partially dry the residue and filter paper by placing them on paper towelling.

(ii) Place the residue and the filter paper on a tared watch glass.

(iii) Place the watch glass, filter paper and residue on a 400 ml beaker containing approximately 200 ml of water.

(iv) Boil the water for 10 or 15 minutes.

(v) Remove the watch glass and contents from the beaker and allow them to cool to room temperature.

(vi) Determine the total mass.

(vii) Repeat the heating procedure for 5 minutes. Cool the watch glass and contents and again determine the total mass. If the total mass is observed to be constant, one may assume that the paper and residue are dry.

(c) OVEN DRYING

This is a rapid and convenient device for drying residues. The temperature of the oven must be high enough to dry but not decompose the residue or filter paper. Ovens are usually operated in the temperature range 100°-110°C. The filter paper and residue are both placed on a tared watch glass in the oven. After 10 or 15 minutes the watch glass and contents are removed from the oven, cooled and their total mass is determined. This heating procedure is repeated for five minutes. The watch glass and its contents are cooled and the total mass is again determined. If the total mass is observed to be constant, one assumes that the paper and residue are dry. Residues should dry completely in 10 to 15 minutes.

1. Measuring pipette
2. Thermometer
3. Double burette clamp
4. 4-inch ring and retort
5. Graduated cylinders
6. Erlenmeyer flasks
7. Test-tube holder

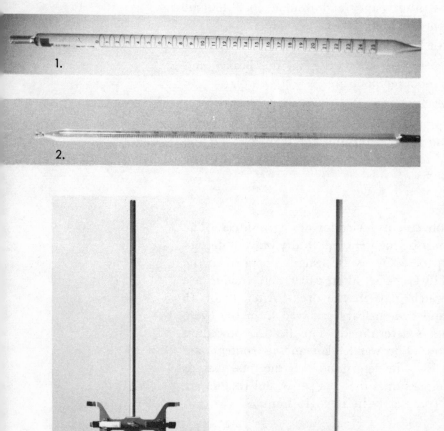

1.

2.

6.

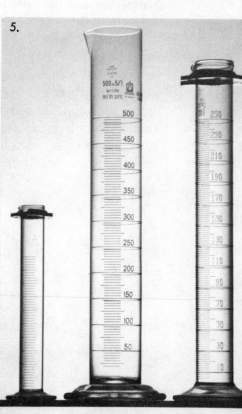

5.

3.

4.

8. Triangular file

9. Crucible tongs

10. Wing top

11. Spatula

12. Porcelain Mortar and Pestle

13. Porcelain evaporating dish

14. Porcelain crucible and lid

15. Tripod and Bunsen burner

16. Test-tube rack

17. Funnel support

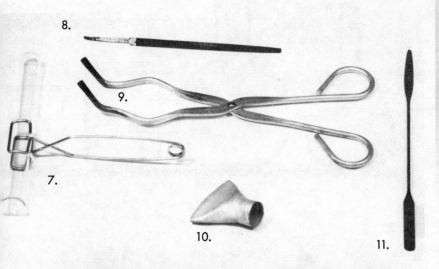

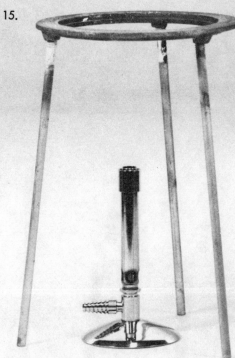

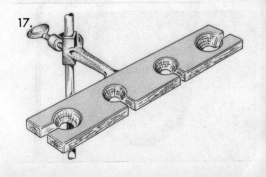

18. Mortar and Pestle

19. U drying tube

20. Volumetric flask 250 ml

21. Florence flask 500 ml

22. Beakers 250 ml   100 ml

23. Separatory funnel

24. Straight drying tube

25. Cork borers

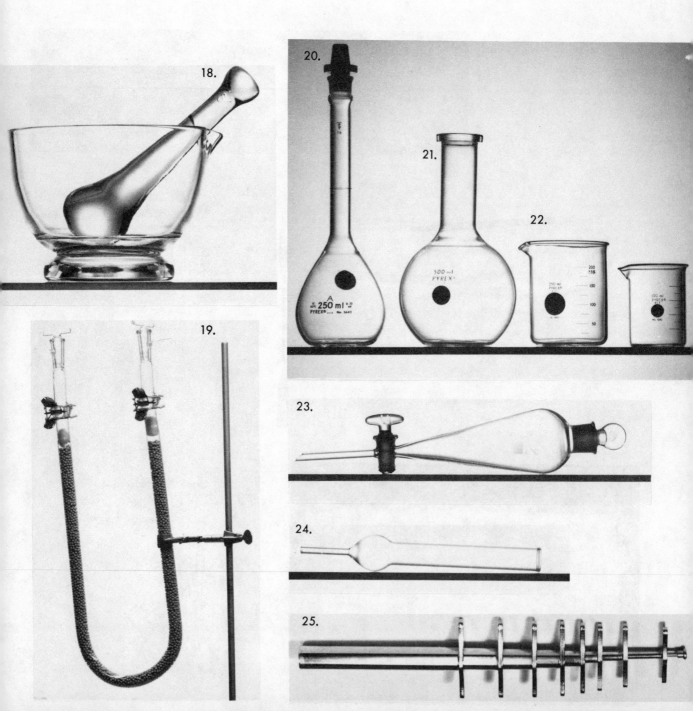

26. Plastic wash bottle

27. Watch glass

28. Glass plate

29. Petri dish

30. Transfer pipette

31. Burette

32. Wide-mouth bottle

33. Stemless funnel

34. Funnel

35. Dropping bottle

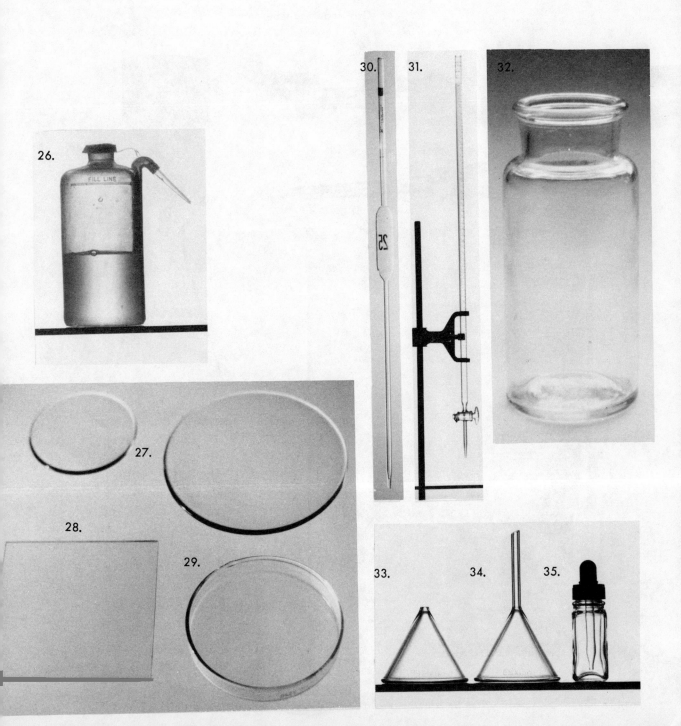

36. Pinch clamp
37. Screw clamp
38. Utility clamp
39. Clamp holder
40. Clamp

41. Water aspirator
42. Retort stand
43. Buchner funnel in suction flask
44. Reagent bottle
45. Deflagrating spoon
46. Gas measuring tube

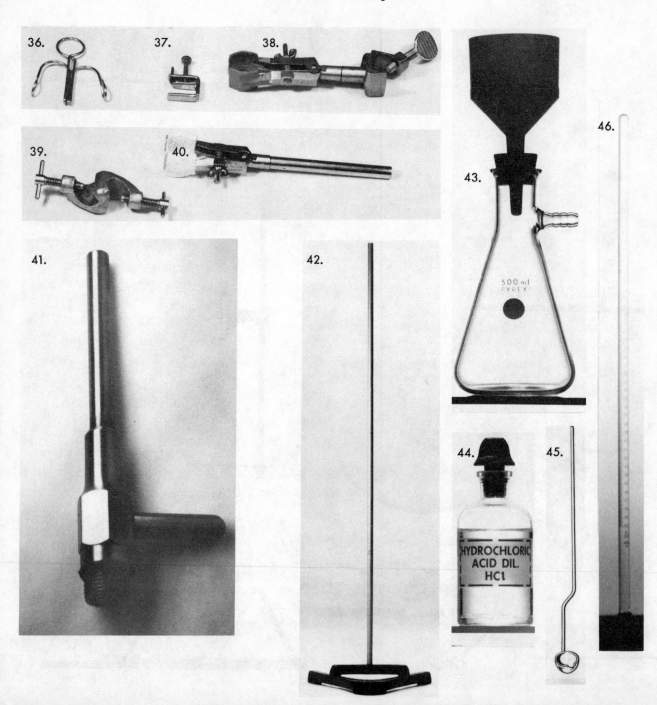

47. Clay triangle
48. Wire triangle
49. Wire gauze
50. Wire gauze with asbestos centre
51. Test-tube brush

52. Distilling flask
53. Thistle tube
54. Stirring rod
55. medicine dropper
56. Water-cooled condenser
57. Test tubes

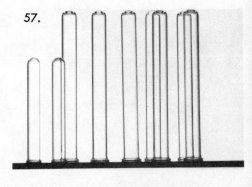

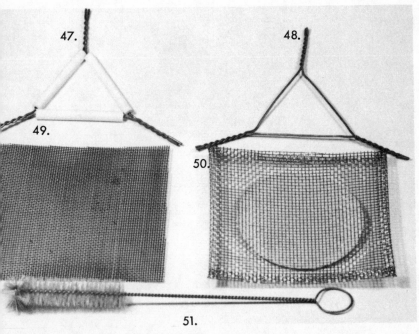

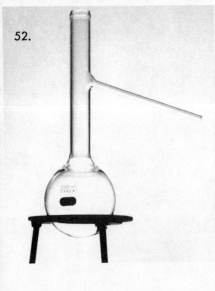

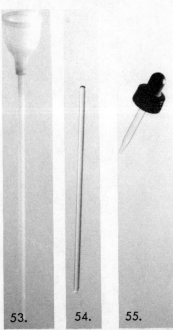

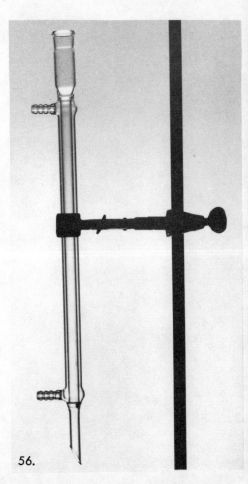

II EXPERIMENTS

EXPERIMENT 1-1

Creating a Model

In the same way that a reader conjures up a mental picture of the situation described by a writer in a story, scientists construct models to help them understand and explain phenomena which are much more difficult to describe in words. Thus, our concept of "atoms" is a model of the composition of matter.

A satisfactory model is one which will help us to understand the phenomenon we are studying and which is in agreement with our observations. While no one has "seen" an atom with the naked eye, our observations show us that matter behaves as though it were made of particles like atoms. We can ascribe to these particles certain characteristics which help explain why matter behaves as it does.

In this experiment you will try to develop a model which will explain certain observations you will make. It doesn't matter whether your model is the correct model. You will be successful if you develop an adequate model.

Procedure

1. Examine the sealed box provided. You may take any action you wish within classroom limitations except that you may not open or mutilate the box.

2. You are not to try to identify the object in the box. Since the box is sealed and will not be opened, you will never know whether or not you were right. Instead, you are to try to suggest what the object in the box is like. Your suggestion then becomes a model for the contents of the box.

3. Having decided on a model for the contents of the box, think of any other means of examination which you might use to improve upon your model.

4. Suggest a method you could employ to test your model.

5. Compare your model with those of other students using other boxes and attempt to develop a theory about the contents of the entire group of boxes.

6. Examine other boxes and decide whether your observations support your theory.

Questions for Thought and Discussion

1. What is your model for the contents of the box?

2. How else could the box be examined to assist in developing your model?

3. How could you test your model?

4. What is your theory about the contents of the entire group of boxes?

5. Why is your theory similar to a scientific theory?

6. What would you predict regarding the contents of the remaining two boxes in a group of 1000 if you found that your model satisfactorily explained the behaviour observed with 998 of them?

EXPERIMENT 1-2

The Precision and Uncertainty of
Measured Quantities

The accuracy of any measurement depends upon the precision of the measuring instrument. To "measure accurately" is to measure to the limits of precision afforded by the instrument available. Many instruments used in chemistry are designed to provide the experimenter with a degree of precision far greater than is found in everyday experience. Thus the common quantities, mass and volume, are often measured using precise chemical balances and volumetric glassware.

This experiment will introduce you to the use of such equipment. The precision of the measuring instrument will be considered as each measured quantity is recorded. Your teacher will instruct you regarding the use of the type of balance provided in your laboratory. The techniques to be employed in using a burette and a graduated cylinder are shown in Figure E-1.

Procedure

Part I

1. Accurately determine the mass of a clean, dry 100 ml flask (or beaker) and record this value.

   The above reading, and all subsequent readings, should be recorded using the appropriate number of significant figures. Information concerning significant figures is provided in Chapter I and in Appendix B of the text.

2. Pour the liquid indicated by your teacher into the 50 ml burette until the level is between the 35 ml and 50 ml marks. Accurately read and record this level.

3. Draw off about 10 ml of the liquid into the 100 ml flask then accurately read the burette again. Record this reading.

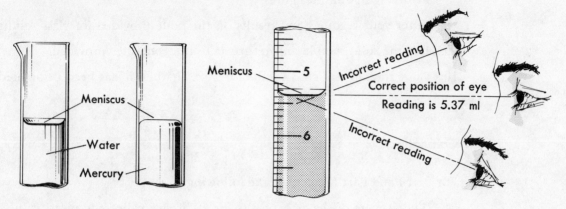

Figure E-1. *Measuring a liquid with a graduated cylinder or a burette.*

4. Calculate the volume of the liquid from the two readings and record this volume using the proper number of significant figures.

5. Accurately determine the mass of the container and liquid and record the reading.

6. From the two mass determinations calculate the mass of the liquid.

7. Calculate the density of the liquid, observing the rules for calculations involving significant figures.

8. Enter your readings and results on the table provided for class results.

9. Return the liquid to the container provided.

10. Copy the table of class results for Part I when it has been completed.

Part II

1. Partly fill a clean graduated cylinder with water.

2. Accurately read the volume of water and record the reading.

3. Accurately determine the mass of a piece of the solid assigned. The piece should be about as large as a walnut.

4. Carefully slide the solid lump into the graduated cylinder to avoid water loss by splashing.

EXPERIMENT 1-2

5. Accurately read the volume of water in the graduate and record the reading.

6. From the two graduate readings calculate the volume of the solid.

7. Calculate the density of the solid, observing the rules for calculations involving significant figures.

8. Enter your readings and results on the table provided for class results.

9. Dry the solid sample and return it to the container provided.

10. Copy the table of class results for Part II when it has been completed.

Calculations

For Part I and Part II calculate the following:

1. The average of the class results for each part, called the mean value.

2. The deviation of each result from the mean value.

3. The mean deviation for the class results.

4. The mean deviation for the class as a percentage of the mean value (the mean relative deviation).

5. The deviation of your result from the mean value.

6. The relative deviation of your result.

Questions for Thought and Discussion

1. Which instrument in this experiment is capable of the most precise measurement?

2. What is the uncertainty involved in reading
   (a) the burette   (b) the graduate   (c) the balance?

3. What volume would be occupied by 1.00 kilogram of the substance you used
   (a) in Part I of the experiment   (b) in Part II of the experiment?

EXPERIMENT 2-1

The Melting Point of a Solid

Substances are distinguished from each other by their properties. Measurement of these properties, often with considerable precision, is an activity of much importance in chemistry. It is not sufficient to say that a substance is conductive, brittle or blue; how conductive, how brittle and how blue are typical of the questions which most often must be answered in research, industry and other fields of science.

The melting point of a pure substance is one of the key physical properties used for identification. In this experiment you will determine the melting point of a solid.

Procedure

1. Describe the solid assigned to you.

2. Fit a thermometer with a small piece of rubber tubing and a cut rubber stopper (Figure E-2).

3. Thrust the open end of a capillary tube (melting point tube) down onto the pile of solid. Now turn the capillary tube upright and gently tap the bottom of the tube on the surface of the desk until the powder falls to the bottom.

4. Repeat this procedure until the solid is 3 to 5 mm deep in the bottom of the tube.

5. Insert the capillary tube into the ring of rubber tubing on the thermometer. Adjust the capillary tube until the solid in the bottom is opposite the bulb of the thermometer (Figure E-2).

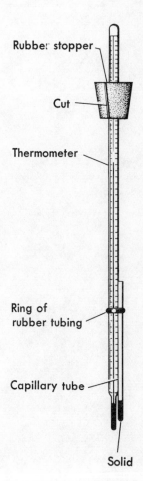

Figure E-2.

6. Add water to a 250 ml beaker until the beaker is three quarters full.

7. Place the beaker on a wire gauze supported by an iron ring and retort stand above a burner (Figure E-3).

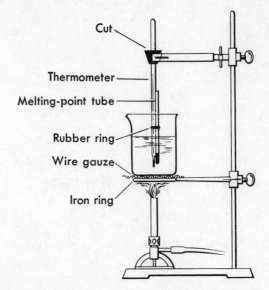

Figure E-3.

8. Clamp the thermometer, at the rubber stopper, in such a position that the bulb of the thermometer is in the middle of the water. Be sure that the open end of the capillary tube never goes below the surface of the water (Figure E-3).

9. Ignite the burner and rapidly heat the water to about 60°C.

10. Lower the flame and continue heating gently so that the temperature of the water rises slowly.

11. Record the temperature at which the solid melts.

12. Compare your result with others in the class.

13. Compare your result with the accepted value for this substance.

Questions for Thought and Discussion

1. Give several qualitative properties of the substance you used.

2. Give one quantitative property of the substance you used.

3. If two solid substances decompose on heating, that is, they have no melting point, how else might they be distinguished from each other?

4. The substance you used was probably an organic substance. What does this tell you about its composition?

EXPERIMENT 2-2

Chemical Changes

A chemical change is one in which a new substance is formed. This means that the properties of the substances formed during a chemical change, or chemical reaction as it is called, will be different from the properties of the substances used up during the change. Each different substance has its own distinctive chemical name. These names can be used to write a simple word equation which represents a chemical reaction. In later experiments you will have an opportunity to write equations in the more useful form with which you may be familiar, using formulas.

In this experiment the properties of substances will be examined and compared to determine whether the substances have undergone physical or chemical changes. The data table recommended in procedure 1 should be prepared before the laboratory period.

Procedure

1. Prepare a data table in the following form and fill in this table as the experiment proceeds.

	Iron	Sulphur	Mixture before heating Proc. 6—7(c)	Residue after heating Proc. 7(d)
	Procedures 1—5			
Appearance				
Odour				
Action with hydrochloric acid			—	
Effect of magnet				
Effect of heat				—

2. (a) Obtain some powdered iron and powdered sulphur on separate, labelled pieces of paper. Enough of each to cover a twenty-five cent piece will be sufficient.

 (b) Carefully smell each substance.

3. (a) Pour about 3.0 ml of dilute hydrochloric acid solution into each of two test tubes (18 × 150 mm).

 (b) Add a pinch of powdered iron to one test tube and a pinch of powdered sulphur to the other.

 (c) Warm each test tube slightly over a low burner flame.

 (d) Observe any changes. Cautiously smell near the mouth of each test tube.

CAUTION: Never check the odour of any substance by inhaling vigorously with your nose close to the material. Instead, waft some of the fumes toward your nose with your hand and sniff cautiously.

---

4. Starting with another pinch of iron and sulphur bring a magnet close to each substance.

5. (a) Using clean and dry test tubes (18 × 150 mm) place a pinch of iron in one test tube and a pinch of sulphur in another.

 (b) Heat each test tube over a low burner flame until no further changes occur.

6. (a) On a piece of white paper, mix a pinch of iron with a pinch of sulphur until the colour of the mixture is uniform.

 (b) Examine the mixture under a hand lens.

 (c) Bring a magnet close to the mixture.

7. (a) Prepare another mixture of iron and sulphur as in procedure 6(a).

 (b) Place this mixture in a porcelain crucible and support the crucible above a burner using a clay triangle, iron ring and retort stand (Figure E-4).

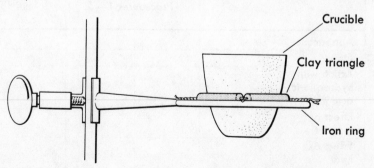

Figure E-4.

EXPERIMENT 2-2

CAUTION: The fumes produced during this procedure should be kept at a minimum. Avoid using a larger quantity of the chemicals than is recommended and conduct the reaction close to a vent or in a fume hood if possible. During the heating procedure keep your face away from the crucible.

(c) Heat the crucible, gently at first, then strongly, until no further changes occur.

(d) Allow the crucible to cool somewhat, then carefully break up the residue in the crucible with the end of a stirring rod.

(e) Reheat the crucible briefly, to remove any sulphur that remains.

(f) Allow the crucible to cool until it can be touched.

(g) Bring a magnet close to the residue in the crucible.

(h) Cautiously smell near the mouth of the crucible.

(i) Add about 1 ml of dilute hydrochloric acid to the residue in the crucible.

(j) Cautiously smell near the mouth of the crucible.

Questions for Thought and Discussion

1. If iron and sulphur are both elements, what must be true about their composition?

2. Why would you expect the properties which you observed in this experiment to be the same for iron and sulphur anywhere in the world?

3. Was the experiment in any way quantitative? Give your reasons.

4. Giving your reasons, state where in the experiment you encountered each of the following:
   (a) a pure substance
   (b) a homogeneous substance
   (c) a solution
   (d) a physical change
   (e) a chemical change
   (f) a change in state

5. Was there a chemical change involved in this experiment other than the one you selected in (4e)? Explain.

6. If there was a chemical change, what information would you require to complete a simple word equation for the reaction: iron + sulphur?

7. Write a detailed description of one pure substance using only the physical and chemical properties observed in this experiment.

EXPERIMENT 2-3

Families of Elements

The chemical elements are divided into two broad classifications, metals and nonmetals. You have encountered the general properties associated with each of these groups in everyday life and in previous experiments. In this experiment, you will examine some representative elements in each group to decide whether it is possible to divide metals and nonmetals into subgroups on the basis of similarities in properties.

Procedure

Part I

1. Arrange four test tubes (18 × 150 mm) in a test tube rack and fill each one-quarter full with water.

2. Obtain small pieces of each of the following metals, one at a time, *as they are required.*
   (a) Freshly cut sodium on a pin.
   (b) Freshly cut potassium on a pin.
   (c) A calcium granule or shaving.
   (d) Magnesium ribbon, freshly rubbed with emery paper.

CAUTION: Potassium and sodium must never be touched against the skin. Handle these two metals with great respect following the teacher's directions. Avoid touching the calcium granule with moist fingers.

---

3. After briefly noting the effect of air on each metal, quickly drop one of the metals into the water in one of the test tubes and observe the changes that occur. Wait until the changes for this metal are complete before adding the next metal to the water in a second test tube. Repeat this procedure for the remaining two metals.

4. Where it seems appropriate, test the gas produced by holding a blazing splint at the mouth of the test tube.

5. If there is no reaction evident, heat the test tube slightly over a low burner flame.

CAUTION: Do not heat strongly nor allow the contents to boil. This might cause the contents to be ejected.

---

6. To each test tube add pieces of red and blue litmus paper.

Part II (optional)

1. Mix enough sodium chloride to cover a twenty-five cent piece with the same amount of manganese dioxide and place the mixture in a test tube (18 × 150 mm).

2. In another test tube, place a similar mixture of sodium bromide and manganese dioxide.

3. In a third test tube, place a similar mixture of sodium iodide and manganese dioxide.

4. Add 5 drops of water to each test tube.

5. To each test tube (that is, to all three test tubes) add about 0.5 ml of concentrated sulphuric acid. Pour the acid, a drop at a time, down the side of the test tubes (Figure E-5).

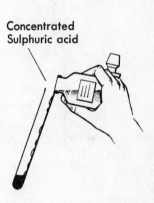

Concentrated Sulphuric acid

Figure E-5.

CAUTION: Handle the concentrated acid carefully as instructed by your teacher. Never add any water to concentrated acid. Avoid spilling or splashing. Any acid that does get on skin or clothing should be rinsed off immediately with plenty of running water.

---

6. If necessary, warm the test tubes gently to produce a reaction. Watch the space above the reaction mixture and look for any deposits forming around the mouth of the test tube.

Part III

1. Obtain three closed gas bottles containing
   (a) chlorine gas
   (b) bromine vapour
   (c) iodine crystals.

2. Line a deflagrating spoon with asbestos shreds, then have your teacher place a small amount of red phosphorus on the asbestos (Figure E-6).

3. Remove the stopper from the gas bottle of chlorine and lower the deflagrating spoon and phosphorus into the bottle. Keep the spoon away from the sides and bottom of the gas bottle. Close the mouth of the bottle as much as possible using a glass plate (Figure E-7).

Deflagrating
spoon

Phosphorus

Asbestos

Figure E-6.

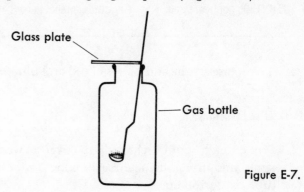

Glass plate

Gas bottle

Figure E-7.

4. Keep the spoon in the bottle until the reaction has ceased. Note the nature of the reactants and the products.

5. Place the hot deflagrating spoon on an asbestos pad and allow it to cool. If there is any reason to suspect that some of the phosphorus has not reacted, hold the spoon in a Bunsen flame until no further reaction occurs, then allow it to cool on the asbestos.

6. Clean the asbestos out of the deflagrating spoon using a glass stirring rod and place it in a container indicated by your teacher.

7. Rinse out the gas bottle with water.

8. Repeat procedures 2, 3, 4, 5, 6 and 7 using the bottle of bromine vapour.

9. Repeat procedures, 2, 3, 4, 5, 6 and 7 using the bottle containing iodine crystals. In this case it may be necessary to loosen the rubber stopper and warm the gas bottle slightly over the burner before placing the deflagrating spoon in the bottle.

10. Repeat procedures 2, 3, 4, 5, 6, 7, 8 and 9 using a small piece of freshly cut sodium metal instead of phosphorus. In each case the deflagrating spoon must be warmed slightly before being lowered into the bottle.

11. Repeat procedures 2, 3, 4, 5, 6, 7, 8 and 9 using a strip of copper foil instead of the phosphorus. The copper strip must be held by tongs and warmed gently before being inserted into the bottle.

Questions for Thought and Discussion

1. What properties of metals did you observe in the samples used in this experiment?

2. What other properties would you expect the metals to have?

3. What was the first chemical change you observed in the experiment?

4. What gas was produced by the reaction of the metals with water?

5. In what way did the metals have a similar chemical property? Into what two groups could they be divided with respect to this property?

6. What other property from this experiment could be used to divide the metals into the same two groups?

7. Compare the variety of physical states found in metals with that for nonmetals.

QUESTIONS 8 TO 11 ARE OPTIONAL

8. To what class of compounds do sodium chloride, sodium bromide and sodium iodide belong?

9. What were the three substances produced, in the gaseous state, in the test tubes?

10. Were these substances metals or nonmetals? Why?

11. What similarities were observed in the preparation of these three substances? What differences?

12. In what ways do chlorine, bromine and iodine have similar chemical properties?

13. Are the above elements identical in exhibiting these chemical properties?

14. Barium belongs to the same chemical family as magnesium. What properties would you expect barium to exhibit?

15. Would you expect sulphur to belong to the same chemical family as chlorine, bromine and iodine? Why or why not?

16. Predict the activity of chlorine, bromine and iodine in reacting with hot steel wool.

EXPERIMENT 2-4

A Quantitative Study of Chemical Changes

Pure substances have constant composition and therefore constant properties. Since elements are simple pure substances, it is not difficult to conceive of a model in which all the particles of the element are the same. Compounds, however, are composed of elements which have combined together chemically. If the composition of a compound is constant, its constituent elements should always be present in amounts having the same ratio to each other.

In this experiment, you will examine at least one oxide and attempt to separate the oxygen from the other element. The mass relationship of the two elements will be compared.

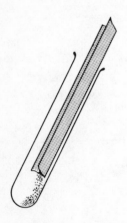

Figure E-8

(see also Figure I-20)

Procedure

1. Accurately determine the mass of a clean dry test tube (18 × 150 mm) containing a loose plug of glass wool inserted in its mouth.

2. Remove the plug of glass wool then using a piece of paper as a trough (Figure E-8 and Figure I-20) add about 1 g of mercury (II) oxide to the test tube. Your teacher will give you approximately 1 g of the solid. Use the whole sample provided. Avoid getting the oxide on the test tube walls. (Alternatively, the sample may be added using a small spatula). Replace the plug of glass wool.

3. Being careful to keep as much of the oxide as possible in the bottom of the test tube, accurately determine the mass of the test tube and contents.

4. Clamp the test tube loosely near the mouth and on an angle (Figure E-9). Place a burner below the test tube in a position so that the flame will heat the oxide but not the upper portion of the test tube.

5. Heat the mercury (II) oxide gently at first then gradually increase the temperature until the oxide is being heated strongly.

6. Heat strongly for 7 to 10 minutes until no further significant changes occur.

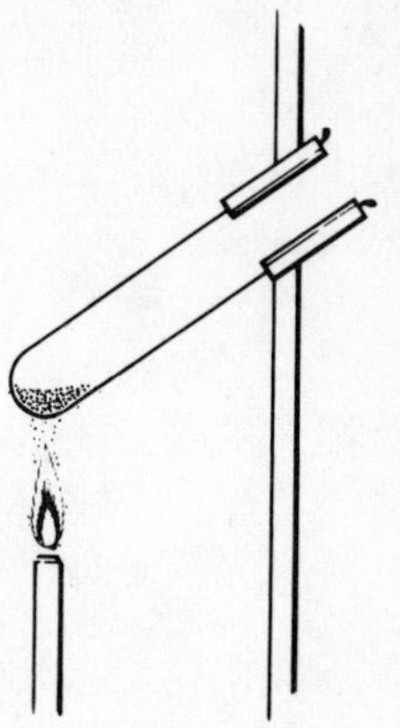

Demonstration: During this heating procedure your teacher will demonstrate the effect of introducing a glowing splint into the mouth of a test tube in which mercury (II) oxide is being strongly heated. It would be unwise to conduct this part of the experiment using the test tube you are heating, since deposits from the splint might interfere with the mass relationships you are examining.

7. Discontinue heating and allow the test tube and contents to cool to room temperature.

8. Accurately determine the mass of the test tube and contents. Be careful that nothing spills from the test tube.

Figure E-9.

CAUTION: Do not attempt to remove the contents of the test tube.

---

9. Stopper the test tube and return it to your teacher for cleaning.

CAUTION: Mercury is poisonous. Avoid getting mercury on your hands, but if you do, wash them immediately.

Calculations

1. Calculate the mass of the oxide used in the experiment.

2. Calculate the mass of the contents of the test tube (the residue) after the heating procedure.

3. Calculate the loss in mass during the heating procedure.

4. Express the loss in mass as a percentage of the mass of the original sample.

5. Express the mass of the residue as a percentage of the mass of the original sample.

6. Enter your results on the table provided for class results and copy the completed table.

7. Calculate the class mean for the results from calculation 4.

8. Calculate the class mean for the results from calculation 5.

9. Calculate the average deviation relative to the mean value.

10. Calculate the deviation of your result relative to the mean value.

Questions for Thought and Discussion

1. Did a chemical reaction occur when you heated the oxide? Explain your answer.

2. Was a metal produced during the decomposition? Give reasons for your answer. What metal was it? Was the metal like most other metals with which you are familiar?

3. What was the other element produced during the decomposition? Give a reason for your choice.

4. The values obtained from calculations 4 and 5 give the percentage composition of the oxide. Was the percentage composition of the oxide constant for all values recorded throughout the class?

5. What chemical laws are illustrated in this experiment by
   (a) the mass of the mercury left + the mass of the oxygen lost = the mass of the original mercury (II) oxide?
   (b) the percent mercury by mass in mercury (II) oxide is constant?

Alternate Procedure Using Lead Dioxide

Following the above procedure it is possible to decompose other oxides by heating. One other oxide that may be used is lead dioxide. In this case the yellow substance remaining after the decomposition of lead dioxide is called lead monoxide. The following calculations and questions apply if lead dioxide is decomposed.

1. Express the amount of oxygen that was removed from lead dioxide (during the thermal decomposition) as a percentage by mass of the original lead dioxide.

2. Yellow lead monoxide can be converted to lead metal reacting it with hydrogen. It is found to be 92.88% lead. Use this data to calculate the percentage of lead in the lead dioxide you used.

3. Calculate the masses of oxygen combined with 10 g of lead in (a) lead mondioxide, (b) lead oxide. How do these two masses of oxygen compare?

4. What chemical law is illustrated by the ratio calculated in 3?

EXPERIMENT 3-1

Electrons: Their Characteristics

Procedure

Part I

1. Rub an ebonite rod with wool (or flannel) and suspend the rod from a thread and stirrup (Figure E-10).

2. Rub a second ebonite rod with wool and bring this ebonite rod close to the suspended ebonite rod.

3. Rub a glass rod with silk and bring the glass rod close to the suspended ebonite rod.

4. Remove the suspended ebonite rod from the stirrup and replace it with a glass rod that has been rubbed with silk.

5. Rub a second glass rod with silk and bring this glass rod close to the suspended glass rod.

6. Rub an ebonite rod with wool and bring it close to the suspended glass rod.

7. Attempt to pick up small pieces of dry paper using a wool-rubbed ebonite rod and then a silk-rubbed glass rod.

Part II   Demonstration

The following demonstrations will be carried out by the teacher to show:

1. The production of a spark through air between the terminals of an induction coil.

Figure E-10.

2. The effects produced between cathode and anode of a discharge tube as the air is gradually removed by a vacuum pump.

3. The discharge between the electrodes in a set of tubes at successive stages of evacuation.

4. The production of cathode rays in a Crookes tube fitted with (a) a Maltese cross and (b) a fluorescent screen.

5. The effect of bringing a magnet near the Crookes tube fitted with a fluorescent screen.

6. The operation of a cold cathode ray tube and the effect of electric and magnetic fields on cathode rays.

Questions for Thought and Discussion

1. State the law of electrostatic attraction and repulsion.

2. (a) What constitutes a negative electrostatic charge?
   (b) What constitutes a positive electrostatic charge?
   (c) State Coulomb's law in words.

3. What method is used to charge the rods?

4. What explanation can be offered for the effects produced between the cathode and the anode of a discharge tube as air is slowly removed?

5. What is suggested by the fact that cathode rays: (a) cast a shadow, (b) are deflected by a magnetic field and (c) are deflected by an electric field (repelled by the negative plate).

6. Give a description of the electron in terms of the observed experimental facts.

7. On the basis of these experiments are we justified in concluding that the electron is a fundamental particle of matter? If so, why? If not, why not?

8. How could we experimentally discover whether or not the electron is a fundamental particle?

9. Two characteristics which would describe such a fundamental particle would be the *charge* and the *mass* of the particle. How might we determine these characteristics experimentally?

EXPERIMENT 3-2

Evidence of Emanations from Radioactive Materials

The movement of charged particles through gases can be observed using a device known as a *cloud chamber*. Charged particles moving through a gas leave a trail of positive and negative ions. The operation of any cloud chamber depends on the observed fact that vapours condense more readily around these positive and negative ions than around neutral particles or in open space.

Procedure

1. (a) Fill a 1 litre boiling flask with water then pour the water out and clamp the flask securely to a retort stand.

   (b) Fit the flask with a 2-holed stopper, glass elbow tubes, heavy walled rubber tubing and clamps as shown in Figure E-11. Connect one of the lengths of rubber tubing to a vacuum pump.

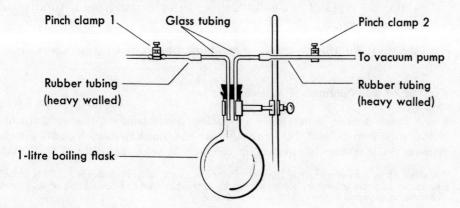

Figure E-11.

(c) With clamp 1 closed, open clamp 2 and evacuate the flask. Observe the flask closely.

2. (a) With the flask still evacuated close clamp 2.

   (b) Place a glowing splint that is still smoking near the open end of the rubber tubing that has been sealed off with clamp 1. At the same time, open clamp 1 slowly, thus releasing the vacuum and at the same time introducing a *small* amount of smoke into the flask.

   (c) Close clamp 1, open clamp 2 and turn on the vacuum pump for a few seconds. Observe the flask closely.

3. (a) Place alcohol in the cloud chamber.

   (b) Place the cloud chamber on dry ice.*

   (c) Illuminate the cloud chamber diagonally from above.

   (d) Insert the radioactive source and observe carefully.

Note: More detailed instructions on the operation of a specific cloud chamber will be supplied by the manufacturer.

Questions for Thought and Discussion

1. Explain the action observed in step 1 (c).

2. Compare the action observed in 2 (c) with that of 1 (c). Explain why there is such a sharp difference.

3. Who discovered the emanations from the elements uranium and radium?

4. What makes up the emanations produced by radioactive materials?

5. Why do we say that this type of decay is spontaneous?

6. Name, state the composition of, and compare the ionization abilities of the three types of emanations that can originate from naturally radioactive materials.

7. Account for the fog-track phenomena observed in this experiment.

Construction and Operation of a Cloud Chamber

A cloud chamber is one means of making atomic particles, that is, the paths of atomic particles, visible. This happens in much the same way that a high flying airplane becomes visible through its vapour trail (contrail). A Scottish physicist, *C. T. R. Wilson,*

---

*A cloud chamber not requiring the use of dry ice might be considered here. This would be necessary in areas where dry ice is not readily available. A brief description of such a cloud chamber is included at the end of this experiment.

working on the problem of cloud formation at the Cavendish Laboratory in Cambridge, first developed this device in 1912.

These instruments are extremely useful. Many important discoveries have been made with their help. Today they are used largely to "take a look" at some new phenomena. Other equipment has since been constructed which has the advantage of automatically selecting and counting the particles one wishes to study.

(a) *Construction*—Figure E-12 shows the basic construction of a cloud chamber.

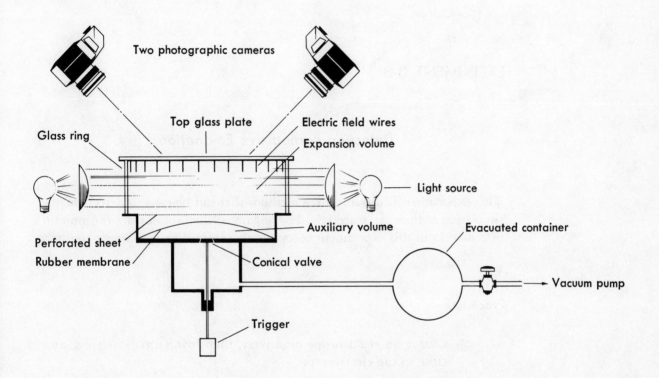

Figure E-12. *A schematic diagram of a cloud chamber.*

(b) *Operation:*

When the trigger is pulled, the valve opens and the rubber membrane flattens as the air below it rushes into the evacuated container. The moist air in the expansion volume expands and cools, and if a fast-moving charged particle passes through the moist air at that instant, the particle forms a trail of droplets which is characteristic of the particle. A stereoscopic photograph of the trail of droplets is taken by the two cameras. Between expansions, the electric-field wires clear the chamber of ions.

EXPERIMENT 3-3

Detecting Radioactive Emanations

This experiment illustrates three methods that can be used to detect emanations from radioactive materials. The apparatus used to measure the amount of radiation in this experiment is commonly referred to as a Geiger counter.

Procedure

1. (a) Charge an electroscope negatively, then bring a radioactive source close to the electroscope.
   (b) Charge the electroscope positively and repeat the procedure in (a).

2. (a) Place a lead object directly in front of a strip of unexposed photographic plate that is still enclosed in its light protective wrapper.
   (b) Place a radioactive source in front of the film for several seconds (Figure E-13).

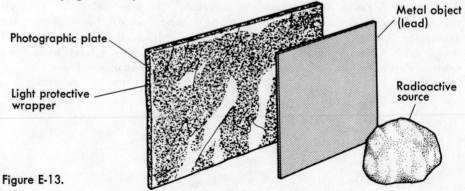

Photographic plate

Light protective wrapper

Metal object (lead)

Radioactive source

Figure E-13.

(c) Have the film developed and examine it in a future laboratory period.

3. Set up the Geiger counter to measure background radiation.

4. Place each radioactive source, in turn, 50 cm. from the detector and measure the radiation from each source.

5. Choose one radioactive source and place it at each of the following distances from the detector. For each distance measure the radiation.

    (a) 50 cm.   (b) 25 cm.   (c) 12.5 cm.

6. (a) Place the most active source a convenient distance from the detector.

    (b) Measure the radiation when the following materials are placed, in turn, between the source and the detector.

        (i) air only
        (ii) a sheet of paper
        (iii) a book
        (iv) one sheet of aluminum
        (v) two sheets of aluminum
        (vi) three sheets of aluminum
        (vii) one sheet of lead
        (viii) two sheets of lead
        (ix) three sheets of lead
        (x) a brick.

7. Measure the radiation from a luminous watch dial.

Questions for Thought and Discussion

1. Explain the effect of radioactive emanations on
   (a) a charged electroscope and (b) a photographic film.

2. Define radioactivity.

3. What property is useful in identifying radiation?

4. What are isotopes?

5. Of the three common isotopes of hydrogen, which one is radioactive?

6. What happened to the intensity of the radiation striking the detector as the source was moved closer to the detector?

7. Of the materials tested, which constituted the best shield against radiation?

Construction and Operation of a Geiger-Müller Tube

The emanations from radioactive materials will ionize atoms by knocking off electrons. This property is utilized in the Geiger-Müller tube which is used for measuring radiation. The device consists of a metal tube made airtight with insulating stoppers and filled with air at about 1/10 atmospheric pressure. A thin wire running through the centre of the tube serves as the positive electrode while the metal tube itself forms the negative electrode. A voltage source and a light, buzzer or electrometer are connected in series with these electrodes. The potential applied is kept well below the sparking potential but is still sufficient to produce a thousandfold multiplication of the primary ions and pulses big enough to affect an electrometer. Such tubes were first developed to detect alpha (α) particles. The counter's deflections, each due to the passage of a single alpha particle, are recorded.

In 1928 Geiger and Müller discovered that this same tube, with some slight modifications, could be used to count beta (β) particles and gamma (γ) rays. If the voltage is high enough, any particle entering the counter, even if it creates only a single ion, will start off a discharge. Geiger and Müller found a way of treating the counter so that this discharge would immediately "quench itself", leaving the counter ready to record another particle almost at once. The entire volume within the tube is sensitive and the pulses produced are quite big. They found it possible, with little additional amplification, to drive a meter which would advance one unit for each particle. From this point on counting was automatic. All the physicist had to do was read the meter at the beginning and end of a certain period and take the difference. A few years later the speed of counting was increased with the invention of *scalers*. This led to a more detailed analysis of radiations with the result that substances could be identified from the radiations they emitted.

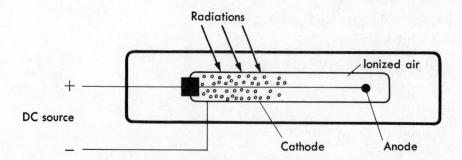

Figure E-14. *Geiger-Müller detector.*

The simplest form of the Geiger-Müller detector is shown in Figure E-14. The metal tube serves as the cathode and the central wire as the anode. These are connected to a D.C. source and in series with a light bulb. Under these conditions the bulb does not glow because the circuit across the tube is open. If the gas in the tube is ionized, however, the ionized gas conducts electricity and the bulb glows. When a particle from a radioactive atom passes through the tube it ionizes the gas and the bulb glows. Using appropriate electronic attachments, a similar detector can be made which counts both the number and kinds of particles entering the tube. Detecting devices used today are much more complex than the one described. They generally have attachments which will determine the energy of the particles as well as count the number of particles.

EXPERIMENT 3-4

The Energy of Electrons: Atomic Spectra of the Elements

The electrons of an atom can exist at different energy levels. When shifting from higher to lower energy levels these electrons emit energy in the form of light. This experiment is designed to illustrate how the visible light emitted by atoms in an excited state can be used to identfy the atoms in the sample.

Procedure

Part I

1. The following saturated solutions are provided.
   a potassium salt
   a sodium salt
   a lithium salt
   a calcium salt
   a barium salt
   a strontium salt
   a copper salt.

2. Pour one of these salt solutions into a 100 ml beaker to a depth of about 1 cm and label the beaker with the name of the solution.

3. Mark one end of a strip of asbestos with the name of the salt solution to be used. Soak the opposite end of the asbestos in the solution.

4. Adjust a burner until the flame is as colourless as possible.

5. Clamp the dry end of the asbestos to a retort stand and adjust the clamp until the wet end of the asbestos is in the colourless flame and about 6 cm above the burner (Figure E-15).

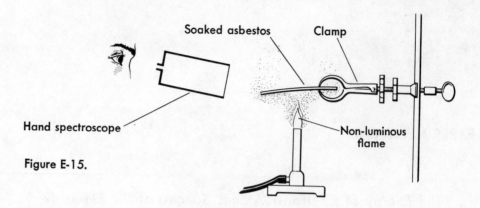

Figure E-15.

6. Record the colour of the flame.

7. Using the spectroscope from the spectrum kit, observe the coloured flame.

8. Record the most predominant features of this spectrum, noting particularly the relative positions and the colours of the most prominent lines. If the spectrum should fade during this procedure, dip the asbestos into the same solution again then return it to the clamped position for further observation.

9. After completing a description of the spectrum, set this strip of asbestos aside for possible use in Part II. Retain the solution in the beaker as well.

10. Repeat procedures 2 - 9 for each of the saturated salt solutions provided.

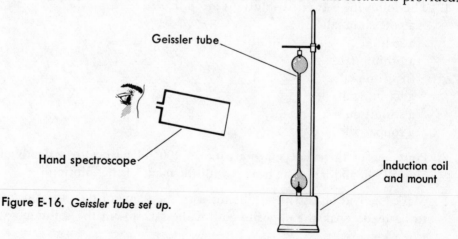

Figure E-16. *Geissler tube set up.*

11. Using the spectrum kit observe the spectra of various gases in the excited state in Geissler tubes (Figure E-16). The following gases may be used:

> hydrogen
> helium
> neon
> mercury vapour
> nitrogen
> oxygen

CAUTION: Your teacher will connect the Geissler tubes to an induction coil. Follow instructions carefully when observing these gases and do not touch the leads to these tubes.

---

12. Compare the spectra of these gases with those provided in a text or chart.

Alternate Procedure for 11 and 12:

Instead of using the hand spectroscope from the spectrum kit, the Geissler tubes may be attached to a larger demonstration spectroscope.

Part II (Optional)

You will be provided with one or more "unknown" solutions. Each solution will be one of the saturated salt solutions provided for Part I.

Try to identify this solution as follows:
1. Follow procedures 2 to 8 of Part I using the unknown solution.

2. Compare the spectrum of the unknown with the spectra recorded in Part I. If there is any doubt when making comparisons from the recorded data, use the strips of asbestos set aside in Part I to observe the spectra of the "known" solutions again.

3. Name the unknown solution.

Questions for Thought and Discussion

1. Define the term "spectrum of a substance".

2. What is significant about the fact that the spectra produced by these solutions are *line* spectra?

3. Where does the light energy which constitutes the spectrum of a substance, originate?

4. What determines the colour of the light?

5. Each bright line in the hydrogen spectrum is made up of light of a definite wavelength coming from excited hydrogen atoms. To what did Bohr relate this in the hydrogen atom? What did this indicate about the orbits that could be occupied by the electron in the hydrogen atom?

6. What did Bohr say about the amount of energy that the electrons in an atom could absorb or radiate?

7. (a) What is a photon?
   (b) What did Bohr imagine concerning the action of an electron when it (i) collides with a photon, (ii) radiates energy?

8. What is meant by the "ground state of an atom"?

9. How can line spectra be used in chemical analysis to identify substances?

An Introduction To The Experimental Work Associated With Chapter 5

A study of periodic classification and the relationship of periodic classification and atomic structure illustrates how the elements can be arranged systematically according to similar chemical properties. Here is a means of simplifying the study of chemistry. A vertical column of elements in the periodic table is known as a *group* or *family* and contains elements having similar properties. Within a group there is a gradation in these common properties. For example, the metallic activity of the elements in a group increases in intensity as the atomic number increases while the nonmetallic activity decreases. A horizontal column of elements in the periodic table is known as a *period*. The elements within a given period also exhibit a gradation in properties. In this case a gradual change from metallic to nonmetallic activity is noted as one moves from left to right across any period in the table. Four atomic properties, namely, ionization energy, electron affinity, electronegativity and atomic (and ionic) radii, are particularly useful in predicting and explaining chemical properties of the elements. This series of experiments related to Chapter 5 is designed partly to illustrate the concepts developed in the chapter and partly to provide an opportunity to apply these ideas in explaining observed experimental data.

EXPERIMENT 5-1

The Periodic Classification as a Predictive Device

One of the great values of the periodic classification of the elements is its usefulness in making predictions. Not only is it possible to predict the existence of elements missing from the classification but it is also possible to predict, with surprising accuracy, the properties of these elements. These predictions are based on the position of the element in the classification relative to other elements and the properties of these other elements.

In this experiment, imagine that you are Mendeléev and that you are faced with the problem of predicting the properties of three missing elements, A, B and C, in the classification.

Procedure

1. Use the data provided in the partial periodic table below (Table 1) to predict the properties of elements A, B and C which occupy the blank squares in the table. Record your predictions in tabular form similar to tables 2, 3 and 4. Base your predictions on the properties of neighbouring elements and the apparent trends that occur as you move across a period or down a group in the table. The properties of the elements which you will predict are shown in the code square below. The arrangement of the values given in each square of table 1 corresponds with the arrangement in this code square.

```
Atomic number

                    Symbol

Density                         Ionization
(g cm⁻³)                        Energy(ev)

Atomic                          Melting
Radius                          Point
(Å)                             (°K)
```

CODE SQUARE

2. Obtain the accepted values from a handbook or from your teacher. Compute the difference between the correct and predicted values.

3. Use the data from table 1 and any other source to indicate the trends in the atomic properties listed to the right, left, and below table 5. Put arrowheads on the lines to indicate the trends.

Table 1

1A	IIA	IIIA	IVA	VA	VIA	VIIA
3 Li 0.53 5.4 1.23 452	4 Be 1.82 9.3 0.89 1557	5 B 2.3 8.3 0.80 2310	6 C 3.5 11.3 0.77 3530	7 N 1.03 14.5 0.74 63	8 O 1.4 13.6 0.74 54	9 F 1.54 17.4 0.72 55
11 Na 0.97 5.1 1.57 370	12 Mg 1.74 7.6 1.36 923	13 Al 2.7 6.0 1.25 932	14 Si 2.4 8.1 1.17 1680	15 P 2.36 11.0 1.10 317	16 S 2.03 10.4 1.04 392	17 Cl 1.56 13.0 0.99 172
19 K 0.80 4.4 2.03 337	20 Ca 1.55 6.0 1.74 1124	31 Ga 5.89 6.0 1.25 303	32 A	33 As 5.72 10 1.21 814	34 C	35 Br 3.1 11.8 1.14 266
37 B	38 Sr 2.6 5.7 1.91 1073	49 In 7.3 5.8 1.50 430	50 Sn 7.3 7.3 1.41 505	51 Sb 6.68 8.6 1.41 900	52 Te 6.24 9.0 1.37 723	53 I 4.93 10.4 1.33 387
55 Cs 1.9 3.9 2.35 301	56 Ba 3.5 5.2 1.98 1123	81 Tl 11.85 6.1 1.55 575	82 Pb 11.3 7.4 1.53 600	83 Bi 9.8 8 1.52 5.44		

Table 2 Element number 32: Element A

	Predicted	Actual	Difference
Number of electrons in the energy level with highest principal quantum number			
Density			
Melting point			
Ionization energy			
Atomic radius			

Table 3   Element number 37: Element B

	Predicted	Actual	Difference
Number of electrons in the energy level with highest principal quantum number			
Density			
Melting point			
Ionization energy			
Atomic radius			

Table 4   Element number 34:   Element C

	Predicted	Actual	Difference
Number of electrons in the energy level with highest principal quantum number			
Density			
Melting point			
Ionization energy			
Atomic radius			

Table 5

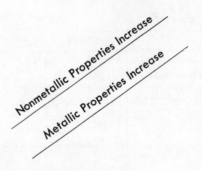

	IA	IIA	IIIA	IVA	VA	VIA	VIIA	O	
	3	4	5	6	7	8	9	10	
	11	12	13	14	15	16	17	18	
	19	20	31	32	33	34	35	36	
	37	38	49	50	51	52	53	54	
	55	56	81	82	83	84	85	86	
	87	88							

Atomic Radii Increase
Metallic Properties Increase

Ionization Energies Increase
Electronegativity Increases

Nonmetallic Properties Increase
Atomic Radii Increase
Ionization Energies Increase
Electronegativity Increases

Nonmetallic Properties Increase
Metallic Properties Increase

Questions for Thought and Discussion

1. What is the relationship between the number of the group in which an element is placed for the representative elements and the number of electrons in that element having the highest principal quantum numbers?

2. Is the trend in ionization energies paralleled by a corresponding trend in metallic to nonmetallic characteristics? Justify your answer.

3. What can you say about the nature of the elements enclosed by the solid coloured line in table 5?

4. Which is the most metallic element of group VA? What is the reason for your choice?

5. Which is the most metallic element in period 5? What is the reason for your choice?

EXPERIMENT 5-2

The Elements of Group 1A And Their Compounds

CAUTION: 1. Wear safety glasses and plastic aprons throughout this experiment. 2. The metals used in this experiment must be handled with forceps at all times. Do not place any of these metals in water except as directed in the procedure. Follow the teacher's instructions explicitly.

Procedure

1. Observe a freshly cut piece of sodium. Note its lustre, hardness and any changes that take place when it is exposed to air.

2. *Demonstration*
   Test the electrical conductivity of sodium by touching the electrodes of the conductivity apparatus (Figure E-17) to the ends of a short piece of the metallic solid.

CAUTION: Use forceps. Keep your face away from the mouth of the test tube.

3. (a) Add a piece of sodium the size of a small pea to 5 ml of water in a test tube.
   (b) Hold a burning splint at the mouth of the test tube as the reaction occurs.
   (c) After the reaction has stopped, add a few drops of phenolphthalein indicator (or pieces of red and blue litmus paper) to the contents of the test tube.

CAUTION: Use forceps. Keep your face away from the mouth of the test tube.

Electrodes

Conductivity apparatus

Figure E-17.

4. *Demonstration*

    (a) Add a piece of sodium the size of a small pea to 5 ml of dilute hydrochloric acid solution (0.5 M) in a test tube.

    (b) Hold a burning splint at the mouth of the test tube during the reaction.

5. *Demonstration*

    Repeat steps 1 to 4 using small pieces of (a) lithium and (b) potassium.

6. (a) Prepare a solution by adding 0.1 g of sodium peroxide to 10 ml of water in a test tube.

    (b) Add several drops of phenolphthalein indicator (or pieces of red and blue litmus paper) to the solution.

    (c) Repeat procedures (a) and (b) using lithium oxide (or peroxide) and then potassium peroxide.

Questions for Thought and Discussion

1. Justify the grouping together of the elements in the periodic table based on the results of these experiments.

2. What do the results of these experiments indicate about the relative reactivity of lithium, sodium and potassium?

3. Account for these differences in reactivity in terms of the ionization energies of these metals. Base your explanation on the different factors which affect the ionization energies of elements.

4. Would you expect cesium, element 55, to be more or less reactive than potassium? Justify your answer.

5. Does the evidence from this experiment suggest that metallic elements form acidic or basic oxides?

EXPERIMENT 5-3

The Elements of Group IIA And Their Compounds

The success of this experiment depends on a careful comparison of the properties of these elements. Accurate observation is essential. The observations should be recorded in chart form.

Procedure

1. (a) Observe a freshly cut (or filed) piece of calcium. Note its lustre, hardness and any changes that take place when it is exposed to air.

   (b) Clean a strip of magnesium ribbon, using emery paper, and compare its properties with those noted for calcium in (a).

2. *Demonstration*

   (a) Test the electrical conductivity of calcium by touching the electrodes of the conductivity apparatus to the ends of a short piece of the metallic solid.

   (b) Repeat this procedure using a short piece of freshly cleaned magnesium.

3. (a) Add a piece of calcium to 5 ml of water in a test tube. Hold a burning splint at the mouth of the test tube as the reaction proceeds. After the reaction, add pieces of red and blue litmus paper to the contents of the tube (or a few drops of phenolphthalein indicator).

   (b) Repeat procedure (a) using a small piece of magnesium. If necessary, warm the test tube to initiate a reaction.

(c) Wet a small piece of asbestos. Squeeze any excess water out of it. Pack the asbestos into the bottom of the test tube. Place 0.1 to 0.2 g of magnesium turnings in the same test tube to form a layer on top of the asbestos. Insert a stopper and delivery tube assembly into the test tube. Prepare a second test tube to collect the gas by the downward displacement of water (Figure E-18). Heat the wet asbestos until droplets of liquid form at the mouth of the test tube. Now heat the magnesium turnings strongly at the junction between the asbestos and the metal, occasionally directing the flame at the wet asbestos. At the same time insert the open end of the delivery tube under the open mouth of the test tube in the water trough. Continue heating until a test tube of the gas produced has been collected. Remove the test tube from the water trough. Hold the gas-filled test tube in an inverted position and bring a burning splint to its mouth. Allow the test tube, containing the reaction mixture, to cool to room temperature. Add 10 ml of distilled water to the reaction mixture and shake vigorously. Filter this mixture and test the filtrate with red and blue litmus paper (or a few drops of phenolphthalein indicator).

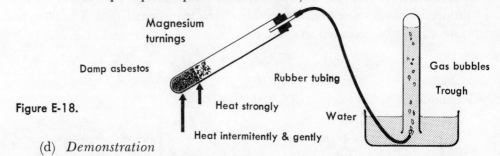

Figure E-18.

Magnesium turnings

Damp asbestos

Rubber tubing

Gas bubbles

Trough

Heat strongly

Water

Heat intermitently & gently

(d) *Demonstration*

Repeat part (c) of this experiment by passing steam over hot magnesium turnings as described in the Guide to the Laboratory Sessions on page 274.

4. (a) Add a small piece of calcium to 5 ml of dilute hydrochloric acid in a test tube. Hold a burning splint at the mouth of the test tube during the reaction.

   (b) Repeat (a) using a small piece of magnesium.

5. (a) Prepare a solution by adding a small amount of calcium oxide to 5 ml of water in a test tube. Test this solution with pieces of red and blue litmus paper (or a few drops of phenolphthalein indicator).

   (b) Repeat (a) using the oxides of magnesium and barium.

6. (a) Place 1 g of calcium sulphate in a test tube and add 5 ml of water. Stopper the test tube and shake vigorously until no more solid dissolves. Label this test tube, then set it aside and continue with procedure (b).

EXPERIMENT 5-3

(b) Repeat procedure (a) using separate samples of magnesium sulphate and barium sulphate.

(c) If the solid used in any of these test tubes does not dissolve completely, filter the contents of the test tube and retain the filtrate. (For a description of the technique of filtering see Part I(c), Section 6, Laboratory Techniques, page 35 of this manual).

(d) Perform a flame test on each filtrate in turn to determine whether a solution has formed. Consult experiment 3-4 on the technique involved in making these flame tests.

7. (a) Add 1 ml of sodium carbonate solution to 5 ml of calcium chloride solution.

(b) Repeat (a) using solutions of magnesium and barium chloride instead of calcium chloride.

Questions for Thought and Discussion

1. Justify the grouping of these elements together in the periodic table on the basis of the results of these experiments.

2. What do the results of these experiments indicate about the relative reactivity of calcium and magnesium?

3. Account for the differences observed in reactivity in terms of the ionization energies of these metals. Base the explanation on the different factors which affect the ionization energies of elements.

4. What do the results of Experiments 5-2 and 5-3 indicate about the relative reactivity of calcium and magnesium compared to that of sodium and potassium? Account for any differences in terms of the ionization energies of these metals. Base the explanation on the different factors which affect the ionization energies of elements.

5. Does the evidence collected in this experiment suggest that metallic elements form acidic or basic oxides?

6. Do you think barium, element number 56, would react with hydrochloric acid? If so, explain why and how you think it would.

7. Strontium, element number 38, forms an oxide which reacts with water. Would you expect the solution to be acidic or basic? Why?

8. What trends in solubilities of the sulphates of these metals is indicated by the results obtained in this experiment?

9. What conclusion can be reached about the solubilities of the carbonates of these metals?

10. Referring to this experiment and experiment 5-2, state some properties of metals.

EXPERIMENT 5-4

The Elements of Group VIIA and Their Compounds

In this experiment, as in Experiments 5-3 and 5-2, the properties of the elements within a group are compared with one another. Record the observations made in this experiment in chart form and later compare these observations with those recorded when the elements of Groups IA and IIA were being examined.

CAUTION: This experiment should only be performed in a room equipped with fume hoods and having adequate ventilation facilities.

Procedure

Part I   Chlorine

Demonstration

1. Observe a sample of chlorine as it exists under normal room conditions. Note its colour, odour and physical state.

2. Collect seven bottles of chlorine. Note the density of chlorine relative to air.

3. To one bottle of chlorine add 20 ml of water. Close the bottle with a solid rubber stopper and shake vigorously. Test the resulting solution with pieces of red and blue litmus paper. Note all of the changes observed.

4. **CAUTION:** Handle the sodium and potassium with forceps.

(a) Place a small piece of sodium on a deflagrating spoon lined with asbestos. Warm the metal gently and lower it into a second bottle of chlorine.

(b) Repeat this procedure using a small piece of potassium and a third bottle of chlorine.

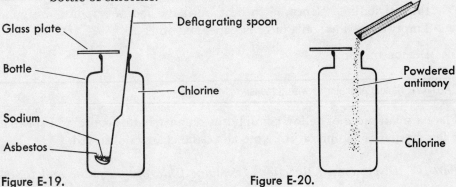

Figure E-19.

Figure E-20.

5. Heat a strip of copper foil held in forceps and, when red hot, thrust it quickly into a fourth bottle of chlorine.

6. Warm a small pinch of powdered antimony on a scoop and sprinkle it into a fifth bottle of chlorine.

7. Place a small amount of red phosphorus on a deflagrating spoon lined with asbestos paper and lower it into a sixth bottle of chlorine. It will be necessary to warm the phosphorus.

Part II Bromine

Demonstration

1. Observe a sample of bromine as it exists under normal room conditions. Note its colour, odour and physical state.

2. Collect seven bottles of bromine. Note the density of bromine relative to water and to air.

3. Repeat procedures 3 to 7 inclusive of Part I using bromine vapour in place of chlorine.

Part III Iodine

1. Observe a sample of iodine as it exists under normal room conditions. Heat it gently without melting. Note its colour, odour, density relative to air, physical state and the effect of gentle heating.

2. Place some iodine in two separate test tubes (18 × 150 mm).

3. To one tube containing iodine add 20 ml of water. Stopper the tube with a rubber stopper and shake vigorously. Test the resulting solution with pieces of red and blue litmus paper. Note all of the changes observed including the density of iodine relative to water.

4. Heat the crystals of iodine in a second tube until iodine vapour fills the tube. Sprinkle a pinch of warm powdered antimony into this test tube of iodine. Continue to heat until the iodine vapours are gone. Empty the residue on a piece of paper and observe.

5. Demonstration

CAUTION: Handle phosphorus with forceps.

Place a small piece of yellow phosphorus on an asbestos gauze and sprinkle a few crystals of iodine on it. Note all of the changes observed.

Part IV   Displacement Reactions Involving Chlorine, Bromine and Iodine

---

CAUTION: Handle carbon tetrachloride in a well-ventilated area only. Avoid inhaling the vapour and do not let the liquid come in contact with your skin.

---

1. Add 1 ml of carbon tetrachloride to each of three test tubes (13 × 100 mm).

2. Add 2 ml of chlorine water to one of the above test tubes. Stopper the test tube and shake the contents. Note any change observed.

3. Repeat procedure 2 using (a) bromine water instead of chlorine water, (b) iodine water (iodine dissolved in potassium iodide solution or iodine dissolved in ethanol and water) instead of chlorine water.

4. Add the solution or liquid indicated in the chart below to three separate test tubes (13 × 100 mm). Follow the suggested order and perform the intermediate shaking procedure as indicated in the chart. Label each test tube. Note all changes observed.

Successive Operations	Test Tube 1	Test Tube 2	Test Tube 3
1.	potassium chloride (3 ml)	potassium bromide (3 ml)	potassium iodide (3 ml)
2.	carbon tetrachloride (1 ml)	carbon tetrachloride (1 ml)	carbon tetrachloride (1 ml)
3.	Stopper each test tube and shake the contents for a few seconds.		
4.	chlorine water (2 ml)	chlorine water (2 ml)	chlorine water (2 ml)
5.	Stopper each test tube and shake the contents for a few seconds.		

5. Repeat procedure 4 using (a) bromine water in place of chlorine water, (b) iodine water instead of chlorine water.

Questions for Thought and Discussion

1. Justify grouping these elements together in the periodic table on the basis of the results of these experiments.

2. What do the results of these experiments indicate about the relative reactivity of chlorine, bromine and iodine?

3. (a) Account for these differences in reactivity in terms of the ionization energies (or electron affinities) of these nonmetals basing the explanation on the different factors which affect the ionization energies (or electron affinities) of these elements.

   (b) List these elements in ascending order of their electronegativities.

4. Would you expect fluorine, element 9 or astatine, element 85, to be more or less reactive than chlorine? Justify your answer.

5. Does the evidence collected in these experiments suggest that the halogens are acid formers or base formers?

6. Generally speaking, how do the ionization energies of metals compare with those of nonmetals?

7. Compare the properties of these elements with the properties of the elements of Group IA or Group IIA.

EXPERIMENT 5-5

The Elements of Period Three And Their Compounds

In the previous three experiments the properties of the elements within a group of the periodic table were examined. Some of the procedures in this experiment are similar to those in the previous experiments but it is the elements of a *period* that are being compared. Again it is essential to record the observations accurately and to compare carefully the properties of the elements in the period. Use chart form for recording the observations.

Procedure

Part I   Properties of the Elements

Demonstration

1. Observe each of the elements in period three in its uncombined form. Note any changes that occur when a freshly cut surface is exposed to air.

---

2. CAUTION: If yellow phosphorus is used in this procedure it must be kept completely immersed in water while the test is carried out. Handle this yellow phosphorus with forceps only. Red phosphorus can be used in this procedure. Similarly, handle the sodium with great care and use forceps. The kerosene can be removed from the sodium by patting it with a dry paper towel.

Test the electrical conductivity of the elements of Period Three that are *solids* by touching the electrodes of the conductivity apparatus to the ends of a short piece of each solid. Predict the electrical conductivity of solid chlorine and argon.

3. Add a small amount of each element to water in a test tube. If no reaction occurs, warm the mixture. The action of chlorine with water can be observed by bubbling the gas through water. The activity of magnesium with steam can be demonstrated by passing steam over hot magnesium turnings. (Caution: See guide to the laboratory sessions.) Retain these solutions for procedure 4.

4. Test each solution produced in procedure 3 with hydrogen-ion test paper or universal indicator solution.

5. CAUTION: Use an extremely small portion of sodium for this procedure. Handle the sodium with forceps and wear safety glasses. It is recommended that the reaction with sodium be done as a demonstration.

Add a small amount of each element to a solution of 2M hydrochloric acid. If no reaction occurs the mixture can be warmed and a more concentrated acid solution can be used.

Part II   Structures of The Elements

1. Assemble models of the crystals representative of the metals sodium, magnesium and aluminium using two-inch styrofoam spheres. Refer to Figure E-21 for the arrangement, or *packing* of the atoms.
   Nine spheres will be required for the model of the sodium crystal, 17 spheres will be required for the model of the magnesium crystal, and 14 spheres will be required for the model of the aluminum crystal. The spheres can be linked together using pipe cleaners.

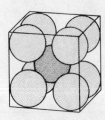
Sodium

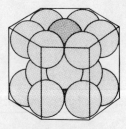
Magnesium

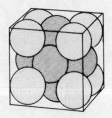
Aluminum

Figure E-21.

Alternate Procedure

Construct three plastic containers of suitable size and shape that they will just hold the two-inch spheres in the arrangement indicated in each of the three diagrams in Figure E-21. These containers can be constructed using Scotch tape and acetate sheets unless a more permanent arrangement is desired. Once the containers are prepared, insert the styrofoam spheres as indicated in Figure E-21.

The packing of the spheres in the case of magnesium and aluminum represents the closest possible packing of identical spheres (atoms or ions).

2. Construct a model of the silicon crystal using one-inch styrofoam spheres and pipe cleaners. Consult Figure E-22 for the appropriate arrangement.

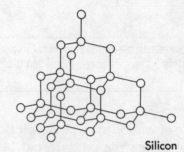

Figure E-22.

Silicon

3. Construct models of the molecules of phosphorus, sulphur, chlorine and argon according to Figure E-23 using two-inch styrofoam spheres.

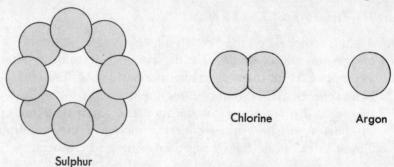

Phosphorus

Sulphur

Chlorine

Argon

Figure E-23.

Part III   Properties Of The Compounds Of These Elements

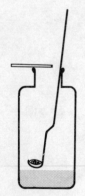

Figure E-24.

1. CAUTION: Handle the sodium with forceps and wear safety glasses.

(a) Remove any liquid from a piece of sodium using blotting paper. Line a deflagrating spoon with asbestos. Place a piece of sodium the size of a pea in the deflagrating spoon and warm the sodium with a burner.

(b) Once the reaction begins, lower the deflagrating spoon into a gas bottle containing 10 ml of water. Cover the gas bottle with a glass plate and allow the reaction to continue.

(c) When the reaction is complete, remove the deflagrating spoon and shake the beaker and contents, keeping the glass plate in position.

(d) Add red and blue litmus to the contents of the beaker.

2. (a) Hold one end of a 6 cm strip of magnesium ribbon with tongs and ignite the other end in the burner flame. Hold the burning magnesium over a beaker so that the product drops into the beaker.

(b) Add 5 ml of water to the product and heat gently. Add pieces of red and blue litmus paper to the contents of the beaker.

3. (a) To 5 ml of 0.1M aluminum nitrate solution, add 1 ml of 6M ammonia-water solution. Shake the test tube. Allow any solid formed to settle and pour off the supernatant liquid.

(b) Wash this solid several times by adding a small amount (2 or 3 ml) of distilled water, shaking the contents of the test tube, allowing the solid to settle again and pouring off the supernatant liquid. (This process is called washing by decantation, see Figure I-42.)

(c) Suspend the solid in distilled water and test with pieces of red and blue litmus paper. Allow the solid to settle again and pour off the supernatant liquid.

(d) Remove the pieces of litmus paper and transfer half of this solid to a second test tube. Retain these two test tubes and their contents for a later procedure.

4. Add 0.3g of hydrous silicon dioxide (silica gel) to 10 ml of distilled water. Add pieces of red and blue litmus paper to this mixture.

5. (a) Put a piece of red phosphorus the size of a matchhead in the asbestos-lined bowl of a deflagrating spoon. Ignite it in a burner flame and lower it into a gas bottle of air containing 10 ml of water.

(b) Cover the gas bottle with a glass plate and shake the contents.

(c) Add pieces of red and blue litmus paper to the contents of the bottle.

6. Repeat procedure 5 using a piece of sulphur the size of a small pea.

7. Test 10 ml of a 0.5 M solution of perchloric acid with pieces of red and blue litmus paper.

8. (a) Place a small amount of the relatively insoluble white powder produced from the burning of magnesium (procedure 2) in each of two test tubes. Add 1 ml of 6M sodium hydroxide to one test tube and 1 ml of 6M hydrochloric acid to the other.

(b) Repeat procedure (a) above using the two test tubes retained from procedure 3.

(c) Repeat procedure (a) using a small amount of hydrous silicon dioxide (silica gel) in each of two test tubes.

9. In each of the three parts of this procedure two substances are reacted together to form a *hydride* of one of the elements in the periodic table. Hydrides are compounds containing hydrogen and one other element. It is these hydrides whose properties we are comparing, not the reactants.

Note: Since the hydrogen compound (a hydride) of phosphorus is poisonous and flammable, the hydrogen compound (a hydride), of nitrogen the corresponding element in period two, is substituted in (c) to show variations in properties of the hydrides of the elements.

(a) Place 1 g of sodium chloride in a test tube. Clamp the test tube then add 2 ml of 6M sulphuric acid. Heat the tube gently. Insert moistened pieces of red and blue litmus paper into the vapour in the upper part of the test tube.

(b) Repeat procedure (a) using 1 g of iron (II) sulphide in place of the sodium chloride.

(c) Repeat procedure (a) using 1 g of ammonium chloride solid and 2 ml of 6M sodium hydroxide solution.

Questions for Thought and Discussion

1. What is the trend in the electrical conductivity of these elements?

2. Which of the elements appear to have reacted with air?

3. (a) What trend in reactivity with water is indicated?
   (b) Are the solutions acidic or basic?
   (c) Arrange the elements in order of their ability to react with water to liberate hydrogen gas.

4. Silicon has a much higher melting point than aluminum. How can this be explained in terms of the change in crystal structure which occurs?

5. How do the magnitudes of the melting points and boiling points of phosphorus, sulphur, chlorine and argon compare with those of the first four elements in the period?

6. What do the results of procedures 1 to 7 of Part III indicate about the reaction of the oxides of the representative elements with water?

7. In what way does the slightly soluble compound of aluminum formed in procedure 8(b) (Part III) differ in its behaviour from that of the slightly soluble compounds of the *other* elements (that is, magnesium and silicon) in the period?

8. What do the results of the litmus test indicate about the relative acidic properties (acidity) of the water solutions of the respective hydrides of nitrogen, chlorine and sulphur?

9. How would you expect the water solution of the hydride of phosphorus to compare in acidic properties (acidity) with those of nitrogen, chlorine and sulphur?

10. What gradation(s) in properties, as one moves across this period from left to right, is (are) indicated by the results of these experiments?

11. How can the change in metallic (or nonmetallic) activity as one moves from left to right across a period be accounted for?

12. Is the trend in ionization energies paralleled by a corresponding trend in metallic and nonmetallic characteristics? Use the elements of Period Three to illustrate.

EXPERIMENT 6-1

Models to Illustrate Bonding

In this experiment we shall construct and study boundary surface models to represent pure *s* and *p* atomic orbitals. Having established this representation for single atoms, we shall then use these models to illustrate σ and π bonding which occur when atoms combine to form molecules.

Procedure

Part I   Models Of Atomic Orbitals

1. Construct a model of an *s*-orbital by placing white, red and blue plastic tubes into the corresponding coloured holes of the white 4″ diameter sphere. The mutually perpendicular rods represent the *X*, *Y* and *Z* axes of three dimensional space.

   (a) What does this model actually represent?

   (b) Draw a boundary surface diagram of a 1*s* oribtal in your notebook.

   (c) How do 2*s* and 3*s* orbitals differ from the 1*s* orbital?

   (d) Which elements, other than the transition elements, have differentiating electrons that half-fill or completely fill valence *s*-orbitals?

2. Construct a model of $2p_x$, $2p_z$ and $2p_y$-orbitals using a 6-pronged (octahedral) connector. Fasten pairs of white, red and blue plastic tubes and matching colour lobes to this connector.

   (a) What does this model actually represent?

   (b) Draw a boundary surface diagram of these 2*p*-orbitals in your notebook.

   (c) How do 3*p* and 4*p*-orbitals differ from 2*p*-orbitals?

(d) Which elements, other than the transition elements, have differentiating electrons that paritally fill or completely fill valence p-orbitals?

Part II   Models of Covalent Bonds

1. Construct a second model of an s-orbital and a second model of p_x, p_y and p_z-orbitals. Now demonstrate the s-s, s-p and p-p overlaps that produce σ bonds using the previously constructed models of s and p-orbitals. Arbitrarily choose the X-axis, say the white plastic tubes, as the one along which bonding occurs. Overlapping of the orbitals can be simulated by placing the models behind one another, overlapping the appropriate orbitals slightly and viewing the whole model directly from the front.

(a) Draw a boundary surface diagram in your notebook of each overlap you are able to demonstrate. Shade in the overlap regions appropriately.

(b) What conditions must be true in ideal atoms before atomic orbitals can overlap to form a bond?

2. Now demonstrate the overlaps which produce π bonds by bringing together two models of p-orbitals. Again, overlap the models slightly by placing one behind the other and viewing them directly from the front.

(a) If you label p-orbitals as p_x, p_y and p_z and assume σ bonding occurs along the X-axis, which overlaps produce π bonds?

(b) Draw boundary surface diagrams in your notebook of π bonds produced by overlap of p-orbitals, being careful to label the axes clearly.

(c) What is the maximum number of electrons that can occupy one π bond orbital?

Part III   Models of Diatomic Molecules

Using orbital and covalent bond models as outlined in Parts I and II, demonstrate the bonding in each molecule listed below. Describe this bonding in detail by answering the questions associated with each molecule.

1. THE HYDROGEN MOLECULE

Using models of 1s orbitals, show the overlap of atomic orbitals that occurs when this molecule forms.

(a) What type of bond is formed?

(b) Write the electronic configuration and orbital box representations for two approaching hydrogen atoms. In the orbital box representations be sure to consider the spins of the interacting electrons.

(c) Draw and label a boundary surface diagram showing all of the orbitals in this model of the hydrogen molecule, H_2. Label the axes and shade in appropriately the region where orbitals overlap to form a bond.

(d) Compare the diagram in (c) with the electron-dot representation for the hydrogen molecule.

(e) Write the orbital box representation to indicate the bonding in the hydrogen molecule.

2. HALOGEN MOLECULES

Using models of the p-orbitals of separate halogen atoms show which orbitals overlap to form a bond. Make an arbitrary choice in selecting the bond axis.

(a) What type of bond is formed?

(b) Write the complete electronic configuration and corresponding orbital box representations for two approaching bromine atoms. Be sure to consider the spins of the interacting electrons.

(c) Draw and label a boundary surface diagram showing all of the orbitals in this model of the bromine molecule, Br_2. Shade in appropriately the region where orbitals overlap to form a bond.

(d) Compare the diagram above with the electron-dot representation for the bromine molecule.

(e) Write the orbital box representation to indicate the bonding in the bromine molecule.

3. THE OXYGEN MOLECULE

Demonstrate the overlap of atomic orbitals for this molecule by bringing together two models of p-orbitals along an arbitrarily selected bonding axis.

(a) What types of bonds are formed?

(b) Write the complete electronic configuration and orbital box representations for two approaching oxygen atoms.

(c) Draw a labelled boundary surface diagram showing all of the orbitals in the model of the oxygen molecule, O_2. Shade in appropriately the regions where orbitals overlap to form bonds.

(d) Compare the diagram above with the electron-dot representation for the oxygen molecule.

(e) Write the orbital box representation for the oxygen molecule.

(f) Are there any unpaired electrons in these representations of molecular oxygen? Explain.

4. THE NITROGEN MOLECULE

Bring models of p-orbitals of separate nitrogen atoms together and note the overlaps that can occur.

(a) What types of bonds are formed?

(b) Write the complete electronic configuration and orbital box representations for two approaching nitrogen atoms.

(c) Draw a labelled boundary surface diagram showing all of the orbitals in the model of the nitrogen molecule, N_2. Shade in appropriately the regions where orbitals overlap to form bonds.

(d) Compare the above diagram with the electron-dot representation for the nitrogen molecule.

(e) Write the orbital box representation for the nitrogen molecule.

(f) Are there any unpaired electrons in these representations of molecular nitrogen?

5. HYDROGEN HALIDE MOLECULES

Show the overlap of atomic orbitals for these molecules by using models of s and p atomic orbitals for the hydrogen and halogen atoms respectively.

(a) What type of bond is formed?

(b) Write complete electronic configurations and the corresponding orbital box representations for approaching hydrogen and fluorine atoms.

(c) Draw and label a boundary surface diagram of the hydrogen fluoride molecule, HF, showing all of the orbitals in the model. Shade in the overlap regions.

(d) Compare the above diagram with the electron-dot representation for the hydrogen fluoride molecule.

(e) Write the orbital box representation for this molecule.

EXPERIMENT 7-1

Further Models to Illustrate Bonding

In Experiment 6-1 boundary surface models were constructed to represent pure atomic orbitals. These models were used to illustrate σ and π bonding in diatomic molecules. In Experiment 7-1 these ideas are extended as boundary surface models are constructed to represent the following *hybrid* orbitals: *sp*, *sp²*, *sp³*, *sp³d*, *sp³d²*. These models are then used to illustrate the bonding that occurs and the shapes of molecules involving two, three, four, five and six electron-pairs in the valence level of the central atom.

A boundary surface model for a hybrid orbital should consist of two lobes, one much larger than the other, that is, ∞. For convenience, the smaller lobe is omitted from the models we are constructing. A single yellow lobe in these models represent the larger lobe of any hybrid orbital. Notice too, that *any* hybrid orbital is represented by the yellow lobe despite the fact that the size of these lobes differs with the different types of hybridization. A single black lobe represents a filled or non-bonding hybrid orbital. Black plastic tubing is used to support all hybrid orbitals.

Procedure

Part I   Models of Hybrid Orbitals

1. *sp-hybrids*, two electron-pairs in the valence level of the central atom. Fasten a piece of the black plastic tubing to each prong of the 6-pronged (octahedral) connector. Assuming that one yellow lobe represents one hybrid orbital, choose the appropriate number of yellow lobes to represent *sp* hybridization in an atom. Place these lobes on the plastic tubing to correctly illustrate the way in which these orbitals are oriented in space about the atom.

Draw a boundary surface diagram to illustrate the *sp*-hybrid orbitals

(a) separately

(b) superimposed.

2. *sp²-hybrids*, three electron-pairs in the valence level of the central atom.

Using the 5-pronged (trigonal bipyramidal) connector, black plastic tubing and yellow lobes construct a model to represent *sp²* hybridization in an atom.

Draw a boundary surface diagram to illustrate *sp²*-hybrid orbitals

(a) separately

(b) superimposed.

Continuing with the procedure by following the pattern established in 1 and 2, construct models for the following hybrid orbitals:

3. *sp³-hybrids*, four electron-pairs in the valence level of the central atom, 4-pronged (tetrahedral) connector.

4. *sp³d-hybrids*, five electron-pairs in the valence level of the central atom, 5-pronged (trigonol bypyramidal) connector.

5. *sp³d²-hybrids*, six electron-pairs in the valence level of the central atom, 6-pronged (octahedral) connector.

Part II Models of Polyatomic Molecules

1. (a) Using the appropriate connector, black plastic tubing and yellow lobes construct a model to represent the hybrid orbitals that result from the electrons in the valence level of the beryllium atom, Be. What type of hybridization occurs in the beryllium atom?

(b) Construct a separate model showing the $2p$ atomic orbitals of a fluorine atom, F.

(c) Using these two models demonstrate the overlap that is possible between beryllium and fluorine orbitals. It is important to remember that each *p*-orbital of the fluorine atom model consists of a *pair* of lobes while each hybrid orbital of beryllium is represented by a single lobe.
Write the chemical formula for this molecule.

(d) What type(s) of bond is formed in this molecule?

(e) Write the electronic configurations and orbital box representations for Be and F atoms in the ground state.

(f) Write the orbital box representation for Be in the first excited state and in the hybridized state. Indicate the hybrid orbitals with brackets.

(g) Draw and label a boundary surface diagram showing all of the orbitals in the model of this molecule. Shade in appropriately the region where orbitals overlap to form a bond.

(h) Indicate the bond angle(s) and molecular shape of this molecule.

(i) Write the orbital box and electron-dot representations for this molecule.

(j) `In what respect would the model differ if it had been constructed to represent the molecule that forms when beryllium and chlorine atoms combine?

2. Repeat procedure 1 but substitute a boron atom, B, for the beryllium atom.

3. (a) Repeat procedure 1, parts (a) to (i) inclusive. This time substitute a carbon atom, C, for beryllium and use a hydrogen atom instead of the fluorine atom indicated in part (b).

   In some molecules involving hybrid orbitals one or more of these orbitals may contain an electron-pair that is not involved in bonding, that is, a non-bonding pair of electrons. The presence of such a pair of electrons affects the geometry of the resulting molecule because a non-bonded pair of electrons occupies a greater volume than a bonded pair. In the procedure that follows a single black lobe will represent the hybrid orbital of a non-bonded electron-pair.

   (b) Remove one of the yellow lobes from the model of the carbon atom and replace it by a black lobe which represents a non-bonded electron-pair.

       (i) How would the presence of the non-bonded electron-pair affect the geometry of the remaining sp^3 hybrid orbitals in the molecule? How do the bond angles compare with the bond angles of the tetrahedral arrangement?

       (ii) The ammonia molecule, NH_3, is a typical example of this arrangement. Three hydrogen, H, atoms are bonded to the hybrid orbitals of the central nitrogen atom, N. Show that this arrangement is possible by writing the orbital box representations for the nitrogen atom in the ground and hybridized states and for the hydrogen atom in the ground state. Indicate the hybrid orbitals with brackets. Note the non-bonded electron-pair in the valence level.

       (iii) Draw and label the boundary surface diagram for an ammonia molecule. Clearly label the bond angles and shade in appropriately the regions where orbitals overlap to form a bond.

   (c) Returning to the original model of the carbon atom, remove two of the yellow lobes and replace them by two black lobes representing two non-bonded electron-pairs.

       (i) How would the presence of this second non-bonded electron-pair affect the bond angle between the remaining two sp^3 hybrid orbitals in the molecule?

EXPERIMENT 7-1

(ii) The water molecule, H_2O, is an example of this arrangement. Show that this is the case by following a procedure similar to 3(b)(ii) above.

(iii) Repeat procedure 3(b)(iii) for the water molecule.

4. Following procedure 1, substitute a phosphorus atom for the beryllium atom and complete the procedure to illustrate the hybridization and geometry in the molecule PF_5. In drawing the boundary surface diagram the fluorine atom can be represented merely as (F) and overlapped appropriately with the hybrid orbitals of the phosphorus.

3. Following procedure 1, substitute a sulphur atom for the beryllium atom and complete the procedure to illustrate the hybridization and geometry in the molecule SF_6. Again, the convention (F) may be used for convenience to represent the fluorine atom in the boundary surface diagram.

Part III   Boundary Surface Diagrams for Molecules Involving C-C Bonds

Each molecule listed below contains two carbon atoms bonded to one another by single, double or triple covalent bonds. The hydrogen atoms are bonded in turn to the carbon atoms.

Molecular Formula	Compound
C_2H_6	ethane
C_2H_4	ethene (ethylene)
C_2H_2	ethyne (acetylene)

Using the ideas gained in experiments 6-1 and 7-1 and working with the same models, it is possible to establish the geometry of the three molecules above. To direct your thinking consider the answers to the following questions:

(a) What are the covalences of C and H?
(b) With due regard for the covalences, what is the rough arrangement of atoms in the molecule?
(c) What are the orbital box representations for C and H in the ground state?
(d) Is promotion of electrons necessary?
(e) What types of hybridization occurs?
(f) Write the orbital box representation and show the hybrid orbitals.
(g) What type(s) of bonding occurs in the molecule?

(h) What is the shape of the molecule?

(i) Draw the boundary surface diagram of the molecule.

Questions for Thought and Discussion

1. Experiments show that boron trifluoride and fluoride ion react as follows:

$$BF_3 + F^- \rightarrow BF_4^-$$

(a) What type of bonding occurs between the boron trifluoride and the fluoride ion? Be specific.

(b) From a consideration of the number of electron pairs about the boron atom in this species BF_4^- what type of hybridization is evident?

(c) What is the bond angle?

2. In the molecule PF_3 the bond angle F-P-F is found to be 100.0°. By reasoning from the electronic configuration of the atoms

(a) indicate the type of hybridization,

(b) describe the shape of the molecule, and

(c) explain the bond angle of 100°.

3. During the experiment you established the hybridization, shape and bond angles for the molecule sulphur hexafluoride, SF_6. Molecules of sulphur difluoride, SF_2, and sulphur tetrafluoride, SF_4, have also been isolated. For both molecules it is found that all the fluorine atoms within a molecule are identical in their chemical behaviour. Establish the probable molecular shape and bond angle(s) for each molecule. Show your reasoning clearly.

4. Consider the compound hydrogen fluoride, HF.

(a) How many electrons of the fluorine atom with principal quantum number 2 are involved in the H-F bond and how many are not?

(b) Considering the fluorine atom as the central atom in this molecule, how are the bonded and non-bonded electrons probably arranged about this central atom? Explain your reasoning. Is there any reason to suspect that hybridization occurs? If so, what type of hybridization would you expect?

(c) Based upon the arguments you presented in answering question 4(b), how would you expect the bonded and non-bonded electrons to be arranged around the atoms in each of the following molecules:

(i) F_2 (ii) O_2 (iii) N_2 (iv) HCl (v) CO? Would you expect hybridization to occur?

EXPERIMENT 8-1

The Nature Of Covalent Bonds (Demonstration)

CAUTION: Carbon disulphide is very poisonous, volatile and inflammable. Never use it near to an open flame or without adequate ventilation. Carbon tetrachloride is also very poisonous and volatile. It should only be used if adequate ventilation is available. Ideally this experiment should be performed in a fume cupboard.

Procedure

1. Bring (a) a charged ebonite rod, (b) a charged glass rod up to an uncharged pith ball and note what is observed.

2. Bring (a) a charged ebonite rod, (b) a charged glass rod up to a positively charged pith ball and note what is observed.

3. Repeat procedure 2 using a negatively charged pith ball and note what is observed.

4. Bring (a) a charged ebonite rod, (b) a charged glass rod up to a steady, slow moving stream of the following liquids:

    (i) water (from a tap)
    (ii) carbon disulphide
    (iii) carbon tetrachloride

The carbon disulphide and carbon tetrachloride should be placed in separate burettes that are clamped to a retort stand. Allow each liquid to run from the burette into a beaker placed directly below it on the laboratory desk. Use a fume hood if one is available (Figure E-25).

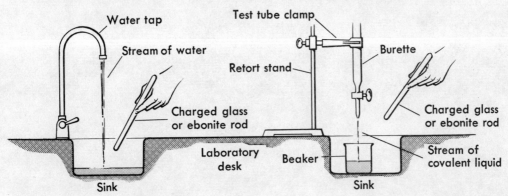

Figure E-25. *An apparatus to test the influence of electrostatic charge on streams of covalent liquids.*

5. Summarize the results by completing a data table in your notebook like the one that follows.

DATA TABLE

Effect on	Charged Ebonite Rod	Charged Glass Rod
pith ball (neutral)		
pith ball (positively charged)		
pith ball (negatively charged)		
water, H_2O		
carbon disulphide, CS_2		
carbon tetrachloride, CCl_4		

Questions for Thought and Discussion

1. How does the behaviour of the liquids studied compare to the behaviour of a neutral or a charged pith ball when under the influence of (a) a charged ebonite rod and (b) a charged glass rod?

2. Do all of the liquids behave in the same way under the influence of an electrostatic charge?

3. Based upon these experimental results, what do you suppose the electrical nature of molecules of these covalent liquids may be?

4. Formulate a model, based upon your present knowledge of structure and bonding, which will explain the experimental results and provide support for the validity of the supposition made in question 3.

EXPERIMENT 8-2

Covalent Molecules

In this experiment you are provided with a molecular model set from which the models of various molecules will be constructed. Check the list of contents of this model set with the actual contents of the box and report any discrepancies. Always use the longest set of spring connectors for multiple bonds. To answer the questions at the end of the experiment, consult tables of (a) *electronegativities* and (b) *electronegativity difference and percentage ionic character* found in your text. At the end of the experiment, reassemble the kit into the pattern shown on the box cover.

Procedure

Two sets of models will be assembled using the molecular model sets in this experiment.

Set 1. Consists of models of the molecules: hydrogen, chlorine, oxygen, nitrogen, hydrogen chloride, bromine chloride, hydrogen bromide.

Set 2. Consists of models of the molecules: water, carbon dioxide, hydrogen sulphide, ammonia, methane, carbon tetrachloride, methyl chloride.

1. Assemble the first set of seven models and have them checked by the teacher. Complete a Data Table like the one that follows.

2. Take these models apart and proceed similarly with the second set.

DATA TABLE

Short Form	Electron-dot Representation	Bond Type (polar or nonpolar)	Shape of Molecule	Kind of Molecule (polar or nonpolar)
Set 1 H_2 Cl_2 O_2 N_2 HCl $BrCl$ HBr				
Set 2 H_2O CO_2 H_2S NH_3 CH_4 CCl_4 CH_3Cl				

Questions for Thought and Discussion

1. Calculate the electronegativity difference and percentage of ionic character for each of the following bonds:

    (a) H-O   (b) H-N   (c) H-Cl
    (d) Br-Cl   (e) H-S   (f) H-C
    (g) Cl-Cl   (h) C-O   (i) K-Br
    (j) Na-O

2. Classify each of the following as ionic, polar covalent, or nonpolar covalent molecules:

    (a) Br_2 (b) $MgCl_2$ (c) CCl_4 (d) HI
    (e) CO_2 (f) H_2O (g) N_2 (h) NaI

3. Both water and carbon dioxide are triatomic molecules. Explain why one of these is polar and the other is nonpolar.

EXPERIMENT 8-2

EXPERIMENT 8-3

Bonding Capacities Of Atoms, Shapes and Polarities
Of Molecules

This experiment examines the electron population of the *valence-level* of a number of atoms. The valence-level electrons of an atom are all those electrons past the last noble gas configuration.

From a knowledge of the valence-level electrons it is possible to predict the formulas and shapes of covalent molecules. This experiment is only concerned with the *covalent bonds* formed when each of two atoms donates one electron to form a shared pair of electrons.

You will receive five coloured styrofoam spheres. Each sphere is a simple model of one of the representative (nontransition) elements in periods 2, 3, 4, 5 and 6 of the Periodic Table. Each of these "atoms" has eight tacks (white or black) stuck to its surface. The white tacks represent the electrons in the energy level of the atom with the highest principal quantum number. The black tacks represent "electron vacancies". Notice that these electrons are the valence electrons of these atoms since we are dealing with representative elements only. The valence electrons and "vacancies" are arranged as they might be found in the isolated atoms in their ground state, that is, they are arranged in orbitals. Some orbitals contain two electrons (two white tacks). Others contain one electron and one "vacancy" (one white and one black tack). Still others contain no electron, a double "vacancy" (two black tacks). The vacant *d*-orbitals are not shown in these models.

You may make the following assumptions:

(a) All bond distances and strengths are equivalent for a given central atom.

(b) Hybrid orbitals are formed by mixing the characteristics of pure atomic orbitals.

(c) The *d*-orbitals are vacant and available for bonding.

(d) Each atom must contribute one electron to the pair being shared by two atoms. Thus the condition for forming a covalent bond is one electron and one vacancy (a white-tack, black-tack combination).

(e) The electrons rearrange themselves to make a maximum number of orbitals available for bond formation (white-tack, black-tack combinations) in atoms which have some orbitals with two electrons (two white tacks) and others with no electrons (two black tacks).

Prepare a data table similar to the one given below before the laboratory period. Fill in this table as you proceed with the experiment.

Procedure

1. For each atom determine the number of electrons in the energy level with the highest principal quantum number (which in representative elements is also the number of valence-level electrons).

2. Write the valence-level electronic configuration of each atom. Do not show the principal quantum number but indicate the electron population of the individual *p*-orbitals.

3. (a) Determine the maximum number of single covalent bonds each atom is capable of forming by contributing one electron to a shared pair. Assume the atoms have at least three principal energy levels.

   (b) Determine the type of hybridization that occurs when the maximum number of other atoms bond to the given atom. (Assume the models represent atoms of the representative elements from Row 3 in the Periodic Table.)

4. Write the bond angles that you would expect to observe between atoms bonding to the central atom in each of the molecules formed if the central atom forms the maximum number of single bonds.

5. Indicate the shape of each of the molecules formed when the central atom forms the maximum number of single bonds with other atoms.

6. Assume that a covalent compound is formed when each atom reacts with chlorine and, using the code letters, write the short forms for the compounds formed.

7. Indicate whether the covalent bonds are polar or nonpolar.

8. Assume that all of the chlorine compounds are covalent and indicate whether the molecule is polar or nonpolar.

DATA TABLE

COLOUR	YELLOW	RED	GREEN	BLUE	WHITE
CODE LETTER	A	B	C	D	E
number of electrons in the energy level with the highest principal quantum number					
electronic configuration of the orbitals in the energy level with the highest principal quantum number					
maximum number of single covalent bonds atom can form					
type of hybridization when all valence electrons are used to form single covalent bonds					
bond angles between atoms attached to central atom					
shape of molecule that would be formed					
formula of covalent chlorine compound					
polar or nonpolar bond(s)					
polar or nonpolar molecule					

Questions for Thought and Discussion

1. Do NH_3 and BF_3 have the same shape? Explain. Can both NH_3 and BF_3 form coordinate covalent bonds? Explain the differences.

2. Is it possible for bromine to form a compound such as BrF_7? Can fluorine form a compound FBr_7? Explain your answers.

3. Predict the shapes of the following molecules or ions:

   (a) CCl_4 (b) BCl_3 (c) CaH_2

   (d) PH_3 (e) H_3O^+ (f) PO_4^{3-}

4. Write the electron-dot diagram for each of the chlorine compounds listed in the data table.

5. Write the electron-dot formula for each of the following molecules or ions and predict their shapes.

   (a) sulphur trioxide, SO_3 (d) sulphate ion SO_3^{2-}

   (c) carbonate ion CO_3^{2-} (b) sulphite ion, SO_4^{2-}

EXPERIMENT 8-4

The Oxidation States of Some Transition Elements

Many elements exhibit more than one oxidation state. Such behaviour is a typical characteristic of transition elements. In this experiment the oxidation states of three transition elements, chromium, manganese and iron are investigated. It is important to note carefully the colours and colour changes throughout the experiment. Prepare the table shown in procedure 3 to summarize your results before coming to the laboratory.

Procedure

Part I Chromium, Cr

1. Add 5 ml of aqueous ammonia, NH_3, to 5 ml of chromium (III) sulphate, $Cr_2(SO_4)_3$, solution. Repeat this experiment using 5 ml of sodium hydroxide, NaOH, solution. Now add an excess of sodium hydroxide solution to the second test tube. Note what is observed in each case.

   When aqueous ammonia or sodium hydroxide solution is added to chromium (III) sulphate, the insoluble solid chromium (III) hyroxide, $Cr(OH)_3$, is formed. On the addition of excess sodium hydroxide a soluble substance sodium chromite, $NaCrO_2$, is formed. What is the oxidation state of chromium in the sodium chromite? Save this solution for procedure 3.

2. To 5 ml of potassium chromate, K_2CrO_4, solution add a hydrochloric acid, HCl, solution until a definite colour change occurs. Record this colour change.

   In this reaction potassium chromate is converted to potassium dichromate, $K_2Cr_2O_7$. What is the oxidation state of chromium in (a) potassium chromate and (b) potassium dichromate?

3. To 5 ml of the alkaline chromite solution from procedure 1, add hydrogen peroxide, H_2O_2, solution until a colour change occurs. Record this colour change.

   The reaction of the sodium chromite with hydrogen peroxide produces a new chromium compound in solution. What new substance is formed? What is the oxidation state of chromium in this compound?

4. Repeat procedure 2 using sulphuric acid, H_2SO_4, solution instead of hydrochloric acid solution. Continue adding this acid until a definite change occurs. To this resulting solution add hydrogen peroxide solution until another colour change occurs. Record the colour changes in each case.

   To which oxidation state is the chromium in the dichromate converted in the reaction with hydrogen peroxide? What change in oxidation state did the chromium undergo?

5. To 5 ml of chromium (III) sulphate solution add 2 pieces of mossy zinc. Heat gently until a colour change occurs. Record the observations carefully.

   This colour is characteristic of chromium in the 2+ oxidation state.

   Decant the solution and shake it with air in the test tube until another colour change occurs. Record the observations carefully.

   In which oxidation state is chromium stable in the presence of air?

Part II Manganese, Mn

1. Add 5 ml of sodium hydroxide solution to 5 ml of manganese (II) sulphate, $MnSO_4$, solution. Add 10 ml more of the sodium hydroxide solution. Note what is observed in each case.

   Compare the behaviour of manganese (II) hydroxide, $Mn(OH)_2$, to that of chromium (III) hydroxide, $Cr(OH)_3$, in the presence of excess sodium hydroxide solution. Has the oxidation state of manganese changed as a result of this treatment with sodium hydroxide?

2. Mix one gram of manganese dioxide, MnO_2, solid with 1.5 g of sodium hydroxide solid and 1.5 g of potassium nitrate, KNO_3, solid in an evaporating dish. Heat until the mass melts, then let it cool. Add water to the dish and stir. Filter the contents of the dish into a cylinder half-filled with water. What is the colour of the filtrate?

   This is the characteristic colour of the manganate ion, MnO_4^{2-}.

   To 10 ml of this solution add nitric acid solution until the solution is acid to litmus paper. Filter. What is the colour of the filtrate?

   This is the characteristic colour of the permanganate ion, MnO_4^-. The brown deposit left on the filter paper is manganese dioxide. What is the oxidation state of manganese in manganate ion, permanganate ion, and manganese dioxide?

Part III   Iron, Fe

Qualitative Tests for Fe²⁺ and Fe³⁺ Ions in Aqueous Solution

Although these ions can be identified from their characteristic colours in aqueous solution, it is often more conclusive to use the qualitative ion tests that are illustrated below (procedures 1 and 2). In each case a solution is prepared which contains the ion to be identified. Addition of the appropriate reagent causes the characteristic colour change which establishes the presence of the ion. Such ion tests are very sensitive. In subsequent procedures these tests are used to determine which form of iron is present in solution.

1. TEST FOR IRON (II) ION, Fe^{2+}, THE FERROUS ION

    (a) Prepare 6 to 8 ml of a dilute solution of iron (II) sulphate, $FeSO_4$, or any other soluble iron (II) salt. Divide this solution into two equal parts.
    In what form would you expect the iron to be present in this solution? Note the colour of the solution. What is the oxidation state of this iron?

    (b) To one part of this solution add a few drops of potassium ferricyanide, $K_3Fe(CN)_6$, solution.

    (c) To the other part of this solution add a few drops of potassium thiocyanate, NH_4CNS, solution.
    Which procedure, (b) or (c), should prove useful in establishing the presence of this form of iron in solution? Retain these tests for reference later in the experiment.

2. TEST FOR IRON (III) ION, Fe^{3+}, THE FERRIC ION

    Prepare 6 to 8 ml of a dilute solution of iron (III) chloride, $FeCl_3$, or any other soluble iron (III) salt. Divide this solution into two equal parts and repeat procedures 1(b) and 1(c) above. Answer the same questions posed in procedure 1 and retain these tests for later reference in the experiment.

    Record the results from procedures 1 and 2 in tabular form.

3. Add finely powdered iron, Fe, solid to a test tube until it just fills the rounded portion at the bottom of the tube. Pour in about 2 ml of dilute hydrochloric acid solution. Filter the mixture while the reaction is still taking place. Immediately divide the filtrate into two equal parts and repeat procedures 1(b) and 1(c).
    In what form is the iron in the resulting solution when iron and dilute hydrochloric acid react? What is the oxidation state of this iron? What colour was the solution before procedures 1(b) and 1(c) were carried out?

114   EXPERIMENT 8-4

4. Add iron (III) oxide, Fe_2O_3, solid to a test tube until the rounded portion at the bottom of the tube is just filled. Pour in about 5 ml of dilute hydrochloric acid solution and heat the mixture slightly. Filter the mixture and divide the filtrate into two equal parts. Repeat procedures 1(b) and 1(c).

   In what form is the iron in the solution resulting from the reaction between iron (III) oxide and dilute hydrochloric acid? What is the oxidation state of the iron? What colour is this solution?

5. Add a few drops of sodium hydroxide solution to 6 to 8 ml of dilute iron (III) chloride solution.

   Note the colour of the precipitate that forms. What is the oxidation state of the iron in this precipitate? Refer to Part I, procedure 1 as a guide to your reasoning.

6. Add a few drops of sodium hydroxide solution to 6 to 8 ml of a dilute solution of iron (II) ammonium sulphate, $Fe(NH_4)_2(SO_4)_2$, (or freshly prepared iron (II) sulphate, $FeSO_4$). Allow the resulting mixture to stand for 10 to 15 minutes. Periodically shake the mixture and watch for colour changes.

   Note the colour and establish the oxidation state of the precipitate that forms when the sodium hydroxide is added. What change in oxidation state occurs as the precipitate stands in air? What evidence suggests this change? Which oxidation state of iron appears to be most stable in air?

7. Pour about 4 ml of dilute iron (II) chloride, $FeCl_2$, solution into a test tube. Slowly add a few drops of chlorine water, $Cl_2(soln)$, to the same test tube and shake the solution. Divide this solution into two parts and repeat procedures 1(b) and 1(c).

   What effect has the chlorine water on the iron (II) chloride solution? What ions are present in solution now that were not present before? Does the oxidation state of iron change? What evidence confirms this view?

8. Pour 5 ml of dilute iron (III) chloride solution into a test tube. Add an equal volume of dilute tin (II) chloride, $SnCl_2$, solution (or a small portion of finely divided zinc). Shake the test tube, then divide the solution into two equal parts. (If zinc is used the mixture must be filtered after the reaction and the filtrate divided into two equal parts.) Repeat procedures 1(b) and 1(c). Compare the results of these tests with the results from procedure 2 of this experiment.

   What form(s) of iron was present in the test tube before the addition of the tin (II) chloride solution? What form(s) was present after this addition? What change in oxidation state has occurred? What evidence confirms this view? What three oxidation states of iron have been observed in Part III of this experiment?

Summarize the results of these experiments in the following table. The table should be copied and completed as in the example. Interpret the results.

	Oxidation State	Electron Populations 3d	4s	Colour
Cr^0	0	⑦⑦⑦⑦⑦	⑦	silvery
Cr^{2+}				
Cr^{3+}				
CrO_2^-				
CrO_4^{2-}				
$Cr_2O_7^{2-}$				
Mn^0				
Mn^{2+}				
MnO_2				
MnO_4^{2-}				
MnO_4^-				
Fe^0				
Fe^{2+}				
Fe^{3+}				

Questions for Thought and Discussion

1. The colour you have recorded above for the species $Cr_2O_7^{2-}$ is said to be the typical colour for this oxidation state of chromium. But the solution containing this species was a potassium dichromate, $K_2Cr_2O_7$, solution. Perhaps this colour is due to the presence of the potassium ion and not the presence of the dichromate ion. Briefly outline a procedure that you might carry out to determine (a) whether this colour is due to the potassium ion, K^+, or the dichromate ion, $Cr_2O_7^{2-}$, (b) whether all dichromates exhibit the same colour in aqueous solution.

2. From your knowledge of electronic structure, suggest a reason for there being a typical colour associated with a given oxidation state of an element.

EXPERIMENT 8-4

EXPERIMENT 9-1

The Formula of a Compound

The chemical formula for any substance must always be determined experimentally. From a knowledge of atomic structure and from these experimentally determined formulas, it is possible to establish a set of rules that will facilitate formula writing and remove much of the sheer "memory work" aspect of such an exercise. Ultimately, however, this set of rules depends on the original experimental procedures used to establish the formulas. In this experiment two elements are combined quantitatively and produce a compound whose formula must be determined.

CAUTION: This experiment should only be performed in a laboratory with excellent ventilation facilities. Ideally, it should be performed only in a fume cupboard.

Procedure

1. Determine the mass of a clean, dry crucible. If it is washed before using, heat the crucible and allow it to cool to room temperature before finding the mass.

2. Cut the lead foil into strips about 1.0 cm wide and 2.0 cm long. Place between 2.5 g and 3.0 g of these strips *loosely* in the crucible. Accurately determine the mass of the crucible + the lead.

3. Add enough powdered sulphur to the crucible to completely cover the lead. Make sure that the sulphur is in contact with all the lead surface.

4. Support the crucible in a clay triangle on a tripod (or on a retort ring attached to a retort stand) and place it under a ventilated hood or in a fume cupboard. Heat the crucible strongly with a hot flame. The

sulphur melts and reacts with the lead. The excess sulphur burns and forms gaseous sulphur dioxide.

5. When no more sulphur vapour is leaving the crucible, place it on a wire gauze using tongs. Allow the crucible to cool to room temperature. Find the mass of the crucible + its contents, now a compound of lead and sulphur.

Calculations

The position of sulphur in the periodic classification indicates that the chemical behaviour of sulphur is similar to that of oxygen. Lead forms several oxides including PbO, PbO_2 and Pb_3O_4. Thus when lead and sulphur combine, the possibility of forming PbS, PbS_2 or Pb_3S_4 should be considered.

The lead and sulphur used in this experiment are naturally occurring samples of these elements. Thus the masses of individual atoms of these elements are represented by their respective atomic weights. Assuming that atoms are neither created nor destroyed during this chemical reaction, the ratio with which the lead and sulphur atoms have combined can be determined by dividing the mass of each element that reacted by the atomic weight of that element (the atomic weight being the weighted average of the masses of the isotopes present in a naturally occurring sample of the element). The ratio of the quotients is the same as the ratio of the number of atoms in the formula of the compound. Make the calculation as follows:

1. Find the mass of lead used.

2. Find the mass of sulphur consumed.

3. Divide the mass of lead used by its atomic weight, and the mass of sulphur used by its atomic weight.

4. Find the ratio between the quotients, "rounding off" to the nearest whole numbers because only whole numbers of atoms are involved in compounds.

Questions for Thought and Discussion

1. What evidence is there that a chemical reaction took place?

2. What is the formula for the compound of lead and sulphur according to your calculations? How does this compare with the results of the rest of the class?

EXPERIMENT 9-1

3. What other formula could be considered to be equally correct for this compound?

4. What type of compound is formed?

5. Assuming that the formula determined in this experiment is correct, what are the oxidation states of lead and sulphur in this compound?

6. (a) What is the name of this compound?
   (b) Could it be named in any other way?

7. What is the mass in grams of one mole of this compound?

8. Would you expect this compound to be predominantly ionic or covalent? Why?

EXPERIMENT 10-1

The Packing of Atoms and Ions in Crystals

In this experiment some of the ways in which atoms pack together to form metallic crystals will be studied. Three types of packing will be considered: (1) hexagonal close packing, (2) cubic close packing (face-centred cubic packing), (3) body-centred cubic packing. The coordination number of the particles in each of these structures will be determined. Some of the ways of packing ions of different radii in lattices of ionic crystals will also be considered. The importance of the radius ratio of cations and anions in determining the coordination number in these crystals will be observed. In addition, some of the methods of packing covalently bonded atoms to form three-dimensional covalent crystals will be considered.

Procedure

Part I   Packing Arrangements Involving Spheres of One Size Only

1. SOME GENERAL CONSIDERATIONS ON THE PACKING OF SPHERES

    (a) Determine how many 2-inch spheres you can pack around a single 2-inch sphere when all spheres are in the same plane. Is this number dependent upon the size of the sphere? Check your prediction.

    (b) Place additional loose spheres above and below the centre sphere so that they all touch it. What is the coordination number for this type of closest packing?

    (c) The three spheres in the top layer can occupy a position directly above a comparable bottom layer or they may be twisted through an angle of 60° and still have the same coordination number. Check this to satisfy yourself that it is true.

2. HEXAGONAL CLOSE PACKING – MODEL A

(a) Connect the groups of spheres you used in procedure 1 with tooth-picks (or short lengths of pipestem cleaners) to obtain the layers shown in Figure E-26.

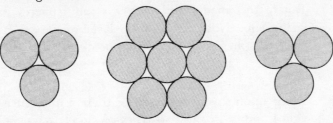

Figure E-26. *Layers for hexagonal close packing.*

(b) Place a layer of three spheres on the desk with the apex of the triangle facing you.

(c) Now place the layer of seven spheres over the three spheres such that the centre sphere fits closely into the depression of the first layer.

(d) For the top layer, place the other layer of three spheres over the central sphere of the second layer such that they are directly oriented over those of the first layer. What is the coordination number for this type of close packing? Many metals such as beryllium, magnesium and zinc have hexagonal close packing structures. Retain this model for use in procedure 4.

3. CUBIC CLOSE PACKING OR FACE-CENTRED CUBIC PACKING – MODEL B

(a) Construct the layers illustrated in Figure E-27 using 2-inch spheres and toothpicks as before.

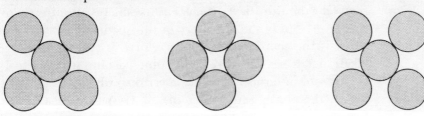

Figure E-27. *Layers for cubic close packing.*

(b) Place the first layer (5 spheres) flat on the desk. Place the second layer (4 spheres) on it such that the spheres rest in the spaces between the corner spheres of the first layer. Now add the third layer such that its spheres are directly over those in the first layer. Study the model carefully. Why is it called a face-centred cubic arrangement? Many metals including copper, silver, gold and aluminum have cubic close packing structures.

4. COMPARISON OF HEXAGONAL CLOSE PACKING WITH CUBIC CLOSE PACKING

(a) Return to the hexagonal close packing model, A. Arrange it such that the top layer is not directly over the first layer but is rotated 60° with respect to it.

(b) Rotate this model and look for four spheres forming a square facing you. Now take the top layer off model B and place it on the four spheres you located on model A. Note that this new model contains a face-centred cube, just like model B but tilted toward you.

(c) Based upon this comparison, is there a difference in the coordination number in the two types of close packing? How should the densities compare when spheres of comparable size and mass are involved in each of these types of packing? Most metals do not crystallize in both of these forms. What does this indicate about the directional nature of the bonds between atoms in these metals?

5. BODY-CENTRED CUBIC PACKING — MODEL C

(a) Construct the layers shown in Figure E-28 using 2-inch spheres. Leave a space of approximately 1/4 inch between the spheres as shown.

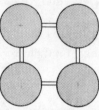 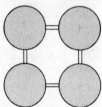

Figure E-28. *Layers for body-centred cubic packing.*

(b) Place a single sphere in the centre of the first layer (4 spheres) and then add the third layer such that its spheres are directly over the first layer. Study the symmetry of this model and justify its name. What is the coordination number for this type of packing? The alkali metals have body-centred cubic packing structures. Is there any reason, in terms of valence electrons, why these metals crystallize in this form, while most metals crystallize in a close-packed form?

Part II Ionic Crystals

Packing Arrangements Involving Different Ions

1. THE CRYSTAL LATTICE STRUCTURE OF SODIUM CHLORIDE

(a) Since sodium ions have a diameter of 1.90 Å, and chloride ions have a diameter of 3.62 Å, one-inch spheres will be used for sodium ions and two-inch spheres will be used for chloride ions in order to approximate their relative sizes in the lattice model.

(b) Use Model B with its two-inch spheres for the face-centred cubic arrangement of the chloride ions. Insert thirteen one-inch spheres, representing sodium ions, into the holes between the chloride ions in each layer. These can be held in place with toothpicks. Note that the Na^+Cl^- lattice is an interpenetrating set of face-centred cubes—one involving sodium and one chloride ions.

(c) What type of ion surrounds each sodium ion? Each chloride ion? What is the coordination number of the sodium ion and of the chloride ion in this close packing structure?

(d) Note that in order to achieve this type of lattice there must be a favourable relationship between the radii of the two spheres which will permit a given sphere to fit into a given hole in the lattice. What is the radius ratio for Na^+/Cl^- ions? Account for the stability of this type of packing in terms of interionic forces.

2. THE CRYSTAL LATTICE STRUCTURE OF ZINC SULPHIDE (WURTZITE)

(a) Since the zinc ion has a diameter of 1.5 Å and the sulphide ion has a diameter of 3.7 Å, ¾-inch spheres will be used for zinc ions and two-inch spheres will be used for sulphide ions in order to approximate their relative sizes in the lattice model.

(b) Use Model A with its hexagonal close packing arrangement to represent the lattice of the larger sulphide ions, S^{2-}. Attach one of the smaller ¾-inch spheres, representing the zinc ion, Zn^{2+}, directly above each of the larger spheres in each of the three layers of Model A using short lengths of the toothpicks.

(c) Place the large layer on the table top with the small spheres pointed down. Place one of the small layers on the large layer in such a way that the smaller spheres fit into alternate depressions. Invert the two layers and place the other small layer, with small spheres pointing up, above the larger layer so that each sphere on the top layer is directly above a sphere on the bottom layer.

(d) What is the coordination number of the spheres representing zinc ions in this close packing structure?

(c) What is the radius ratio for Zn^{2+}/S^{2-} ions?

3. THE CRYSTAL LATTICE STRUCTURE OF CESIUM CHLORIDE

(a) Since the cesium ion has a diameter of 3.36 Å and the chloride ion has a diameter of 3.68 Å, two-inch spheres will be used for both the cesium ions and the chloride ions in order to approximate their relative sizes in the lattice model.

(b) Use Model C with its body-centred cubic packing arrangement to represent the cesium chloride lattice where the central sphere in the cube is designated as the cesium ion and the spheres at the corners of the cube are designated as chloride ions.

(c) What is the coordination number of the spheres representing the cesium ions in this structure?

(d) What is the radius ratio for Cs+ /Cl⁻ ions?

Part III   Covalent Crystals (Network Solids)

1. THE CRYSTAL LATTICE STRUCTURE OF DIAMOND

(a) Using ¾-inch black spheres and short connectors, construct several models consisting of 5 spheres in a tetrahedral arrangement as shown in Figure E-29.

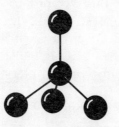
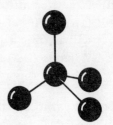

Figure E-29. *Tetrahedral arrangement.*

(b) Following the pattern illustrated in Figure E-30, connect the tetrahedral models to form a model of the diamond crystal. Some spheres will have to be removed as the model develops.

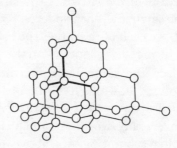

Figure E-30. *The diamond structure.*

2. THE CRYSTAL LATTICE STRUCTURE OF GRAPHITE

(a) Begin the construction of the model of graphite by constructing two hexagons using the ¾-inch black spheres and short connectors (distances between adjacent carbon atoms in a layer of graphite are identical and equal to 1.42 Å).

(b) Using Figure E-31 as a guide, connect the two hexagons above one another using longer connectors to represent the distance between adjacent layers (3.40 Å).

(c) Use the remaining black spheres to build up each layer. Two carbons in the first constructed hexagons will be common to the newly constructed hexagons.

(d) Use long connectors, as required, between the rest of the constructed layers.

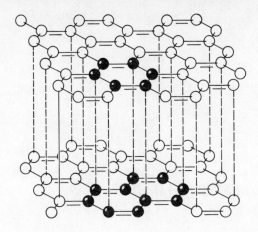

Figure E-31. *The graphite structure.*

Questions for Thought and Discussion

1. Answer all questions asked in the procedure sections.

2. In one type of cubic packing the spheres occupy about two-thirds of the available space, while in the other type they occupy about three-fourths of the available space. Identify which type is which. Which is more dense? Which has the larger number of bonds?

3. From a consideration of the three models constructed in Part II, what relation can you deduce concerning the radius ratio of ions and the coordination number in crystals? In which case is the number of interionic attractions the greater around any given ion?

4. Suppose you have a crystal, AB, with the same packing as sodium chloride in which each of the ions is the same size as the sodium ion and chloride ion respectively, but each is doubly charged, A^{2+} and B^{2+}. Would AB have a higher or a lower melting point than sodium chloride? Suggest a real pair of ions which meets the above criteria and look up the melting point of the corresponding crystal to check your prediction.

5. Suppose you have a crystal, CD, with the same packing as sodium chloride in which each of the ions has the same charge, C^+ and D^-, as Na^+ and Cl^- but the radii of C and D are proportionately larger. Would AB have a higher or a lower melting point than sodium chloride? Suggest a real pair of ions that meets these criteria, and look up the melting point of the corresponding crystal to check your prediction.

6. To how many carbons in (a) the diamond lattice, (b) a layer of graphite is each carbon bonded?

7. What type of hybridization of carbon results in (a) the diamond and (b) the graphite structure?

8. What is the nature of the bonding between layers in graphite?

EXPERIMENT 10-2

Allotropic Forms of Sulphur

If you are not already familiar with the term *allotrope,* you should consult your text before proceeding with this experiment. The experiment is designed to illustrate allotropic forms of this element.

CAUTION: This experiment should only be performed as a class experiment in a laboratory with adequate ventilation facilities.

Although valid for the entire experiment this warning applies particularly to procedure 1. Carbon disulphide is volatile, poisonous and explosively flammable when mixed with air. It should never be used without adequate ventilation and must be kept away from flames.

Procedure

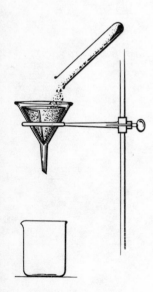

1. Demonstration

   Powder a small lump of roll sulphur in a mortar with a pestle. Dissolve the sulphur in 8 ml of carbon disulphide in an evaporating dish. Stir with a glass rod to hasten dissolving. Let the liquid evaporate spontaneously in a good draft of air in a fume hood or on the sill of an open window. Use a hand lens or binocular microscope to examine the crystals. Describe their shape and appearance.

2. Half-fill a test tube with small pieces of roll sulphur. Adjust a burner to provide a low flame and melt the sulphur at *as low a temperature as possible*. During the heating the liquid should not get much darker than a pale straw colour. Note the viscosity of the liquid. Pour all the molten sulphur into a folded filter paper cone in a funnel supported on a retort ring. (Figure E-32.)

Figure E-32.

Watch it as it cools. As soon as needlelike crystals from the cone form across the surface of the cooling sulphur, pour the excess liquid into a beaker of cold water, unfold the filter paper at once and examine the crystals with a hand lens. Describe their shape and appearance and compare them with those obtained in procedure 1. Keep the crystals obtained in procedure 2 for a few days and examine them closely again for any changes.

3. Half-fill the same test tube used in procedure 2 with small pieces of roll sulphur. Heat the test tube, slowly at first, and note again the colour and viscosity of sulphur when it has just melted. Observe any changes in colour and viscosity that occur when the sulphur is heated more strongly. The viscosity can be observed by periodically tipping the test tube to a nearly horizontal position. Finally, heat the sulphur to boiling and extinguish the burner flame. Note any further changes in colour or viscosity and pour the contents of the tube into a beaker of cold water. At this point, the sulphur may catch fire. Do not become alarmed; the sulphur will burn quietly. After emptying the test tube, any sulphur on it which is still burning can be smothered with a wet towel. Remove the product from the beaker of water and examine it. Keep this product for a few days and examine it again.

4. Demonstration
   Place 0.5 g of zinc dust on an asbestos square. Add an equal bulk of flowers of sulphur and mix the two elements on the square. Heap the mixture up into a conical pile and place the pile in a fume cupboard.

CAUTION: Hold a burner at arm's length and ignite the mixture with the tip of the flame.

Note all changes that are observed. Examine the zinc, sulphur and the material formed during the chemical change with a hand lens. Compare these solids with one another.

Questions for Thought and Discussion

1. What changes occur in the structure of sulphur molecules as sulphur is raised from its melting point to its boiling point?

2. In what different forms may sulphur exist?

3. What changes in structure does the sulphur produced in (a) procedure 2, and (b) procedure 3 undergo when it stands for some time? What type of solid is formed in procedure 3?

4. Which of these forms of sulphur is the most stable?

5. (a) What new substance is formed in the chemical reaction of procedure 4?

(b) Using your knowledge of structure and bonding, account for the chemical change that occurs.

(c) Is the solid formed an ionic, molecular, or covalent crystal?

(d) Into what characteristic geometrical shape does this substance crystallize?

(e) Sketch the unit cell for this crystalline solid.

(f) What physical properties would you expect the solid to exhibit?

EXPERIMENT 10-3

Chemical Bonding

All chemical bonds involve some degree of sharing of electrons between atoms but the degree of sharing varies considerably. For convenience, chemical bonds are divided into categories such as ionic, covalent, polar covalent, etc. Although most chemical bonds involve some combination of these categories, substances can be selected which have chemical bonds of predominantly one category. Such selected substances exhibit properties typical of that type of chemical bond. Part I of this experiment compares the physical properties of substances that have been selected to represent a particular type of chemical bonding. In Part II the rate of a chemical reaction is related to the chemical bonding within the molecules involved. Data tables should be prepared prior to the laboratory period (see tables 1 and 2).

Procedure

Part I   Physical Properties and Chemical Bonds

Use:

potassium iodide, KI, as a typical ionic compound

paradichlorobenzene, $C_6H_4Cl_2$, as typical molecular substance
composed of nonpolar molecules.

silicon dioxide, SiO_2,   as a typical covalent crystal
(a three-dimensional network solid)

and any or all of

calcium, Ca,
aluminum, Al,   as typical metallic crystals
sodium, Na,

1. Smell each substance. If you detect an odour, assume that the substance is volatile. If there is no odour, assume that it is nonvolatile.

2.

Test the hardness of each substance by rubbing and squeezing a small sample between your fingers. Record the hardness as either soft and waxy or brittle and granular. Record your impression before the substance tends to dissolve in any oil or moisture on your fingers. Wash your hands after testing.

Additional evidence related to this property may be obtained by using sodium chloride or calcium carbonate as examples of ionic substances, a piece of candle as an example of a molecular substance, a piece of silicon as an example of a covalent crystal, and magnesium and copper as examples of metallic crystals.

3.

Add paradichlorobenzene to a dry test tube to a depth of 3 cm. Clamp the test tube to a retort stand and heat the sample with a hot flame. Observe the approximate time required for the sample to melt. Allow the contents of the test tube to cool and follow your teacher's instructions regarding disposal of the material.

Repeat this procedure using, in turn, potassium iodide, silicon dioxide and the metal(s) you have been instructed to use.

In each case, use the time required for melting as a basis for identifying the melting points as relatively high or relatively low compared to paradichlorobenzene.

4.

EXPERIMENT 10-3

Place a few crystals or a small piece of each subtance in separate test tubes containing 5 ml of water. Shake or stir, if necessary, and record the relative solubilities of the substances in water.

5. CAUTION: Benzene is a very volatile and flammable liquid. In addition, the vapour is poisonous and contact with the skin is dangerous. Never handle benzene near an open flame. Follow carefully the instructions given below.

You will be provided with stoppered test tubes containing benzene, C_6H_6. Put a few crystals or a small piece of each substance you are testing in separate test tubes. Replace the stopper firmly and shake the contents. Hold the stopper in place with your thumb during the shaking procedure. Record the relative solubilities of the substances in benzene.

6. Demonstration
The teacher will place samples of each substance in separate evaporating dishes or crucibles and test the electrical conductivity of each in the solid state. He will then heat each of the solids and test the conductivity in the liquid state in each case where melting occurs.

Table 1

Property	Molecular paradichlorobenzene $C_6H_4Cl_2$	Ionic potassium iodide KI	Covalent silicon dioxide SiO_2	Metallic metal used
Volatility (high or low)				
Melting point (high or low)				
Solubility in water (soluble or insoluble)				
Solubility in benzene				
Electrical conductivity in the solid state				
Electrical conductivity in the liquid state				
Hardness or texture (brittle or soft)				

Part II   Rate of Reaction and Chemical Bonds

1. Place a few crystals of the ionic compound iron (II) sulphate, $FeSO_4$, in a small beaker (100 ml) and add enough water to dissolve the crystals. Add 2 or 3 ml of 2M sulphuric acid.

2. Using a medicine dropper, add 10 drops of a dilute solution of potassium permanganate, $KMnO_4$, to the iron (II) sulphate solution. Continually stir the contents of the beaker during this addition. Indicate the relative rate of reaction in terms of the time required for the permanganate colour to disappear. Record the observation in table 2.

Table 2

Reaction	Relative Rate of Reaction
iron (II) sulphate (ionic) with potassium permanganate	
oxalic acid (molecular) with potassium permanganate	

3. Place a few crystals of oxalic acid, $H_2C_2O_4$, a molecular substance composed of polar covalent molecules, in a small beaker (100 ml) and dissolve it in water. Add 2 or 3 ml of 2M sulphuric acid.

4. Add 10 drops of the same dilute solution of potassium permanganate used in procedure 2 to the oxalic acid solution. Stir constantly during this addition. Record in table 2 the rate of this reaction compared with that of the reaction between iron (II) sulphate and potassium permanganate.

Questions for Thought and Discussion

1. (a) In terms of the types and relative strengths of bonds, explain the presence or absence of an odour in each of these substances.
   (b) Can a substance be relatively volatile and not have an odour?

2. In terms of the types and relative strengths of bonds, explain the differences in melting points of these substances.

3. Is one comparing the relative strengths of covalent and ionic bonds when comparing the relative melting points of potassium iodide and paradichlorobenzene? Explain.

4. Are the electrons in (a) ionic crystals, (b) molecular crystals, (c) covalent crystals and (d) metallic crystals tightly bound or mobile? What experimental evidence have you to support your answer?

5. Do ionic crystals form ionic liquids? What experimental evidence have you to support your answer?

6. Do nonpolar crystals form ionic or molecular liquids? What experimental evidence do you have to support your answer?

7. Did any of the solids appear to be soft or waxy? Account for any observed differences in hardness of the crystals.

8. Are the intermolecular or intramolecular forces greater in paradichlorobenzene? Explain in terms of your observations.

9. Assuming the results recorded in table 2 are typical, would you conclude that ionic substances in solution are apt to react more or less rapidly than covalent substances? Can you suggest a reason for this?

10. Refer to the Periodic Table or chart of electronegativities and classify the following substances as largely covalent or largely ionic:
(a) KF   (b) ICl (c) NaBr   (d) SO_3 (e) CaI_2.

11. Use the results of the experiment to predict the properties of the substances listed in the following chart.

Properties	LiF	CCl₄	SiC	K or Mg
Melting point (high or low)				
Volatility (high or low)				
Electrical conductivity in the solid state				
Electrical conductivity in the liquid state				
Solubility in water				
Solubility in benzene				
Type of crystal (ionic, molecular, covalent, metallic)				
Type of bond between units at lattice points				
Type of bond between elements in formula				

EXPERIMENT 10-4

Crystal Structure

Crystalline solids are characterized by distinctive geometrical shapes. These shapes are thought to arise from definite orderly arrangements of the constituent atoms. These orderly arrangements can be represented by the unit cell. The *unit cell* is defined as the smallest portion of the space lattice which, when moved a distance equal to its dimensions in various directions, generates the whole space lattice. In this experiment you will first construct models of various unit cells. Assuming that atoms can be represented by rigid spheres, you will then calculate the fraction of the volume of the unit cell that is empty space. Finally, you will construct models of the unit cell of a simple compound and show the relationship between the unit cell and the simplest formula.

Procedure

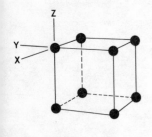

Simple cubic

Figure E-33. (a)

1. (a) Using 1-inch spheres, construct a single unit cell of the simple cubic lattice arrangement shown in Figure E-33 (a). The dots in this figure represent the centres of atoms. Your model should be constructed with the spheres in contact and held together by toothpicks (or pipestem cleaners).

   (b) Using only four more spheres, extend the model in the Y direction so that you end up with two unit cells in contact. Notice that the four spheres in the middle of this arrangement are shared by the two unit cells. Following the same pattern as above add spheres to the model in directions X and Z. Continue adding spheres until the model consists of a large cube made up of 8 unit cells and composed of a total of 27 spheres.

(c) Select any unit cell within the model and observe these 8 spheres closely. The *edge length of a unit cell* is defined as the distance from the centre of a corner sphere to the centre of an adjacent corner sphere. Since the spheres in this model are in contact along the cube edge and all spheres are the same size, the edge length is twice the radius of one sphere or $2r$, where r represents the radius of one sphere. Record this edge length expressed in terms of r in your data table.

(d) Now consider the sphere that is right in the centre of the whole model. How many unit cells surround the sphere? What fraction of this sphere must form a part of each of these unit cells? Record this fraction in the data table. Any sphere lying at the corner of any unit cell that is a cube contributes this fraction of itself to each of the surrounding unit cells. Figure E-33 (a) suggests that apparently the number of spheres per unit cell of this type is 8. However, when the corner spheres and adjacent unit cells are considered, the equivalent of how many spheres form this simple cubic unit cell? Record this value in the data table as the "equivalent number of spheres per unit cell".

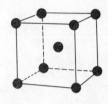

Body-centred cubic

Figure E-33. (b)

2. Construct a single unit cell having the body-centred cubic lattice [Figure E-33 (b)]. Use 1-inch spheres and toothpicks. For a detailed description of the procedure see Experiment 10-1, Part I, procedure 5. Notice that the spheres are in contact along the diagonals of the cube but are not in contact along the edges of the cube. Express the length of the diagonal of the cube in terms of the sphere radius, r, and record this value in the data table. Calculate and record the equivalent number of spheres per unit cell for this body-centred cubic arrangement.

3. Construct a single unit cell having the face-centred cubic lattice [Figure E-33 (c)]. Use 1-inch spheres and follow the detailed procedure given in Experiment 10-1, Part I, procedure 3. Notice that the spheres that run along the diagonals of each face of the cube are in contact. Express the length of a diagonal of any face of the cube in terms of the sphere radius, r. Record this value. Calculate the equivalent number of spheres per unit cell for this face-centred cubic arrangement.

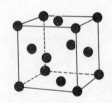

Face-centred cubic

Figure E-33.(c)

4. Using 2-inch spheres for the chloride ions and 1-inch spheres for the sodium ions, construct a single unit cell of the sodium chloride lattice. For a detailed procedure on constructing this unit cell see Experiment 10-1, Part I, procedure 3 and Part II, procedure 1. The completed model should contain 27 spheres, 14 2-inch spheres representing chloride ions and 13 1-inch spheres representing sodium ions. Calculate and record the equivalent number of sodium ions and the equivalent number of chloride ions within this unit cell. Compare these values with the simplest formula for the compound.

5. Construct a face-centred cubic unit cell in which the centre of each face is occupied by a small sphere, X, and each corner position is occupied by a small sphere, X. The remainder of the positions should be occupied by the large spheres, Y. Calculate the equivalent numbers of spheres X and Y within this unit cell. Compare these values with those calculated in procedure 4. What is the simplest formula of this compound?

Data Table

1. SIMPLE CUBIC, UNIT CELL
   Edge length of cube expressed in terms of sphere radius, $r =$
   Fraction contributed by corner sphere to each unit cell $=$
   Apparent number of spheres per unit cell [Figure E-33 (a)] $=$
   Equivalent number of spheres per unit cell $=$

2. BODY-CENTRED CUBIC, UNIT CELL
   Diagonal length of cube expressed in terms of sphere radius, $r =$
   Apparent number of spheres per unit cell [Figure E-33 (b)] $=$
   Equivalent number of spheres per unit cell $=$

3. FACE-CENTRED CUBIC, UNIT CELL
   Diagonal length of face of cube expressed in terms of sphere radius, $r =$
   Apparent number of spheres per unit cell [Figure E-33 (c)] $=$
   Equivalent number of spheres per unit cell $=$

4. SODIUM CHLORIDE, UNIT CELL
   Equivalent number of sodium ions per unit cell $=$
   Equivalent number of chloride ions per unit cell $=$

5. COMPOUND CONTAINING SPHERES X AND Y
   Equivalent number of X spheres (small) per unit cell $=$
   Equivalent number of Y spheres (large) per unit cell $=$

Calculations:

(Volume of a sphere $= \frac{4}{3}\pi r^3$)

1. SIMPLE CUBIC
   Volume of unit cell in terms of $r =$
   Volume of all spheres within the unit cell in terms of $r =$
   Fraction of the unit cell that is empty space $=$

2. **BODY-CENTRED CUBIC**
   Length of an edge of the unit cell in terms of $r =$
   Volume of unit cell in terms of $r =$
   Volume of all spheres within the unit cell in terms of $r =$
   Fraction of the unit cell that is empty space $=$

3. **FACE-CENTRED CUBIC**
   Length of an edge of the unit cell in terms of $r =$
   Volume of unit cell in terms of $r =$
   Volume of all spheres within the unit cell in terms of $r =$
   Fraction of the unit cell that is empty space $=$

4. Simplest formula of sodium chloride $=$

5. Simplest formula of compound $=$

Questions for Thought and Discussion

1. Suppose that each 1-inch sphere used in procedures 1, 2 and 3 represents an atom having an atomic mass of 100.0 a.m.u. and a radius of 1.00 Ångstrom units. Calculate the density of the solid for each of the three arrangements of atoms.

$$1\text{Å} = 1 \times 10^{-8} \text{ cm}$$

2. Which of the arrangements 1, 2 or 3 corresponds to "cubic close packing"? Explain the reason for your choice.

3. In the crystal lattice arrangement of the compound sodium chloride, the distance between the centre of a sodium ion and the centre of an adjacent chloride ion is 2.819 Å. Calculate the density of a perfect crystal of sodium chloride. Compare your result with the accepted value of the density of sodium chloride as given in a handbook of chemistry and physics.

4. Hard spheres, having a radius of r units, are in contact with one another in the arrangement of a simple cubic unit cell. In terms of r calculate the radius of the largest sphere that can fit into the hole in the centre of this unit cell.

   (calculate the length of the cube diagonal in terms of r)

EXPERIMENT 11-1

Pressure-Volume Relationship for Gases: Boyle's Law

In this experiment we examine the effect of a change in pressure on the volume occupied by a given mass of gas. A sample of gas is placed in a cylinder fitted with a movable piston. This mass of gas is now subjected to various pressures by adding, in succession, objects of equal mass to a support attached to the piston. We will assume that the temperature of the gas sample remains constant (at room temperature) throughout the experiment.

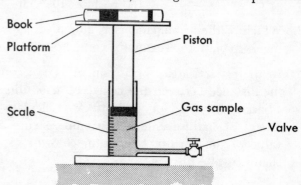

Figure E-34. *Syringe.*

Procedure

Part I   Boyle's Law

1. When you receive the apparatus, the piston will probably be at its lowest position and there will be no gas in the cylinder. A gas sample may be introduced by opening the valve at the end of the rubber tubing and raising the piston until 40 ml to 50 ml of gas (air) are in the cylinder. Close the valve securely. A given mass of gas is now trapped in the cylinder. Press down on the piston then release it. Repeat this procedure, then record the volume of this gas to the accuracy indicated on the cylinder.

2. To increase the pressure on this gas, masses can be added to the platform continuous with the movable piston. A mass of 700 g to 900 g is appropriate. Your textbook may fall within this range. If so, carefully place one textbook on the platform making sure that the textbook is well centred. Record the volume of the gas sample again.

3. A second mass (textbook), identical with the first, is now placed atop the first and the volume recorded.

4. This procedure should be repeated until 5 or 6 identical masses have been added to the platform.

5. Remove all masses from the platform and compare the volume of the gas now with the volume recorded before any masses were added.

6. Record the data in tabular form as outlined below and calculate the reciprocals of the recorded volumes.

Pressure, P (number of identical masses, books)	Volume, V (ml)	$\dfrac{1}{Volume}$, $\dfrac{1}{V}$ (ml^{-1})
0		
1		
2		
3		
4		
5		
6		

7. Plotting pressure, P, as the y coordinate and volume, V, as the x coordinate draw a graph showing the pressure-volume relationship (that is, plot P as a function of V).

8. On a second set of axes plot pressure, P, as the y coordinate and the reciprocal of the volume, $\dfrac{1}{V}$, as the x coordinate.

Questions for Thought and Discussion

1. What does the P-V curve indicate about the relationship between these two quantities?

2. Does the P vs. $\frac{1}{V}$ graph verify your answer to the above question?

3. Express the conclusion drawn from the graphs as a concise statement. This relationship between pressure and volume of gases is known as Boyle's law. Express the same relationship mathematically.

4. What was the purpose of removing all mass from the platform and comparing this volume with the original volume of the gas sample?

5. When there are *no* books on the platform (and assuming that the small mass of piston and platform is negligible), what is the pressure being exerted by the gas?

6. What is the total pressure exerted by the gas when, for example, 3 books are on the platform?

Part II   Extrapolation

The data acquired in this experiment covers a very narrow range of pressure changes. In such cases it is often useful and valid to establish the variables graphically and then assume that these trends continue over a range not covered by the data. Such a process is called *extrapolation*.

Suppose we apply this idea to the P vs. $\frac{1}{V}$ curve. The pressures plotted range in value from atmospheric pressure (no masses on the piston) to, for example, atmospheric pressure + 6 masses on the piston. Using the curve already established, extend the y-axis below the origin using the same scale. Now extend the curve until it intersects with the y-axis.

Questions for Thought and Discussion

1. At the y-intercept the value of $\frac{1}{V}$ is 0. What must be the value of V?

   What must be the pressure exerted on the gas under this condition? What arrangement of the apparatus used in the experiment would give such a pressure?

2. What mass on the platform must correspond to a pressure of one atmosphere? Explain your reasoning.

3. With reference to the data from the experiment, what change occurs in the volume of the gas when the pressure is doubled? Does this agree with your statement of Boyle's law?

4. The validity of our extrapolation has been tested by the above reasoning. What method might be used to test the validity of the extrapolation experimentally using the same apparatus?

EXPERIMENT 11-2

Temperature-Volume Relationship for Gases: Charles' Law

The volume of a given mass of gas varies considerably when the temperature of the gas is increased or decreased. A fixed mass of gas is trapped in a small-bore glass tube with a globule of mercury. The temperature of the gas sample is changed by inserting the tube into water baths at various temperatures. The resulting volumes of the sample are recorded and the relationship between temperature and volume examined.

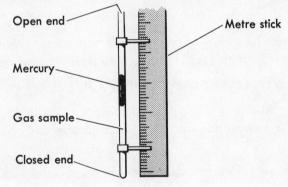

Open end — Metre stick

Mercury

Gas sample

Closed end

Figure E-35.

Procedure

1. When you receive the apparatus, a sample of air about one-half the length of the tube is enclosed by the mercury pellet.

2. An appropriate linear scale (metric units) is attached to the glass tube (Figure E-35). Measure the length of the gas sample enclosed by the mercury. This length measurement will serve to measure the volume of the gas at various temperatures if we assume that the bore of the tube has a uniform area of cross-section. At the same time record room temperature (°C). The above and subsequent results should be recorded in suitable tabular form.

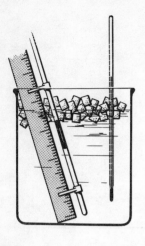

Figure E-36.

3. Prepare a bath of water and ice of suitable size so that the sample of gas in the glass tube can be completely immersed in the mixture. Immerse the tube as shown (Figure E-36) and stir the mixture in the bath. When the mixture of ice and water has reached a constant temperature, record the temperature of the bath and the volume of the gas in the glass tube.

4. Prepare a second bath, using water, and maintain the temperature at 30°C. Immerse the gas sample while the bath is being heated and stirred, and record the temperature of the bath and the volume of the gas in the tube after the temperature of the bath has been constant for 4 or 5 minutes. It is not necessary to maintain the temperature at a value of 30°C exactly, but the temperature must be maintained at some value close to 30°C for 4 or 5 minutes, for example, 25°C or 31°C.

5. Repeat the above for temperatures of approximately 60°C and 90°C (and for as many other temperatures as time permits).

6. Plot the data with temperature (°C) along the x-axis and volume (relative volume) along the y-axis. The scale on the x-axis should extend to the left of the origin and should include values from −300°C to 100°C. The scale on the y-axis need only include positive values.

7. Extrapolate the curve obtained, using a dotted line, until the curve intersects with the x-axis.

Questions for Thought and Discussion

1. Examine the curve obtained from the data. What does this curve indicate about the relationship between temperature and volume?

2. Is the fact that the curve is a straight line of any significance?

3. Explain why it is possible to measure the length of the gas sample in the tube and assume that this is a measurement of the volume of the gas.

4. Of what significance is the x-intercept when the curve is extrapolated?

5. Does it seem likely that data can be obtained for these very low temperatures to verify the extrapolation? Explain.

6. The relationship T vs. V described above is only true when the pressure remains constant. Is it true that the pressure is constant throughout this experiment? If it is, at what pressure is the experiment conducted?

7. Express the conclusion drawn from this experiment as a concise statement. This relationship between the temperature and volume of gases is known as Charles' law. Express the same relationship mathematically.

EXPERIMENT 11-2

EXPERIMENT 11-3

Pressure-Temperature Relationship for Gases

The two previous experiments have examined the relationship which exists between temperature, pressure and volume of a gas sample. By combining the expressions $V \ \alpha \ \dfrac{1}{P}$ and $V \ \alpha \ T$ we arrive at the more general relationship $PV = kT$, where V, P and T represents volume, pressure and temperature respectively of a given mass of gas, and K is a proportionality constant. This expression was developed by using mathematical principles and combining Boyle's and Charles' laws. By rewriting the expression as $P = \dfrac{k}{V} \times T$, we see that the relationship $P \ \alpha \ T$ must be true if the volume, V, and the mass, m, of the gas sample remain constant. In this experiment we shall test this relationship.

A sample of gas is placed in a metal sphere or bulb which is connected with a pressure gauge (Figure E-37). The bulb is submerged in liquids at various known temperatures and the pressures are recorded for each temperature. The relationship between pressure and temperature is established graphically.

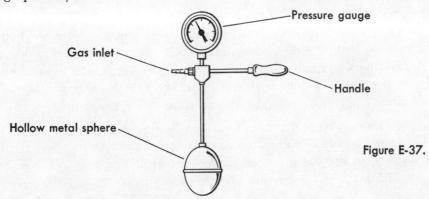

Pressure gauge

Gas inlet

Handle

Hollow metal sphere

Figure E-37.

Procedure

1. Examine the apparatus to insure that the valve core is in position. The pressure gauge should indicate a pressure of 10 to 20 lb in^{-2}. The pressure may be increased a few lb in^{-2} by using a bicycle pump, removing the valve core and adding some air.

2. Prepare a chart to record four values of temperature and pressure.

3. Record room temperature (°C) and if the apparatus has been in the room for at least ten minutes, record the pressure exerted by the gas sample in the bulb at room temperature.

4. At least two baths should be prepared to test the pressure-temperature relationship at other temperatures.

   (a) *Boiling Water Bath*: Add 500 ml of water to a 2-litre beaker, place the beaker on a hot plate and bring the water to a boil.

   (b) *Ice-Water Bath*: While waiting for the water in (a) to boil, add a water and ice mixture to a 2-litre beaker (or a pail) until the beaker is about half full. Stir the mixture well until the temperature approaches 0°C and remains constant. Add ice if required.

   (c) CAUTION: Do not handle dry ice with bare hands.

   Dry Ice—Alcohol Bath (optional): If dry ice (solid carbon dioxide) is available, a third bath may be prepared by adding small pieces of dry ice to alcohol in a dewar flask (or 2-litre beaker) until the temperature (alcohol thermometer) approaches −78°C and remains constant. About 500 ml of the bath should be prepared. Excess dry ice must be continually added to keep the bath at this temperature.

5. Submerge the bulb in the ice-water bath. Keep a thermometer in the bath but do not record the temperature immediately. Stir the bath constantly. When the temperature remains constant, record both the temperature and the pressure exerted by the gas in the bulb.

6. If the dry ice-alcohol bath was prepared, repeat procedure 5 with this bath.

7. Once the water from 4(a) is boiling, turn the hot plate down until a gentle boiling action is maintained. Lower the bulb carefully into the boiling water using the handle provided. Keep a thermometer in the water and *when the temperature of the bath is again constant*, record this temperature and also the pressure of the gas sample.

8. (Optional) Repeat procedures 1 to 7 using a different amount of gas in the bulb. The mass of the gas sample, and consequently the initial pressure, may be increased using the bicycle pump as indicated before. The mass of the gas may be decreased by removing the valve core,

placing the bulb in boiling water, and replacing the valve core while the bulb is still in the water.

9. Plot the results as follows:

   (a) x-axis: Plot temperature (°C) using a scale ranging from $-300°C$ to $+100°C$.

   (b) y-axis: Plot pressure values starting from 0 at the origin. Treat the results from procedures 1 to 7 separately from any results of procedure 8.

10. Allowing for experimental error, what relationship is indicated by the graph? Extrapolate the results, using a dotted line, until the pressure indicated is zero.

Questions for Thought and Discussion

1. What is the significance of the straight line(s)? How does this relate to the expression $P = \frac{k}{V} \times T$?

2. (a) How can the value of the proportionality constant(s) be obtained?
   (b) Derive the units for this proportionality constant.

3. At what point does the extrapolated curve(s) intersect with the x-axis? Why is this significant?

4. What does this experiment tell us with respect to the expression $PV = kT$ which was developed from Boyle's and Charles' laws?

EXPERIMENT 11-4

Gay-Lussac's Law of Combining Gas Volumes

This experiment examines the ratio, by volume, with which two gases react. The apparatus consists of two gas syringes as pictured in the accompanying diagram. A measured volume of hydrogen chloride gas is introduced into one syringe. A measured volume of ammonia is introduced into the other. The hydrogen chloride is then forced into the syringe containing ammonia and the two gases are allowed to react.

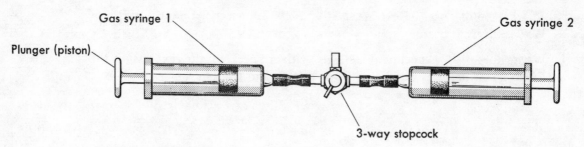

Figure E-38.

Procedure

Part I   Filling one syringe with dry ammonia

1. Place a few millilitres of concentrated aqueous ammonia solution into a large test tube.

2. Stopper the test tube with a one-hole stopper into which has been inserted a drying tube filled with calcium chloride.

3. The opposite end of the drying tube should be stoppered with a one-hole stopper fitted with a "T" valve. The whole assemblage is shown in Figure E-39.

4. Attach the delivery tube from the "T" valve to the 3-way stopcock that connects the two syringes.

5. Warm the aqueous ammonia solution gently, allowing the ammonia produced to pass through the drying tube and out the open arm of the "T" valve.

6. When it can be assumed that all air has been removed from the test tube and drying tube, place a finger over the open end of the "T" valve at the same time turning the 3-way valve to allow ammonia gas to enter syringe 1. To ensure that there is no air in the syringe, pull the plunger out, allow the syringe to fill, then remove the finger from the "T" valve at the same time forcing the plunger in. Repeat this procedure.

7. Introduce 80 ml of ammonia into syringe 1 by withdrawing the plunger to the 80 ml mark and covering the open arm of the "T" valve. When slight outward pressure is evident at the open arm of the "T" valve, syringe 1 is full. Close the 3-way valve with respect to syringe 1 and disconnect the ammonia generator from the 3-way stopcock.

Part II   Filling the second syringe with hydrogen chloride

1. Hydrogen chloride may be produced by adding concentrated sulphuric acid to sodium chloride. Construct a generator as shown in Figure E-40.

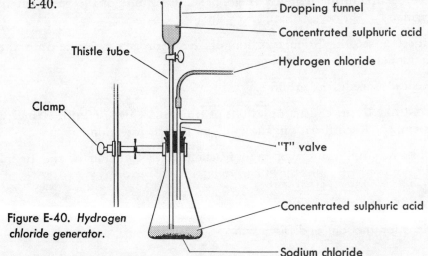

Figure E-40. *Hydrogen chloride generator.*

Dropping funnel
Concentrated sulphuric acid
Thistle tube
Hydrogen chloride
Clamp
"T" valve
Concentrated sulphuric acid
Sodium chloride

2. Cover the bottom of the flask with a thin layer of sodium chloride crystals and carefully add a few drops of concentrated sulphuric acid via the dropping funnel to the sodium chloride. Add more concentrated sulphuric acid as required.

3. Connect the delivery tube from the hydrogen chloride generator to the 3-way stopcock.

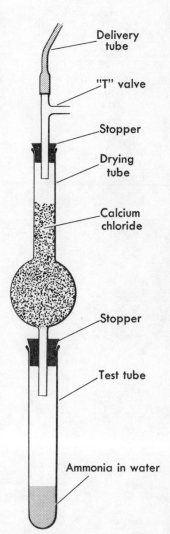

Delivery tube
"T" valve
Stopper
Drying tube
Calcium chloride
Stopper
Test tube
Ammonia in water

Figure E-39. *Ammonia generator.*

4. Turn the 3-way stopcock to allow hydrogen chloride to enter syringe 2. Follow procedure 6 of Part I. *Do not warm the generator.* The production of hydrogen chloride may be increased by adding more concentrated acid.

5. Introduce 50 ml of hydrogen chloride to syringe 2 in a manner similar to procedure 7 of Part I.
   Note: The gases used in this experiment may be supplied from cylinders containing the compressed gases.

Part III   Mixing the gases

1. Turn the 3-way valve to create a passage between syringe 1 and syringe 2.

2. Push the plunger of syringe 2 inwards so that 10 ml of hydrogen chloride are injected into the ammonia. Describe any changes that occur.

3. Close the passage at the 3-way valve between syringe 1 and syringe 2.

4. Measure the volume of hydrogen chloride in syringe 2 and the volume of the materials in syringe 1.

5. Prepare a data table and record (1) the volume of hydrogen chloride injected; (2) the total number of both reactants (that is, the volume of hydrogen chloride left in syringe 2 + the volume of the gases left in syringe 1).

6. Inject a second 10 ml portion of the hydrogen chloride into the ammonia.

7. Repeat procedures 3, 4 and 5.

8. Continue to inject 10 ml portions of hydrogen chloride until syringe 2 is empty. Record data in the table with each injection.

9. Plot the total volume of both reactants as a function of the 10 ml portions of hydrogen chloride injected.

Questions for Thought and Discussion

1. Name the product of the reaction that occurs when the two gases are mixed. Describe this product.

2. Explain, clearly, the significance of the plotted data.

3. What is the ratio, by volume, with which these gases react?

4. Assuming a similar behaviour when other gases are reacted together, state Gay-Lussac's law of combining gas volumes.

EXPERIMENT 11-5

The Composition of Ammonia by Volume

In this experiment ammonia gas is decomposed into its components by passing it over an appropriate catalyst at a high temperature. The products of the reaction are nitrogen gas and hydrogen gas. Once these products are present in the system, the hydrogen gas is removed by allowing it to react with hot copper (II) oxide. The volumes of hydrogen gas and nitrogen gas present are determined and compared with the original volume of ammonia gas used in the experiment. The same apparatus is used here as in Experiment 11-4 except that a silica tube is introduced between the syringes (Figure E-41).

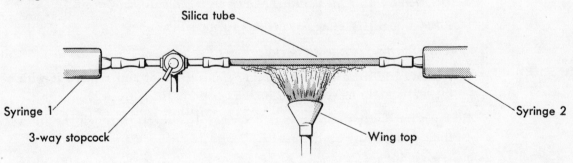

Figure E-41.

Procedure

Part I   Decomposing the ammonia gas

1. Fill the silica tube with grease-free steel wool until the tube is $2/3$ full. The steel wool should be free from rust.

2. Connect the apparatus as shown in the diagram and test whether the apparatus is reasonably air-tight.

3. Using dry ammonia from an ammonia generator (as described in Experiment 11-4) fill syringe 1 with ammonia and flush out the system by passing this ammonia back and forth between the two syringes. If a cylinder of nitrogen gas is available, it may be used for the above instead of the ammonia.

4. Remove all gas from the syringes by using the 3-way stopcock and pressing the plungers inwards.

5. Add 40 ml of dry ammonia to syringe 1. See Experiment 11-4 for the details on how ammonia is added.

6. Place a burner equipped with a wing top under the silica tube and heat the steel wool *strongly* until it is red hot.

7. Pass the ammonia over the heated steel wool by placing one hand on the plunger of each syringe and gently pressing one plunger in while pulling the other out. This prevents any build-up in pressure that might create a leak in the system. Reverse the direction of the plungers several times, thus passing the ammonia back and forth over the steel wool. The volume of the gas should expand during this procedure.

8. Using the plungers, push *all* of the gas back into syringe 1.

9. Turn off the burner and cool the silica tube using a damp cloth.

10. After waiting for the apparatus and gas to reach room temperature, record the total volume of the gases in syringe 1.

Part II   Determining the volumes of hydrogen gas and nitrogen gas

1. Place copper (II) oxide powder in a second silica tube.

2. Turn the 3-way stopcock to *close off syringe 1.*

3. Remove the silica tube containing the steel wool and replace it with the one containing copper (II) oxide powder.

4. Turn the 3-way stopcock so that syringe 1 connects, through the silica tube, with syringe 2.

5. Using a moderate burner flame, heat the copper (II) oxide in the silica tube.

6. Pass the gases back and forth over the heated copper (II) oxide using the technique described in Part I, procedure 7. The volume of the gas should decrease during this procedure.

7. Using the plungers, push *all* of the remaining gas back into syringe 1.

8. Turn off the burner and cool the silica tube using a damp cloth.

9. Wait for the apparatus and gas to reach room temperature, then record the total volume of the gas in syringe 1.

Questions for Thought and Discussion

1. Write a word equation for the reaction that occurs in Part I.

2. What is the purpose of the copper (II) oxide in Part II of this experiment? Does its function differ in any way from that of the steel wool in Part I?

3. Calculate the volume of hydrogen gas produced from the ammonia.

4. What volume of nitrogen gas is produced from the ammonia?

5. Show clearly that these results, within experimental error, are in agreement with Gay-Lussac's law. To do this you will have to assume that the reverse of the above reaction is possible, that is, hydrogen gas and nitrogen gas will combine to form ammonia gas.

6. How are the temperature-pressure relationships inherent in Gay-Lussac's law satisfied in this experimental procedure?

7. Discuss any sources of error that might interfere with the results of the experiment.

8. What name is given to a substance having the function of steel wool in this experiment?

EXPERIMENT 11-6

The Ratio, By Volume, With Which Gases Combine
(Demonstration)

In this experiment two gases, which at room temperature and pressure do not react, are placed in a calibrated glass tube known as a eudiometer tube. A spark is used to cause a reaction to take place and the ratio by volume with which the two gases react is determined.

CAUTION: The reaction that takes place when this mixture is ignited is an explosive one. The eudiometer tube may shatter. All students should be at least 10 to 15 feet away from the apparatus during ignition. To prevent glass from shattering, the eudiometer tube may be wrapped in, for example, Saran wrap. The apparatus should be separated from students and teacher by a shatter-proof glass or wire explosion screen mounted on a solid base. When using a 50 ml eudiometer tube, no more than <u>20 ml</u> of each gas should be used in the tube.

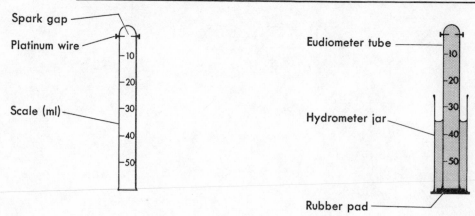

Figure E-42. *50 ml eudiometer tube.*

Figure E-43.

The eudiometer tube is a glass tube of uniform cross-section, calibrated in millilitres. One end of the tube is closed and equipped with a pair of platinum wires as shown in Figure E-42. There is a small gap between these wires. The other end of the eudiometer tube is open.

Procedure

1. Fill an hydrometer jar with water and put a small rubber pad into the bottom of the jar (Figure E-43).

2. Fill a 50 ml eudiometer tube with water, cover the open end of the tube and invert it into the hydrometer jar (Figure E-43).

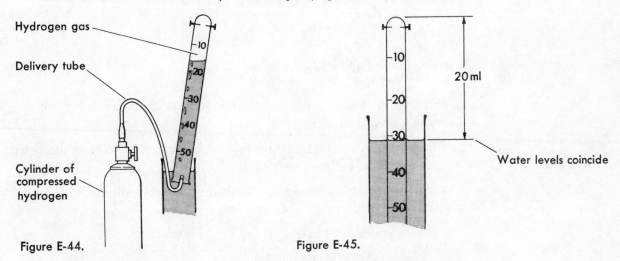

Figure E-44.

Figure E-45.

3. Using a hydrogen gas generator or, preferably, a cylinder of compressed hydrogen, bubble hydrogen gas into the eudiometer tube until 20 ml of hydrogen gas are in the tube (Figure E-44). This volume should be measured when the eudiometer tube has been lowered into the hydrometer jar until the water levels are the same in the eudiometer tube and in the hydrometer jar (Figure E-45).

4. Using an oxygen generator or a cylinder of compressed oxygen, bubble oxygen gas into the eudiometer tube until 20 ml of oxygen gas have been added to the hydrogen gas already in the tube. The total volume of the gases in the eudiometer tube should now be 40 ml and this volume should again be measured using the procedure to adjust the water levels described above.

5. Press the eudiometer tube *lightly* down onto the rubber pad and clamp the tube *firmly* into position. The clamps should be lined with a flexible material such as rubber in order that the tube not strike the rigid metal surface and shatter when the reaction takes place.

6. Connect the platinum wires to the leads of an induction coil which in turn is connected in series with a switch (open) and 3 dry cells (alternately the mixtures may be ignited with a Tesla Coil).

7. Close the switch. Observe carefully.

8. Allow the tube to cool.

9. Adjust the water levels as before and record the volume of the gas now present.

10. Cover the open end of the eudiometer tube with a glass plate or rubber stopper and remove the tube from the water. Keep the water in the tube. Place the tube with the open end upright, remove the glass plate and insert a glowing splint.

Questions for Thought and Discussion

1. What gas or gases remain(s) in the tube after the reaction? Give two reasons for your choice(s).

2. Give a reason for each change in the water level in the eudiometer tube during and after the explosion.

3. From the volume readings establish the ratio by volume with which hydrogen gas and oxygen gas combine.

that is, $\dfrac{\text{volume of hyrdogen gas}}{\text{volume of oxygen gas}} =$ _____

4. This reaction is just one example of the general behaviour of gases when they react. State the law which generalizes this specific example.

EXPERIMENT 11-7

Molecular Weights of Gases

According to Avogadro's principle, equal volumes of different gases at the same temperature and pressure contain the same number of molecules. If this is true, it should be possible to determine the mass of a volume of one gas, then the mass of the *same volume* of a second gas at the same temperature and pressure. The two masses obtained will *represent* the masses of individual molecules of each gas compared with one another.

In this experiment a plastic bag is filled with one gas at room temperature and pressure and the total mass carefully determined. This procedure is repeated for a second gas using the same plastic bag. The masses of these equal volumes of two different gas samples are then compared. These different masses represent the relative masses of the molecules of the two different gases.

Because the gas samples will be quite light, their masses must be determined very carefully to obtain the maximum precision from the apparatus available. In addition, the buoyancy of the gas sample will have to be accounted for. The instructions for filling the plastic bag with the gases must be followed carefully. The same procedure must be used for each gas to minimize variations in pressure.

Procedure

Part I

1. You have been provided with a size 6 one-hole stopper having a deep groove cut around it. Fold the open end of the plastic bag into small pleats around the large end of this stopper and fasten the bag securely to the stopper using a rubber band (Figure E-46).

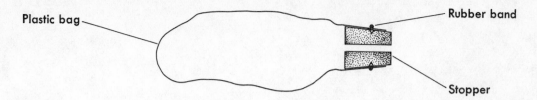

Figure E-46.

2. Insert the tapered end of a medicine dropper into the smaller end of the rubber stopper. Hold the medicine dropper with a cloth and cautiously twist the dropper into the stopper until the stopper holds it firmly (Figure E-47).

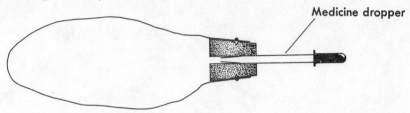

Figure E-47.

3. Remove the bulb from the medicine dropper. Starting at the closed end, squeeze all the air out of the plastic bag by flattening and folding the bag. When all air has been removed, put the bulb back on the dropper (Figure E-48).

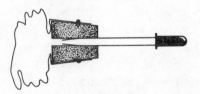

Figure E-48.

4. Determine the mass of the empty plastic bag, stopper and medicine dropper carefully to the nearest 0.01 g (more accurately if possible).

5. A cylinder of compressed oxygen may be used as a source of oxygen gas. Open the valve until a *slow* but steady bubbling action is produced when the open end of the delivery tube is placed below water in a beaker. Note the extent to which the cylinder valve must be opened to produce this steady bubbling action, then close the valve.

6. Remove the bulb from the medicine dropper and attach the dropper snugly, but not tightly, to the delivery tube from the oxygen cylinder (Figure E-49). Allow the oxygen gas to enter until the plastic bag is fully inflated. *Support the plastic bag assembly by the rubber stopper only.*

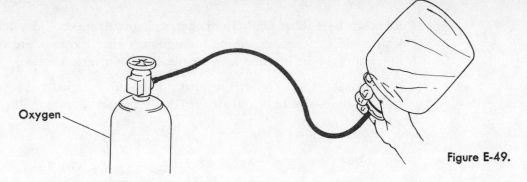

Oxygen

Figure E-49.

7. Once the plastic bag is full, disconnect the delivery tube and hold the assembly in the air for a few seconds. *Do not squeeze the bag.* At this point, any excess oxygen gas will escape and the gas sample will be under room temperature and pressure conditions.

8. Replace the rubber bulb and determine the mass of the plastic bag, oxygen gas, stopper and medicine dropper to the nearest 0.01 g.

9. Record room temperature and atmospheric pressure.

10. As time permits, procedures 6, 7 and 8 may be repeated as a check on the first determination.

Part II

Starting again with the same plastic bag, dry and empty, repeat procedures 5, 6, 7 and 8 exactly as before except that a cylinder of compressed carbon dioxide is used as a source of carbon dioxide gas. Again, as time permits, procedure 10 may be followed. Gases other than carbon dioxide may also be used, for example, nitrogen gas, methane gas, helium gas or one of the freons.

Part III

As discussed in the opening remarks, the buoyant force exerted by the atmosphere on the gas samples in the plastic bag is considerable when compared with the mass of the gas sample. To find the buoyant force exerted on the gas sample, the volume of the gas sample in the plastic bag must be determined.

1. Starting again with the empty, dry plastic bag, fill the bag with air by blowing into the medicine dropper. Pause, as before, to allow the pressure to adjust to atmospheric pressure, then put the rubber bulb back on the medicine dropper.

2. Fill a large bottle with water. Any small-mouthed bottle having a larger volume than the gas sample in the plastic bag will do. Hold a glass plate over the mouth of the bottle and invert the bottle into any large container of water. Remove the glass plate.

3. Remove the rubber bulb from the medicine dropper and replace it with a piece of rubber tubing long enough that the opposite end of the tubing can be inserted into the neck of the inverted bottle.

4. Apply pressure, gently, to the plastic bag and eventually flatten and fold the bag until all of the air has been removed (Figure E-50).

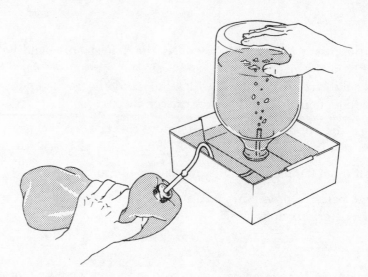

Figure E-50.

5. Pinch the rubber tubing closed, then remove it from the neck of the bottle.

6. Cover the bottle mouth with a glass plate (or insert a rubber stopper) and place the bottle upright on the laboratory bench. Remove the glass plate (or rubber stopper).

7. Using a graduated cylinder, add water to the partially filled bottle until it is full. This volume is the volume of gas that filled the plastic bag.

Calculations

The buoyant force exerted on an object immersed in any fluid is equivalent to the mass of the fluid that the object displaces. When the mass of the plastic bag containing a gas is determined in air, the bag displaces a volume of air approximately equivalent to the volume of the gas sample in the bag. The volume of this gas sample has been determined. Table 1 shows the density (g litre^{-1}) of air at different temperatures and pressures.

EXPERIMENT 11-7

Table 1

Density of Air (g litre^{-1})

Pressure (mm)	Temperature			
	15°C	20°C	25°C	30°C
600	0.97	0.95	0.94	0.92
610	0.98	0.97	0.95	0.93
620	1.00	0.98	0.97	0.95
630	1.02	1.00	0.98	0.97
640	1.03	1.01	1.00	0.98
650	1.05	1.03	1.01	1.00
660	1.06	1.05	1.03	1.01
670	1.08	1.06	1.04	1.03
680	1.10	1.08	1.06	1.04
690	1.11	1.09	1.07	1.06
700	1.13	1.11	1.09	1.07
710	1.14	1.12	1.10	1.09
720	1.16	1.14	1.12	1.10
730	1.18	1.16	1.14	1.12
740	1.19	1.17	1.15	1.13
750	1.21	1.19	1.17	1.15
760	1.23	1.21	1.19	1.16
770	1.24	1.22	1.20	1.18

1. Calculate the apparent mass of oxygen gas in the plastic bag. The apparent mass is the mass of the gas neglecting the buoyancy.

2. Calculate the buoyant force exerted on the plastic bag when filled with a gas, that is, the mass of air displaced by the bag when filled with a gas.

3. Calculate the *actual* mass of the oxygen gas sample which filled the plastic bag.

4. Repeat calculations 1, 2 and 3 for carbon dioxide gas (and for any other gases used).

5. Compare the mass of the carbon dioxide gas sample with the oxygen gas sample by expressing the following ratio as a decimal fraction:

$$\frac{\text{mass of carbon dioxide gas sample}}{\text{mass of oxygen gas sample}} =$$

6. Using the table of atomic weights, determine the molecular weight of oxygen gas, O_2.

7. By setting up the appropriate ratio, use the results from this experiment to determine the molecular weight of carbon dioxide gas.

8. Repeat procedures 5 and 7 for any other gases that were used during this experiment.

EXPERIMENT 11-8

Rates of Effusion

In this experiment a single gas syringe (Figure E-51) equipped with a pin-hole opening is used to measure differences in the effusion rates of various gases. A relationship is then established between the effusion rates and the molecular weights of the gases used. Finally, the molecular weight of an unknown gas is determined.

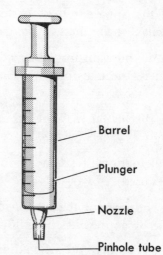

Figure E-51. Gas syringe

— Barrel

— Plunger

— Nozzle

— Pinhole tube

Procedure

Part I   The Relationship Between Effusion Rates and Molecular Weights
The relationship is established for nitrogen, hydrogen and carbon dioxide gases.

1. Support the gas syringe in a vertical position.

2. Connect a small cylinder of compressed nitrogen gas, N_2, to the lower end of the gas syringe (the nozzle) using rubber tubing.

3. Open the valve on the nitrogen gas cylinder *very slightly* (caution) and allow the gas syringe to fill. The plunger should rise slowly.

4. After filling the syringe, disconnect the rubber tubing from the nozzle of the syringe and allow the plunger to fall freely, thus emptying the syringe.

5. Repeat procedures 2, 3 and 4 *two* more times.

6. Fill the syringe again as already described. Remove the rubber tubing from the syringe nozzle and quickly connect the pinhole tube to the nozzle.

7. Measure the time required for the plunger to pass between, for example, the 80 ml and 20 ml marks on the barrel of the syringe. That is, measure the time required for a given volume of gas to effuse.

8. Repeat procedures 2 to 7 using the following gases:
   (a)   hydrogen, H_2.
   (b)   carbon dioxide, CO_2.
   Allow the *same* volume of gas to effuse in each case. Record the results in tabular form.

9. Plot the reciprocal of the time taken for the given volume of each gas to effuse against the square root of the molecular weight of each gas.

Part II   Determining the Molecular Weight of an Unknown Gas

1. You will be provided with a gas whose molecular weight is to be determined. Follow procedures 2 to 7 of Part I and determine the time required for this unknown gas to effuse.

2. Using the graph prepared in Part I, determine the molecular weight of the unknown gas.

3. If time permits determine the molecular weight of a second unknown gas.

Questions for Thought and Discussion

1. With reference to the data table (only) that you have prepared, express *qualitatively* the relationship that exists between rates of effusion and molecular weights of gases.

2. With reference to the plotted results express, both verbally and as a mathematical expression, the *quantitative* relationship that exists between rates of effusion and molecular weights.

EXPERIMENT 11-9

Diffusion of Gases

When any sample of gas or volatile liquid is placed at a given point in a room, the gas (or gas produced as the liquid vapourizes) spreads to all parts of the room. This is true even when there are no convection currents in the room. This process is known as *diffusion*. The rate of diffusion of a gas is measured as the rate at which molecules of a gas diffuse or spread out into a second gas.

In this experiment, two solutions are placed at opposite ends of a glass tube of uniform cross-section. The solutions chosen result in gases which react with one another and form a white solid. We would like to decide (1) whether there is a spreading out or diffusion; (2) whether there is any difference in the rates of diffusion of different gases.

1. Clamp a clean, dry glass tube horizontally.

CAUTION: Handle the solutions provided using medicine droppers only and avoid breathing in the fumes. Keep the tops on the bottles as much as possible.

---

2. Select a piece of absorbent cotton and fashion it into the shape of a small plug that will fit into the end of the glass tube. Repeat for the opposite end of the tube. Alternately, the solutions may be placed in combustion boats and the glass tube stoppered after the boats are in position (Figure E-52).

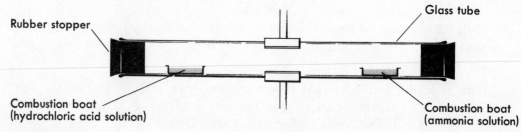

Figure E-52.

Rubber stopper

Glass tube

Combustion boat
(hydrochloric acid solution)

Combustion boat
(ammonia solution)

3. Using forceps and medicine droppers, add 4 drops of concentrated ammonia water (a source of ammonia gas) to one cotton plug and 4 drops of concentrated hydrochloric acid (a source of hydrogen chloride gas) to the other.

4. Simultaneously insert the plugs into opposite ends of the glass tube and note the time. Stopper the ends of the tube. Be careful to note which liquid is on which plug.

5. Record the time again when a white ring first appears inside the tube. This ring is the white solid ammonium chloride.

6. Measure the distance from each cotton plug (the inside edge of the cotton) to the centre of the white ring that forms.

7. Repeat the experiment until two sets of results are in reasonable agreement. Be sure that the tube is clean and dry before each determination.

8. Calculate the rate at which ammonia gas spreads along the tube, expressing this rate in centimeters per minute.

9. Repeat the calculation for hydrogen chloride gas which arises from the concentrated hydrochloric acid.

Questions for Thought and Discussion

1. What two conclusions may be drawn from this procedure?

2. Does the phenomenon of diffusion of gases suggest anything as to the nature of gases?

3. What factor might account for the difference in the rate at which these gases spread out in the tube?

EXPERIMENT 12-1

Melting Point of a Pure Substance

Several methods may be used to determine the melting point of a pure substance. In this procedure the cooling and heating curves are established for the moth repellent, paradichlorobenzene, and from these the melting point is established.

In Part I of the experiment the warm liquid sample is cooled by lowering it into a 400 ml beaker containing water at room temperature. In Part II the warm water in a 400 ml beaker is used as a source of heat to establish the heating curve. In experiments of this type it is essential that the sample be cooled or heated at a constant rate. The temperature of the water and sample before cooling and heating have been selected with this in mind. The amount of water in the bath is also critical. The instructions must be followed carefully to obtain the two curves. Data tables should be prepared prior to the laboratory period as directed in the procedure.

Procedure

Part I   Cooling Curve

1. Add tap water to a 400 ml beaker until the beaker is 3/4 full. This water should be at room temperature (22°C to 30°C).
    Note: If Part I and Part II are to be carried out in the same 40 to 45 minute laboratory period it is advisable to use a second 400 ml beaker, pour in the same amount of water and heat this water to 70°C while carrying out the remainder of Part I. Alternatively, hot water may be provided as you begin Part II.

2. Place about 15 g of the moth repellent, paradichlorobenzene, in a dry, clean test tube.

3. Fasten a clamp near the mouth of the test tube. This clamp should be a type which can later be attached to the retort stand.

4. Using a *low flame,* heat the test tube and paradichlorobenzene gently until it *just melts* (Figure E-53). Place the provided thermometer in the liquid and continue heating gently until the temperature of the liquid is between 67°C and 71°C. The purpose of this procedure is simply to convert the paradichlorobenzene into the liquid state in order to place the thermometer into the sample. The warm liquid is now cooled slowly and the data recorded.

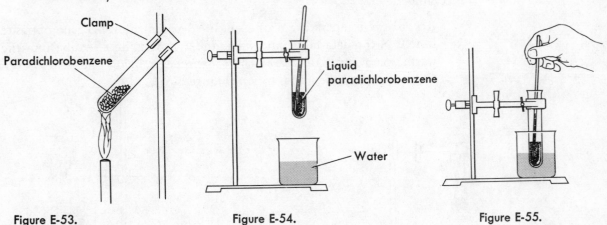

Figure E-53. Figure E-54. Figure E-55.

5. Clamp the test tube above the beaker of cool water (Figure E-54). The next step involves the use of a stopwatch and thermometer. Every 30 seconds the temperature of the cooling liquid must be recorded. A data table should be prepared (before the laboratory period) capable of handling about 18 pairs of readings. One person should handle the stopwatch (is it wound?) and record the data. The other should take the temperature readings to the highest degree of precision warranted by the thermometer he is using. The temperature at which solidification begins and the temperature at which solidification is complete should be noted in the table of data.

6. Record the temperature of the paradichlorobenzene opposite time 0 in the data table and *immediately* lower the test tube into the water. Clamp the test tube into position (Figure E-55). Record the temperature at 30 second intervals. The thermometer should be supported manually with the bulb in the middle of the sample—not touching the sides or bottom of the test tube. The scale should be completely visible —not obscured by the clamp. This position should be maintained until the paradichlorobenzene solidifies.

7. Continue recording until the temperature is in the high thirties.

Part II   Heating Curve

1. Place the 400 ml beaker, still ¾ full of water, on a ring clamp and wire gauze and heat the water until the temperature is approximately 70°C (Figure E-56). Stir the water during this heating procedure. Turn the burner off when the required temperature has been reached.

Add a third column to the previous data table and follow the same procedure for recording time and temperature as in Part I. Record the temperature at which melting begins and the temperature at which melting is complete.

2. Record the temperature of the solidified paradichlorobenzene opposite time 0 in the data table, and *immediately* lower the test tube into the warm water until the paradichlorobenzene is below the water level. Clamp the test tube into position (Figure E-57).

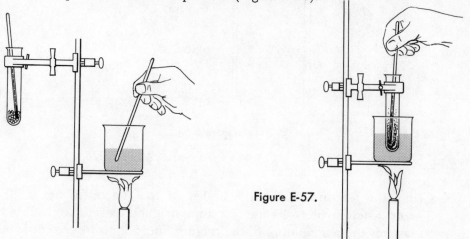

Figure E-56.

Figure E-57.

3. Record the temperature of the paradichlorobenzene every 30 seconds. When the solid becomes free in the test tube, raise and lower the thermometer *gently* as a means of stirring the mixture.

4. Continue the procedure until the temperature of the paradichlorobenzene is about 60°C. Check the temperature of the water bath during this interval and if it should fall below 60°C, warm the water with the burner and keep the temperature between 60°C and 65°C.

5. Remove the thermometer from the paradichlorobenzene.

Plotting The Cooling And Heating Curves

1. Using the data from Part I, plot the temperature (°C) as a function of time (minute). That is, plot the time along the horizontal axis (*x*-axis

or abscissa) and plot the temperature along the vertical axis (y-axis or ordinate.) Choose a scale such that the data plotted along each axis covers approximately the same distance on the page. Plot each pair of values by placing a small x at the appropriate point.

2. Draw a smooth curve through the plotted x's. This is the cooling curve for paradichlorobenzene.

3. Using the same set of axes, plot the data for the heating curve from Part II. Plot each pair of values by drawing a small circle around the appropriate point.

4. Using a coloured pencil, draw a smooth curve through the small circles. This is the heating curve for paradichlorobenzene.

Questions for Thought and Discussion

1. What is the significance of the plateau in:
   (a) the cooling curve?
   (b) the heating curve?

2. From your results, what is the melting point (m.p.) of paradichlorobenzene?

3. From your results, what is the freezing point (f.p.) of paradichlorobenzene?

4. If a larger sample of paradichlorobenzene were used, how would the shape of the curves alter?

5. What use is made of the melting points of pure substances?

EXPERIMENT 12-2

The Vapour Pressure of Liquids
(Demonstration)

A simple mercury barometer may be used to illustrate the vapour pressure of liquids. The space above the mercury in such a barometer may be considered a vacuum since the vapour pressure of mercury is very low. In the experiment the vapour pressures of water, benzene and diethlyl ether are determined using separate barometer tubes at room temperature. The effect of temperature changes on vapour pressure is examined in Part II, using a condenser jacket over the barometer tube in order to vary the temperature.

CAUTION: Do not allow mercury or benzene to come in contact with the skin. Do not inhale either of their vapours unnecessarily. Rubber gloves should be used when handling these liquids.

Procedure

Part I

1. Fill a clean, dry barometer tube with mercury and invert the tube into a cistern of mercury. The cistern should be a thick-walled container and large enough that it can hold easily all of the mercury in the barometer tube in addition to the pool of mercury it already contains. Clamp the barometer tube securely.

2. Measure the height of the mercury column (Figure E-58) to the nearest millimetre.

3. Record room temperature.

4. Repeat procedures 1 and 2 and set up *two additional* mercury barometers. One of these tubes should have the rubber stopper in position (Figure E-59) that will serve to connect the condenser jacket used in Part II.

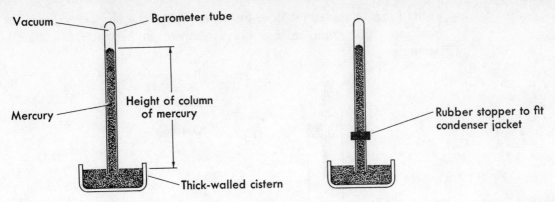

Vacuum — Barometer tube

Mercury — Height of column of mercury

Thick-walled cistern

Rubber stopper to fit condenser jacket

Figure E-58, 59

5. Using a curved medicine dropper, introduce a few drops of water into the mercury column of the first barometer (Figure E-60). If the water does not rise to the surface of the mercury, tap the barometer tube gently until it does. Add enough water that a small amount of water remains on the surface of the mercury.

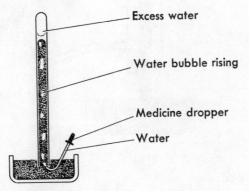

Excess water

Water bubble rising

Medicine dropper

Water

Figure E- 60

6. Measure the height of the column of mercury after the mercury level has remained constant for several minutes.

7. Record the temperature of the room to the nearest half degree (°C).

8. Repeat procedures 5, 6 and 7 using the barometer tube with the rubber stopper but add benzene, C_6H_6, instead of water.

9. Repeat procedures 5, 6 and 7 using the third barometer tube and diethyl ether, $(C_2H_5)_2$ O, instead of water.

10. From the readings obtained, calculate the vapour pressure of water, benzene and diethyl ether at room temperature.

Part II

1. Fit one end of a condenser jacket with a stopper and thermometer and lower the jacket over the second barometer tube (the one from Part I

containing benzene) until it fits snugly into the stopper already in position. The complete assembly is shown in Figure E-61. Clamp securely.

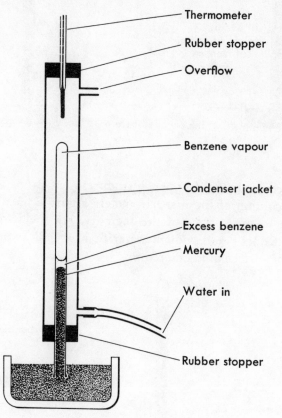

Figure E-61.

2. The lower jacket opening should be connected by rubber tubing to a source of water that can be adjusted to provide hot and cold water. Connect rubber tubing to the upper jacket opening and place the opposite end of this tubing in the sink (overflow).

If an outlet is available at the sink where hot and cold water can be mixed in any proportion and passed through the jacket, it is possible to obtain a series of temperature and vapour pressure readings and to plot these values. If such an outlet is not available the hot and cold water taps may be used to get some idea of the variation in vapour pressure over this temperature range. Alternatively, the bottom jacket opening can be closed and ice water or hot water poured into the upper opening using rubber tubing and a funnel.

3. Allow cold tap water to circulate slowly through the jacket and observe any change in the mercury level.

EXPERIMENT 12-2

4. Record the temperature of the water in the jacket after this value has remained steady for several minutes.

5. Measure the height of the column of mercury.

6. Adjust the mixture of water to provide water that is about 10C° higher in temperature than the cold water added in 3. Allow this water to circulate slowly through the jacket and observe any change in the mercury level.

7. Record the temperature of the water in the jacket after the temperature has remained constant for several minutes.

8. Measure the height of the column of mercury.

9. Repeat procedures 6, 7 and 8 using water temperatures that increase successively by 10C° intervals. Continue until it becomes impossible to record the height of the column of mercury or until the water temperature in the jacket cannot be further increased.

10. From the readings obtained, calculate the vapour pressure of benzene at each temperature recorded.

11. Choose appropriate scales and plot the vapour pressure of benzene as a function of temperature.

12. From the graph, determine the normal boiling point of benzene.

13. Compare the value from procedure 12 with the accepted value.

Questions for Thought and Discussion

1. When water, benzene or diethyl ether is added to the barometer tube, what happens to the mercury level? Carefully explain the reason for this change.

2. What was atmospheric pressure during the course of the experiment?

3. What accounts for the difference in vapour pressure of water, benzene and diethyl ether at a given temperature?

4. Why is the temperature stipulated when the vapour pressure of a liquid is given?

5. What general relationship exists between the vapour pressure of a liquid and temperature? Does this relationship seem reasonable when compared with the theory governing liquid and gaseous behaviour? Explain.

6. At what points in this experiment does a dynamic equilibrium exist?

EXPERIMENT 12-3

Dalton's Law of Partial Pressures

The law of partial pressures states that the total pressure exerted by a mixture of non-reacting gases is equal to the sum of the partial pressures exerted by each gas in the mixture.

$$P_{total} = P_1 + P_2 + P_3 + \cdots \cdot P_n$$

Using basic apparatus found in most laboratories, it is possible to verify this law experimentally.

Design a technique, based on the discussion and experimental work carried out so far, that would verify the law. With the approval of your teacher carry out this procedure.

EXPERIMENT 13-1

The Molar Volume of Oxygen Gas

Potassium chlorate, $KClO_3$, is a white crystalline solid which when heated produces oxygen gas, O_2. In this experiment a known mass of potassium chlorate is heated in a test tube and any gas produced is directed into a gas measuring burette. Since the potassium chlorate loses only oxygen during the heating procedure, any loss in the mass of potassium chlorate represents the mass of oxygen gas produced.

Ideally the gas measuring burette used in this experiment should be calibrated from top to bottom as shown (Figure E-62) and have a capacity of at least 50 ml. There should be a stopcock at the 0 end of the tube. If such a burette is not available, a standard 50 ml volumetric burette can be used.

Procedure

1. Invert the gas measuring burette as shown and clamp it securely.

2. Fit the lower end of the gas measuring burette with an appropriate stopper and rubber tubing and connect the tubing with a levelling bulb. This bulb can be supported using an open-ended iron ring (Figure E-62). The rubber tubing must be long enough that the levelling bulb can be raised to the level of the stopcock.

3. Use a 1-hole stopper and a second length of rubber tubing to connect the upper end of the gas measuring burette with a clean, dry, pyrex test tube (18 × 150 mm). Set up a clamp and retort stand to receive this test tube, then remove the test tube.

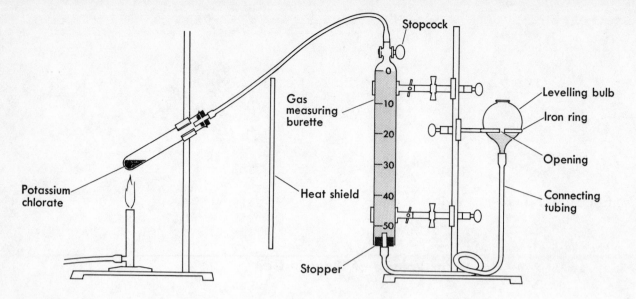

Figure E-62.

4. Support the levelling bulb opposite the 20 ml mark on the gas measuring burette and half fill the reservoir and burette with water. Allow the water to come to room temperature.

5. Add from 0.10 g to 0.15 g of potassium chlorate (reagent grade) to the clean, dry, pyrex test tube. Determine, accurately, the mass of the test tube and its contents.

6. With the stopcock open, raise the levelling bulb until the water in the burette *just touches* the lower opening of the stopcock. Once the water level is steady at this point, close the stopcock.

7. To check for a leak at the stopcock, lower the levelling bulb momentarily. If there is no significant change in the water level at the top of the burette, the stopcock is not leaking.

8. Clamp the test tube containing the potassium chlorate sample into position and connect this test tube to the upper end of the gas burette using the tubing and rubber stopper.

9. Open the stopcock.

10. Again test for leaks by lowering the levelling bulb. The water level will probably drop slightly then remain constant if there are no leaks.

11. Place the heat shield in position. (A sheet of asbestos is sufficient.)

12. Heat the potassium chlorate, gently at first, then gradually increase the intensity of this heating. As the gas collects in the burette, gradually lower the levelling bulb keeping the level of the water in the bulb

roughly opposite the level in the burette. Continue heating until 30 ml to 40 ml of gas have been collected in the gas measuring burette.

13. Stop heating and allow the apparatus to cool to room temperature.

14. Adjust the levelling bulb until the water levels in the levelling bulb and burette are the same. Record the volume of gas collected.

15. Record atmospheric pressure and room temperature.

16. Look up the vapour pressure of water at the temperature recorded in 15.

17. Disconnect the test tube and accurately determine the mass of the test tube and its contents.

Calculations

1. Calculate the mass of oxygen gas produced.

2. What pressure in the gas measuring burette can be attributed to the oxygen gas alone? That is, what is the partial pressure of the oxygen gas? Explain your reasoning.

3. At room temperature and the pressure obtained in 2, calculate the molar volume of oxygen gas.

4. Calculate the molar volume of oxygen gas at STP conditions.

Questions for Thought and Discussion

1. What is the reason for the several adjustments made with the levelling bulb?

2. What is the reason for using the asbestos heat shield?

3. This experiment can be carried out using a 100 ml graduated cylinder in place of the gas measuring burette.
   (a) Draw and label a diagram showing how the apparatus would be arranged to perform the experiment in this way.
   (b) What modifications would be necessary in the procedure?

EXPERIMENT 13-2

The Molar Volume of Hydrogen Gas

In the previous experiment the molar volume of oxygen gas was determined at room temperature and pressure. This value was converted to STP conditions since molar volumes are usually compared at $0°C$ and 760 mm Hg. But the molar volume is the volume occupied by 6.02×10^{23} particles (1 mole of particles). If Avogadro's principle is accepted as correct, at a given temperature and pressure, *1 mole of particles of any gas will occupy the same volume*. In this experiment the molar volume of hydrogen gas is determined and compared with the molar volume of oxygen gas from the previous experiment. If these values are similar under the same temperature and pressure conditions (STP will be used) then the validity of Avogadro's principle is strengthened.

Magnesium metal reacts with dilute acid solutions to form hydrogen gas. In the following procedure a known mass of magnesium is reacted with an excess of dilute hydrochloric acid. The volume of the hydrogen gas produced is determined by using a gas measuring tube. By applying the law of conservation of mass, the molar volume of hydrogen gas is calculated.

Procedure

1. Using emery paper, clean a strip of magnesium ribbon 4.5 cm long.

2. Determine the mass of the magnesium strip as accurately as possible.

3. Add water to a 400 ml beaker until it is ¾ full.

4. Fill a large glass cylinder with water.

5. Using fine copper wire, construct a support for the magnesium in order that it can eventually be suspended in a gas measuring tube (Figure E-63). Do not place the magnesium in position at this time.

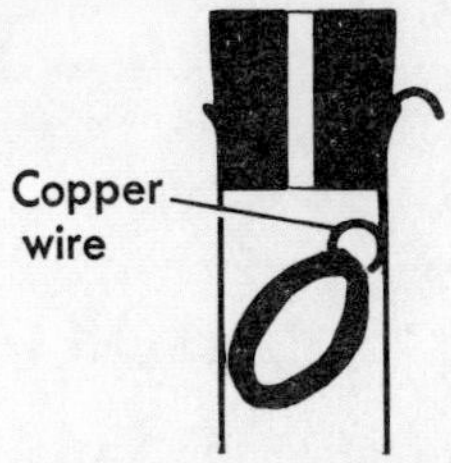

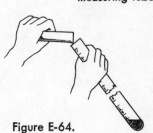

Copper wire

Figure E-63. Top of gas measuring tube.

6. Add 10 ml of dilute hydrochloric acid to the gas measuring tube. Pour the solution carefully down the side of the tube using a 10 ml graduated cylinder (Figure E-64).

7. *Slowly* add water to the gas measuring tube until the tube is full. Keep the measuring tube on an angle and avoid stirring up the 10 ml portion of acid solution in the bottom.

8. Insert the magnesium ribbon supported by the copper wire into the gas measuring tube and hook one end of the copper wire over the edge of the tube. Fix the position of the copper wire by inserting a 1-hole stopper (Figure E-62 and E-65).

Figure E-64.

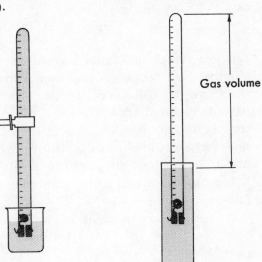

Gas volume

Figure E-65.   Figure E-66.   Figure E-67.

9. Cover the opening in the stopper with your finger and invert the gas measuring tube into the beaker of water (Figure E-66). Clamp the tube into position.

10. After the reaction, allow the apparatus to stand for 10 minutes until it has returned to room temperature. During this time dislodge any bubbles trapped by the copper wire or adhering to the glass by tapping the tube.

11. Cover the stopper opening and transfer the gas measuring tube to the large cylinder.

12. Lower the gas measuring tube until the water levels in the measuring tube and the large cylinder are the same. Measure the volume of the gas collected (Figure E-67).

EXPERIMENT 13-2

177

13. Record atmospheric pressure and room temperature.

14. Record the vapour pressure of water at room temperature.

Calculations

The calculation to determine the molar volume in this experiment involves an understanding of the reaction that occurs. Magnesium metal, Mg(s), reacts with hydrochloric acid which is a solution of hydrogen chloride in water, HCl(soln). One product of this reaction is hydrogen gas, $H_2(g)$. This much of the reaction may be summarized as:

$$\text{magnesium metal} + \text{hydrochloric acid} \rightarrow \text{hydrogen gas}$$

or

$$Mg(s) + HCl(soln) \rightarrow H_2(g) \tag{1}$$

But this expression cannot be complete. According to the atomic theory, atoms are not created or destroyed during chemical reactions. Yet clearly, the above expression indicates that the magnesium and the chlorine atoms have disappeared while there are twice as many hydrogen *atoms* as there were before the reaction. There must be another product formed during this reaction. Chemists have identified this product as magnesium chloride, $MgCl_2$, but we have not seen it form during the reaction because as it forms it remains dissolved in the water. We can now add to expression (1) as follows:

$$\text{magnesium (solid)} + \text{hydrochloric acid (soln)} \rightarrow$$
$$\text{hydrogen (gas)} + \text{magnesium chloride (soln)}$$

or

$$Mg(s) + HCl(soln) \rightarrow H_2(g) + MgCl_2 \text{ (soln)} \tag{2}$$

But notice that this expression still contradicts the atomic theory and the law of conservation of mass. Although each kind of atom is now accounted for before and after the reaction, the expression indicates that there are twice as many hydrogen and chlorine atoms after the reaction as there were before. These extra hydrogen and chlorine atoms must have been present before the reaction. They are accounted for in the expression by placing the coefficient 2 before the hydrogen chloride formula. Thus

$$Mg(s) + 2HCl(soln) \rightarrow H_2(g) + MgCl_2 \text{ (soln)} \tag{3}$$

Expression (3) is known as the *balanced chemical equation* for the reaction of magnesium metal with hydrochloric acid. If we consider each chemical symbol as representing 1 mole of an element then 1 mole of magnesium atoms, 2 moles of hydrogen atoms and 2 moles of chlorine atoms are present both before and after the reaction. Mass is conserved and atoms are neither created nor destroyed.

In our experiment the mass of magnesium and volume of hydrogen gas are known. It is these two components of Equation 3 that concern us. *The equation shows that when 1 mole of solid, 1 Mg(s), reacts with an excess of hydrochloric acid 1 mole of hydrogen gas, 1 H₂(g), is produced.*

1. Calculate the number of moles of magnesium that reacted.

2. What molar relationship will always exist between the magnesium, Mg(s), and the hydrogen gas H(g), when this reaction occurs?

3. How many moles of hydrogen gas were produced in this experiment?

4. What volume does the hydrogen gas from question 3. occupy in the gas measuring tube?

5. What pressure is exerted by this hydrogen gas? In other words, determine the partial pressure of the hydrogen gas.

6. Calculate the volume that 1 mole of hydrogen gas would occupy at room temperature and at the partial pressure of hydrogen gas. *This is the molar volume of hydrogen gas at this temperature and pressure.*

7. Convert the molar volume above to the standard molar volume (STP conditions).

8. Compare this standard molar volume with that obtained for oxygen gas in Experiment 13-1.

Questions for Thought and Discussion

1. What general conclusion can be drawn as to the validity of Avogadro's principle when the results of Experiments 13-1 and 13-2 are compared?

2. Why is a 1-holed stopper used in this experiment rather than a solid stopper?

3. Is there any evidence that the copper wire has reacted with the dilute hydrochloric acid?

EXPERIMENT 13-3

Molecular Weight and Molecular Formula

Procedure

Part I   Determining the Molecular Weight of a Gaseous Substance

You have been supplied with a container filled with a compressed gas whose molecular weight is unknown. In this experiment the relationship between the mass and volume of a small sample of this gas is established. From this information the molecular weight of the gas is calculated.

1. Connect a short length of Tygon tubing to the nozzle of the container of compressed gas.

2. Determine the total mass of the tubing, container and compressed gas as accurately as the balances in the laboratory permit.

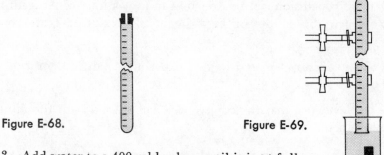

Figure E-68.　　　　　　　　　　**Figure E-69.**

3. Add water to a 400 ml beaker until it is ¾ full.

4. Fill a gas measuring tube (or graduated cylinder) with water and insert a 1-hole rubber stopper (Figure E-68). Be sure that no air is trapped in the tube. Cover the stopper opening, then invert the tube into the beaker of water and remove the stopper. Clamp the tube carefully (Figure E-69).

180　　　　　　　　　　　　　　　　　　　　　　EXPERIMENT 13-3

5. Connect a gas collecting tip to the free end of the Tygon tubing on the container of compressed gas. Depress the nozzle gently and allow a spurt of gas to escape.

Figure E-70.

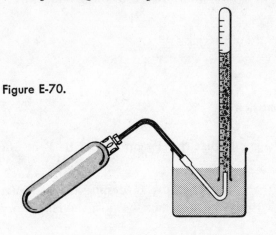

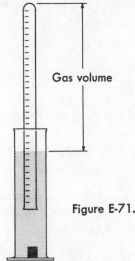

Gas volume

Figure E-71.

6. Place this gas collecting tip under the end of the gas measuring tube in such a position that the Tygon tubing does not come in contact with the water (Figure E-70).

7. Depress the nozzle on the compressed gas container *very slowly and very gently*. Allow gas to collect in the measuring tube until 40 to 48 ml of gas have accumulated (Figure E-70). Be careful that the volume of gas collected does not exceed the calibrated portion of the tube.

8. Wait 10 or 15 minutes until the measuring tube and gas sample have reached room temperature.

9. Adjust the water levels inside and outside the tube until they are the same, then record the volume of the gas collected. If the water levels cannot be adjusted using the 400 ml beaker, insert the rubber stopper into the measuring tube again (under the water), cover the stopper opening and transfer the tube to a glass cylinder filled with water. Remove the rubber stopper, adjust the water levels and record the volume of the gas (Figure E-71).

10. Remove the gas collecting tip (*only*) from the Tygon tubing and again determine the total mass of tubing, container and compressed gas as accurately as the balances in the laboratory permit. Be careful not to release any of the compressed gas during this procedure.

11. Record atmospheric pressure and room temperature.

12. Look up the vapour pressure of water at the above temperature.

13. If time permits, repeat the whole determination.

Calculations

1. Calculate the partial pressure of the unknown gas in the gas measuring tube.

2. Calculate the molecular weight of this gas.

Questions for Thought and Discussion

1. Explain why procedure 6 suggests that the Tygon tubing be kept out of the water.

2. Why is a waiting period necessary (procedure 8) despite the fact that the compressed gas and all equipment used have been in the laboratory for some time?

Part II   Determining the Molecular Formula

When the gas in Part I is analyzed, it is found to contain two elements, carbon and hydrogen. The percentage composition by mass of the compound is

carbon   82.8%
hydrogen 17.2%

Calculate:

1. The simplest formula of the gas.

2. The molecular formula of the gas.

EXPERIMENT 13-4

The Extent of Hydration in a Crystalline Salt

When a solution of a salt remains exposed to the atmosphere, the water of this solution gradually evaporates and the salt itself is left in the container as a crystalline solid. This process is known as *crystallization* and results in crystals of various shapes and colours depending on the geometrical arrangements and electronic configurations of the substances involved. Certain salts, when crystallizing from an aqueous solution, combine with a definite amount of water as the crystals are forming. This water becomes part of the crystalline solid. Such substances are said to be *hydrates* (hydrated salts). The water that forms part of their structures is called *water of hydration*.

In this experiment you will be supplied with one or more hydrates. When a hydrate is heated the water of hydration is removed and the *anhydrous* form of the salt remains. Your teacher will supply you with the formula weight of the corresponding anhydrous salt. Using this procedure, it is possible to calculate the number of moles of water molecules associated with each mole of the anhydrous salt. Prepare a suitable data table before the laboratory experiment.

Procedure

1. Determine the mass of a clean dry crucible and cover.

2. Add crystals of the hydrate to the crucible until the crucible is ¼ to ⅓ full. At the same time record the appearance of this hydrate and the formula weight of the corresponding anhydrous salt as supplied by the teacher.

3. Determine the mass of the crucible, cover and hydrate.

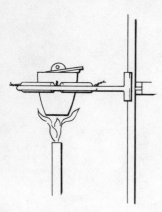

4. Set the crucible on a clay triangle mounted on an iron ring. The crucible cover should be slightly to one side (Figure E-72). Heat the crucible gently for 5 to 7 minutes. When most of the water has been driven off, increase the heat until the crucible bottom becomes a dull red. If the hydrate begins to darken, reduce the heat. Maintain this temperature for 5 minutes. Observe and record any change in the substance during this heating procedure, then allow the crucible and contents to cool (preferably in a desiccator or desicooler).

5. Determine the mass of the crucible, cover and contents as soon as the crucible is cool enough to touch.

6. As time permits, repeat the experiment using a second hydrate.

Figure E-72.

Calculations

Mass of hydrated salt used =
Mass of anhydrous salt =
Mass of water of hydration =
Number of moles of anhydrous salt used in the experiment =
Number of moles of water of hydration in the hydrated salt used =
Number of moles of water of hydration per mole of anhydrous salt =

Compare your results with those of other members of the class using the same hydrated salt.

Questions for Thought and Discussion

1. Does a chemical reaction occur during this experiment? Justify your answer.

2. Why is the mass of the crucible and contents determined immediately after cooling rather than before it has cooled or some time later?

3. Ask your teacher for the chemical name of the anhydrous salt that was produced during this experiment. Write the chemical formula for (a) the anhydrous salt (b) the hydrate.

4. Compare the formula you have written in 3(b) with the accepted formula for this hydrate as found in a handbook of chemistry.

184   EXPERIMENT 13-4

EXPERIMENT 14-1

Reaction of Solid Copper with an Aqueous Silver Nitrate Solution—Verification of the Mole Ratio

This experiment involves a chemical reaction that you have not encountered before. The experiment is divided into two parts. In Part I the reaction is examined qualitatively in order to identify reactants and products. From this information the balanced chemical equation is established using the principles developed in Chapter 14. The mole ratio of silver metal to copper metal is determined from the equation.

If the balanced chemical equation does, in fact, represent both qualitatively and quantitatively the reaction that occurs, it should be possible to verify the mole ratio of silver metal to copper metal experimentally, that is, it should be possible to show *experimentally* that substances react in definite mole ratios. This verification is carried out in Part II. The procedures described in Part II involve standard techniques of quantitative chemical analysis. Great care must be taken to prevent unnecessary loss of reactants or products. Part II is a quantitative procedure and the accuracy of your result will depend upon the care you have taken. A data table for Part II should be prepared before the laboratory period.

Procedure

Part I

The silver nitrate solution used in this procedure has been prepared by dissolving crystals of silver nitrate in distilled water. You will have an opportunity to prepare a similar solution in Part II of this experiment. The solution is kept in dark brown bottles since the compound silver nitrate decomposes in sunlight.

CAUTION: Silver nitrate solid or silver nitrate solution will react with skin causing a dark coloured stain. Avoid contact between these materials and skin or clothing, however, such stains will disappear in a few days.

1. Add about 5 ml of the silver nitrate solution to a clean test tube. Examine this solution carefully and briefly describe it in your notebook.

2. Add a thin strip of copper (0.5 cm × 5 cm) to the same test tube after describing the copper.

3. Observe the contents of the test tube carefully and record any changes that occur.

4. Pour off the remaining solution while retaining any solids that are present in the test tube. Examine and describe these solids carefully.

Questions for Thought and Discussion

1. Is there any evidence to indicate that a chemical change has taken place?

2. From the observations and a knowledge of the reactants, name one of the products of the reaction.

3. There are only two products in this reaction. Having identified one product and knowing the reactants, write the balanced chemical equation for this reaction following the principles outlined in Chapter 14.

4. From the equation determine the ratio of moles of silver produced to moles of copper reacted.

Procedure

Part II

1. Using about 30 cm of copper wire, No. 16, form a coil as illustrated in Figure E-73. The individual coils should be somewhat separated as shown and the straight portion should measure 6 to 8 cm.

2. Determine the mass of this coil as precisely as possible (minimum precision ±0.01 g).

3. Accurately determine the mass of a dry, clean 250 ml beaker.

Figure E-73.

EXPERIMENT 14-1

4. You will be provided with a vial containing 3 to 5 g of small crystals of silver nitrate. Empty the entire contents of the vial into a 250 ml beaker and accurately determine the mass of the beaker plus silver nitrate.

5. Add about 100 ml of distilled water to the beaker. Stir the silver nitrate crystals gently with a glass stirring rod until all crystals have dissolved.

6. Immerse the copper coil in the silver nitrate solution. Bend the straight portion of the copper wire such that the coil can remain suspended from the edge of the beaker (Figure E-74).

Figure E-74.

7. Observe any changes that occur during the first 5 to 10 minutes after the copper is lowered into the solution.

8. Place a watch glass over the beaker and put the beaker aside until the next laboratory period. Make sure that you can identify *your* beaker.

Next Laboratory Period

9. *Do not jar the beaker.* Carefully observe and record any changes.

10. Holding the coil by the bent end, jiggle the coiled portion under the surface of the solution to remove as many crystals from the coil as possible. Any crystals that remain on the coil should be removed by rinsing the coil with distilled water from a wash bottle (Figure E-75). *Remember that this procedure is quantitative.* All crystals that are rinsed off should end up in the beaker, not on the laboratory bench.

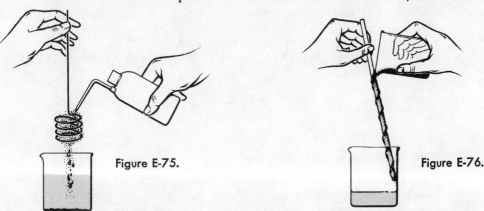

Figure E-75.

Figure E-76.

11. Place the copper coil on a clean watch glass and allow it to dry.

12. Determine the mass of the copper coil after it has dried. Meanwhile carry on with procedure 13.

13. Allow the crystals to settle to the bottom of the beaker. After they have settled, carefully pour off the liquid into a second beaker using a stirring rod as shown in Figure E-76. This process is known as *decanting.* The liquid poured off is known as the *decantate.*

14. A few small particles of copper may be visible among the crystals in the bottom of the original beaker. If this is the case, add 4 to 5 ml of silver nitrate solution from a reagent bottle supplied by your teacher (0.2 M $AgNO_3$) and stir the mixture gently until these reddish-brown particles disappear. Carefully decant this silver nitrate solution following procedure 13.

15. Add about 10 ml of distilled water to wash the crystals free of solution. Use the wash bottle to add this water and pour the water over as many of the crystals as possible. Carefully decant.

16. Repeat this washing process (procedure 15) at least three more times. A few crystals may be lost during these decanting procedures, but if you are careful the mass of material will be very small.

17. The crystals in the bottom of the original beaker must be dried before their mass is determined. Depending on the facilities and time available, this may involve allowing the crystals to stand overnight. Heat lamps, a drying oven or a sand bath may be used. Your teacher will indicate a suitable procedure.

18. Cool the contents of the beaker, then accurately determine the mass of the beaker plus crystals.

19. *Reminder*: Has the mass of the dry copper coil been determined?

Calculations

1. Knowing the mass of the copper coil, calculate the number of moles of copper that reacted.

2. From the mass of the silver, calculate the number of moles of silver produced.

3. Establish the ratio of moles of silver produced to moles of copper reacted.

Questions for Thought and Discussion

1. How does the mole ratio established experimentally in Part II compare with the mole ratio obtained from the balanced chemical equation in Part I?

2. What is the significance of this comparison?

3. One product of this reaction appeared as a precipitate. In what form was the second product? Is there any evidence to verify your answer?

4. A blue coloured solution developed during the reaction. Has this coloured solution been encountered before? If so, where? What is apparently causing the blue colour?

EXPERIMENT 14-2

Determining the Percentage Yield

Whenever a procedure is carried out for the purpose of producing a certain chemical substance, the mass of the product is called the *yield*. When the chemical equation for the reaction is known, it is possible to calculate the theoretical yield for any mass of reactant(s) that is selected. The *theoretical yield* is the mass of product that would be obtained if (1) the reactants were 100 per cent pure, (2) the reaction written in the equation took place completely and (3) none of the products was lost due to the mechanics of the procedure. The theoretical yield is based on calculations from the equation.

In practice, the yield is never as great as the equation predicts. Chemicals are not pure, reactions are not necessarily complete, reactions other than those predicted do occur to some extent and material is lost during experimental procedures. The actual yield obtained by experiment is called the *experimental yield*. It is customary to express the percentage yield for any preparative experiment.

$$\text{percentage yield} = \frac{\text{experimental yield [g]}}{\text{theoretical yield [g]}} \times 100$$

In this experiment a solid is produced when two solutions react. The theoretical yield of this solid is calculated from the equation. The experimental yield is determined by isolating, drying and determining the mass of the solid. The two values are compared in the percentage yield.

Parts I, II and III of this experiment involve calculations that can be performed before the laboratory period. Part IV describes the procedure that will be followed to determine the experimental yield. As in Experiment 14-1, the techniques described here are used frequently in quantitative chemical analysis. The experiment should be carried out with the idea of mastering the techniques as well as the calculations. Only careful experimental work will produce a reasonable yield.

Part I

1. In Part IV a lead nitrate, $Pb(NO_3)_2$, solution will be prepared containing 2.10 g of pure lead nitrate. Calculate the number of moles of this reactant that will be used in the experiment.

2. The second reactant is sodium iodide, NaI. In this case the solution has already been prepared. It is a 0.7M NaI solution and 25 ml of this solution is added to the lead nitrate solution. Calculate the number of moles of this reactant that will be used in the experiment.

2. From the equation determine the ratio:

$$\frac{\text{moles of sodium iodide}}{\text{moles of lead nitrate}}$$

Part II

CALCULATIONS ONLY—DETERMINING THE REACTANT IN EXCESS

The number of moles of each reactant has been determined in Part I. From this information alone it is impossible to predict whether:

(a) there is more sodium iodide than required to react with all the lead nitrate present;

(b) there is more lead nitrate than required to react with all the sodium iodide present;

(c) the amount of each reactant is such that all the sodium iodide reacts with all the lead nitrate.

The theoretical yield cannot be calculated until it is known *which of the reactants is present in excess.* This can be determined using the balanced chemical equation.

1. The solid produced when the lead nitrate solution reacts with the sodium iodide solution is lead iodide. There is only one other product of this reaction. Write the balanced chemical equation for the reaction.

3. From the equation determine the ratio:

$$\frac{\text{moles of sodium iodide that react}}{\text{moles of lead nitrate that react}}$$

3. Compare the above ratio with that calculated in Part I. Is either of the reactants in excess? If so, which one?

Part III

CALCULATIONS ONLY—THE THEORETICAL YIELD

1. In view of the conclusion drawn in Part II, which of the reactants must be used to calculate the theoretical yield? Explain your reasoning.

2. From the mass relationships indicated in the balanced chemical equation, calculate the maximum amount of precipitate, lead iodide, that could be formed, that is, calculate the theoretical yield in this experiment.

Procedure

Part IV

THE EXPERIMENTAL YIELD—PERCENTAGE YIELD

1. Determine the mass of a small, clean and dry piece of paper. Fold the paper once. Using the balance remove approximately 2.4 to 3.0 g of solid lead nitrate from the reagent bottle and add it to the paper (Figure E-77).

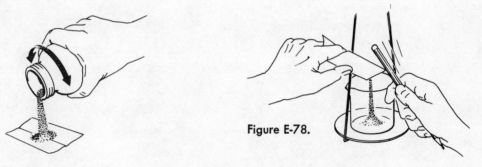

Figure E-77.　　　　　　　　　　　　　　　　Figure E-78.

2. Determine the mass of a clean, dry 100 ml beaker as accurately as possible.

3. Adjust the balance to read 2.10 g *more* than the mass of the beaker. With the beaker on the balance, carefully add lead nitrate from the paper until equilibrium is restored (Figure E-78). Discard any lead nitrate remaining on the paper.

Note: The requirement here is 2.10 g of lead nitrate. *If you wish to know the purity of the lead nitrate, either refer to the reagent bottle or ask your teacher. If this purity is less than 99 percent, calculate the mass of reagent that must be taken from the reagent bottle to give a sample containing 2.10 g of pure lead nitrate. Use this value instead of 2.10 g in procedure 3 above.*

4. Using a graduated cylinder add about 25 ml of distilled water to the beaker and stir until all the solid has dissolved. The mixture can be warmed slightly to increase the rate at which the solid dissolves.

5. Measure out 25 ml of sodium iodide solution into a graduated cylinder (0.7M NaI).

6. While constantly stirring the lead nitrate solution in the beaker, slowly add the 25 ml of sodium iodide solution from the graduated cylinder. Continue stirring for several minutes.

7. Determine the mass of several pieces of filter paper, then calculate the average mass of one piece of filter paper.

8. Fold the filter paper (Figure E-79), moisten it with distilled water from the wash bottle and place it in a funnel. (See Figures I-43 to I-47 for more detail on filtering techniques)

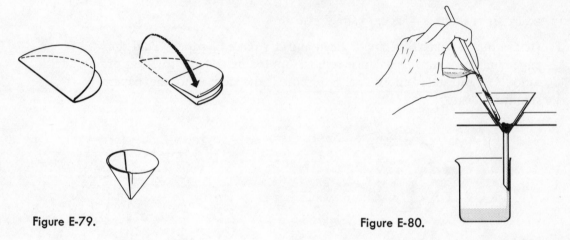

Figure E-79.

Figure E-80.

9. Place the funnel in a funnel holder and adjust the apparatus so that the stem of the funnel touches the edge of a 250 ml beaker placed to receive the filtrate (Figure E-80). If a funnel holder is not available, support the funnel on a clay triangle that rests across the top of a 400 ml beaker.

10. By this time the precipitate in the original beaker will have settled somewhat. Place a glass stirring rod across the top of this beaker, resting the rod in the pouring spout. Grasp the rod and beaker as shown in Figure E-80 and decant the clear liquid into the funnel by pouring it along the glass stirring rod. Some precipitate will get into the funnel, but as much as possible should be kept in the beaker where it will be washed. The stirring rod should be rinsed off into the funnel with distilled water.

11. Use about 15 ml of distilled water from the wash bottle to wash the precipitate in the beaker. Direct this water over as much of the precipitate as possible including any which may have adhered to the sides of the beaker (Figure E-81). Stir precipitate and water briefly then decant the water into the funnel. Again rinse off the stirring rod.

Figure E-81.

12. Repeat this washing procedure with a second 15 ml portion of distilled water. Decant the wash water again.

13. After the filtration is complete, carefully remove the filter paper from the funnel and place it in the beaker with the washed precipitate. Be careful not to lose any of the contents of the filter paper when the transfer is made.

14. Allow the beaker and moist contents to dry overnight. If all beakers are left in one place, be sure you can identify your own.

Next Laboratory Period

15. Accurately determine the total mass of the beaker and its contents when both are thoroughly dry.

Calculations:

1. Determine the mass of precipitate collected in this experiment. This is the experimental yield.

2. Calculate the percentage yield. Refer to Part III for the theoretical yield.

3. Compare your percentage yield with others in the class.

Questions For Thought and Discussion

1. What factors may account for the experimental yield being less than the theoretical yield, or more than the theoretical yield, whichever is the case in your determination?

2. Suggest why substances in solution react more rapidly than in the solid state.

EXPERIMENT 15-1

The Study of Oxygen and Oxides

Oxygen is an extremely important element, not only because it is so plentiful but because it enters into so many reactions which illustrate fundamentals in a beginning chemistry course.

In this experiment you will note several ways of preparing oxygen and some of the properties of oxygen itself. Equations for the methods of preparation are

$$2KClO_3(s) \rightarrow 2KCl(s) + 3O_2(g) \qquad \triangle H \text{ is negative}$$
$$2KNO_3(s) \rightarrow 2KNO_2(s) + O_2(g) \qquad \triangle H \text{ is positive}$$
$$2H_2O_2(l) \rightarrow 2H_2O(l) + O_2(g) \qquad \triangle H \text{ is positive}$$
$$2Na_2O_2(s) + 2H_2O(l) \rightarrow 4NaOH(soln) + O_2(g) \quad \triangle H \text{ is negative}$$

In addition, you will have the opportunity to examine the relationship between the position of an element in the Periodic Table and the properties of its oxide. You will also be able to observe the effect of a catalyst and apply some of the more general oxidation-reduction principles to specific reactions.

The properties of acids and bases have been discussed in terms of their effect on litmus. Litmus is an indicator, one of a large family of indicators used in acid-base reactions. Another member of this family, bromthymol blue, will be used in this experiment because it is more suitable than litmus. An acid can, therefore, be a substance which turns bromthymol blue (BTB) yellow and a base, a substance which turns BTB blue.

Procedure

Part I

1. In a clean, dry test tube, heat about 1 g of potassium chlorate until it has *just* melted. Bring a glowing splint to the mouth of the test tube.

CAUTION: Be careful not to drop ash from the splint into the test tube.

2. Continue heating cautiously and testing with the glowing splint until a definite reaction is observed with the splint.

3. Starting again with a clean, dry test tube, heat about 1 g of potassium chlorate until it has *just* melted. Pointing the test tube away from your face, add a pinch of manganese dioxide to the melted potassium chlorate and again test with a glowing splint.

4. Allow the test tube to cool to room temperature then dissolve as much of the contents as possible by adding hot water to the test tube. Shake or stir the mixture. Filter the mixture and note the nature and quantity of the residue on the filter paper.

5. Allow the filter paper and residue to dry *completely*. Scrape a small portion of this dried residue from the filter paper. Be careful to avoid scraping off bits of filter paper as well. Why?

CAUTION: The residue must be completely dry before continuing with the next procedure. If it is not dry wait until the next laboratory period before performing procedure 6 below.

6. Repeat procedure 3 using a new sample of potassium chlorate and adding a small portion of the thoroughly dried residue.

Parts II, III, IV and V which follow outline different methods that can be used to *prepare* oxygen gas. One of these methods should be used to obtain the oxygen gas required for Part VII. The procedure used to *collect* the oxygen gas is described in Part VI. The instructions given in Part VI should be followed no matter which of Parts II to V is used for the method of preparation.

Part II

1. Calculate the number of grams of potassium chlorate, $KClO_3$, necessary to provide 3.0 litre of oxygen gas at laboratory temperature and pressure.

2. Mix the calculated amount of potassium chlorate with about 2 g of manganese dioxide.

3. Place the mixture in a large test tube (Figure E-82). Avoid contact between any of the mixture and the rubber stopper. Why? Clamp the test tube loosely near its mouth.

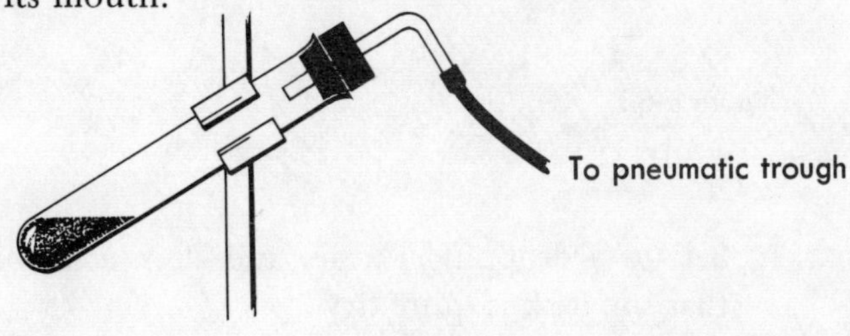

To pneumatic trough

Figure E-82.

4. Heat the test tube gently for about a minute and then heat it **more** strongly, being careful to control the rate of reaction and to **avoid** contact between the molten material and the stopper. Why?

5. Collect the evolved gas as outlined in Part VI.

Part III

1. Calculate the number of grams of potassium nitrate, KNO_3, necessary to provide 3.0 litre of oxygen gas at laboratory temperature and pressure.

2. Place the calculated amount of potassium nitrate in a large test tube (Figure E-82). Clamp the test tube loosely near its mouth.

3. Heat the test tube with a medium flame for about a minute and then heat it strongly.

CAUTION: Great care must be exercised during the heating procedure to avoid contact between the potassium nitrate and the rubber stopper. Why?

4. Collect the evolved gas as outlined in Part VI.

Part IV

1. Set up a thistle tube and flask assembly and place about 2 g of manganese dioxide in the flask. The manganese dioxide will serve as a catalyst for the decomposition of hydrogen peroxide. This reaction is normally very slow at room temperature.

2. Calculate the volume of 5% hydrogen peroxide, H_2O_2, necessary to produce 3.0 litre of oxygen gas at laboratory temperature and pressure.

3. Measure out the calculated volume of hydrogen peroxide and add it slowly through the thistle tube of the flask.

4. Collect the evolved gas as outlined in Part VI.

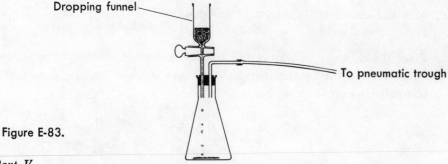

Figure E-83.

Part V

1. Set up a dropping funnel and flask assembly (Figure E-83). Be sure that the flask is quite dry.

2. Calculate the mass of sodium peroxide, Na_2O_2, necessary to produce 3.0 litre of oxygen gas at laboratory temperature and pressure.

3. Very carefully measure out the calculated amount of sodium peroxide in a dry beaker and place it in the bottom of the dry flask.

CAUTION: Do not allow sodium peroxide to touch paper, wood or skin. If it is necessary to remove any spilled solid, brush it into the sink with a dry brush and wash the surface with plenty of water.

---

4. Add water from the dropping funnel, *a few drops at a time,* until a steady stream of gas is produced by the generator.

5. Collect the evolved gas as outlined in Part VI.

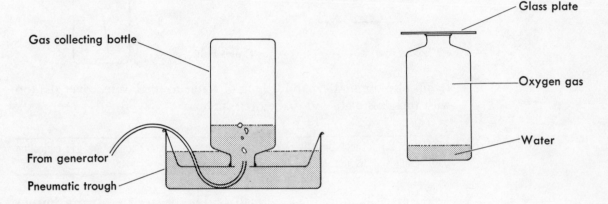

Figure E-84.

Part VI

1. To collect the evolved gas, place the end of the delivery tube in the water of a pneumatic trough (Figure E-84). After allowing the first few bubbles of air to escape, place the tube under the open end of one of the inverted 250 ml, wide mouth bottles filled with water. Be careful not to pinch the end of the delivery tube. A gas collecting tip on the end of the tube will avoid this problem. As the gas is being collected, heat the test tube steadily but gently so that a steady stream of moderate sized gas bubbles rises in the bottle. When this bottle is full of gas, cover the end of the bottle with a glass plate, lift the bottle from the water and place it right side up on the laboratory bench. Keep the glass plate over the mouth of the bottle. Continue this operation until 5 bottles of oxygen gas have been collected.

CAUTION: Never leave the end of the delivery tube under the water when there are no gas bubbles coming from the tube. This permits cold water from the pneumatic trough to back up into the delivery tube and generator which may shatter the apparatus or result in an explosion.

Part VII

1. Using emery paper, clean a 5 cm strip of magnesium ribbon. Coil the magnesium ribbon as in Figure E-85. Hold the coiled magnesium with crucible tongs, ignite the opposite end with a burner flame and lower the magnesium into a bottle of oxygen gas. Allow the ash that forms

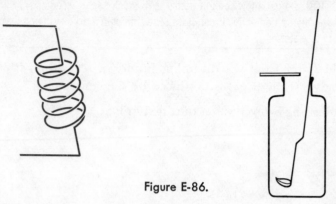

Figure E-85.   Figure E-86.

to fall into the bottle. Add 0.5 cm of water to the bottle, cover the top with the glass plate and shake the contents.

CAUTION: Do not look directly at burning magnesium. Do not touch the gas collecting bottle while the magnesium is burning.

---

2. Using crucible tongs, heat a small bundle of steel wool in a burner flame until it ignites, then lower it into a second bottle of oxygen gas. After the reaction add 0.5 cm of water to the bottle and cover the bottle with the glass plate. Shake the bottle and its contents.

3. Place a small piece of charcoal in a clean deflagrating spoon or hold it in a pair of tongs. After igniting the charcoal in a flame, lower the glowing charcoal into another bottle of oxygen gas (Figure E-86). Allow it to burn until extinguished, then remove the charcoal. Add 0.5 cm of water, then cover and shake the bottle.

CAUTION: Only if the classroom is adequately ventilated should the next two procedures be carried out as class experiments.

---

4. Place a small portion of red phosphorus (about the size of a pencil point) in a deflagrating spoon lined with asbestos. Ignite the phosphorus in a burner flame, lower it into a bottle of oxygen gas and hold the glass plate firmly in place to minimize escape of fumes. Add 0.5 cm of water, then cover and shake the bottle. Burn out any residual phosphorus by holding the spoon in the burner flame.

5. Repeat procedure 4, using roll sulphur instead of red phosphorus.

6. Place a small piece of sodium (about the size of a small pea) in a deflagrating spoon lined with asbestos. Ignite the sodium in a burner flame and lower it into a bottle of oxygen gas. Keep the glass plate over the mouth of the bottle during the reaction. After the reaction, add 0.5 cm of water, then cover and shake the bottle. Burn out any sodium that remains in the spoon by holding the spoon in the burner flame.

7. Add a pinch of boron trioxide, B_2O_3, to 0.5 cm of water in a gas collecting bottle and shake the mixture.

8. To each of the gas collecting bottles containing the oxides shaken with water, add a few drops of bromthymol blue.

Questions for Thought and Discussion

1. What effects does addition of manganese dioxide have on the decomposition of potassium chlorate?

2. What other experimental work can you suggest to determine whether manganese dioxide is a catalyst in the potassium chlorate decomposition?

3. What properties of oxygen are evident from its preparation and collection?

4. Write equations for the preparation of each of the oxides prepared or used in this experiment.

5. Complete the following table using the information obtained from the experiment and that supplied for chlorine (VII) oxide.

Periodic Table		Oxide Formula	Effect of solution on BTB	Equation for Reaction of oxide with water, where occurring
Block	Group			
	I			
	II			
	III			
	IV			
	V			
	VI			
	VII	Cl_2O_7	blue → red	$Cl_2O_7 + H_2O \rightarrow 2HClO_4$
	VIII			

6. Write as hydroxides the formulas for the acids formed in the experiment.

7. How could you determine whether the iron oxide formed in the experiment was acidic or basic?

8. From the location in the Periodic Table of the elements used in this experiment,

   (a) name two other elements that would be expected to form basic oxides,

   (b) name two other elements that would be expected to form acidic oxides,

   (c) write the equation for the reaction between water and the oxide of each element named in (a) and (b).

9. For one element forming a basic oxide and for one forming an acidic oxide, complete the following table:

Element	Elemental Oxidation State	Oxidation State in an Oxide	Oxidation State in an Acid or Base

10. Manganese dioxide acts as a catalyst for the decomposition of potassium chlorate. Predict which other oxides might be worth experimental investigation as substitutes for manganese dioxide in this reaction.

11. What experimental evidence would be required to show that manganese dioxide is not a peroxide?

12. Suggest alternate substances that could be used for the production of oxygen gas if potassium chlorate were unavailable.

EXPERIMENT 15-2

Enthalpy Changes During Physical and Chemical Reactions: A Comparison

The melting of a solid is one example of a physical change. In Experiment 12-1, we found that solid paradichlorobenzene absorbed heat as it melted. Melting or fusion is accompanied by an increase in enthalpy. It follows that the reverse process, solidification, involves a decrease in enthalpy, heat is evolved during the process.

Chemical changes are also accompanied by energy exchanges. We have observed a number of chemical reactions where heat was evolved, particularly in Experiment 15-1, where various substances were burned in oxygen. Paraffin wax is another substance that will burn in oxygen. During the combustion of paraffin wax, heat is evolved, and the system undergoes a decrease in enthalpy.

The purpose of this experiment is to determine quantitatively the enthalpy changes involved in (1) the solidification of paraffin and (2) the combustion of paraffin. Since both the solidification process and the combustion process involve the same substance, paraffin, it is reasonable to compare the two values we obtain for $\triangle H$. Perhaps this comparison will indicate something about the relative amounts of energy involved in a physical versus a chemical change.

In both procedures liquid water is used to absorb the heat given off by the process. The temperature of this water rises as the paraffin solidifies or undergoes combustion. The quantity of heat involved is measured in calories. A *calorie* is the *amount of heat required to raise the temperature of one gram of water one centigrade degree.* Although this quantity varies slightly as the temperature of the water changes, between $8°C$ and $80°C$ it is reasonably constant.

Procedure

Part I   Heat of Solidification

In this procedure a sample of melted paraffin wax is cooled in a beaker of water. As the wax solidifies the temperature of the water rises. Before coming to the laboratory, prepare a data table similar to the one given in the procedure.

1. You will receive a test tube that already contains approximately 10 g of paraffin wax. Determine the mass of the test tube plus paraffin and record this value.

2. A second clean, dry and empty test tube will be provided. Determine the mass of this test tube as a means of knowing the approximate mass of the test tube containing the paraffin. Record this value.

3. Determine the mass of an empty 250 ml beaker and record this value. This beaker will serve as a calorimeter.

4. Half-fill the beaker with tap water that is 1 or 2 centigrade degrees below room temperature. Determine the mass of the beaker plus water and record this value.

5. Half-fill a second 250 ml beaker with tap water and heat the water to the boiling point. *Turn off the burner.* Now place the wax-filled test tube into the boiling water bath and wait until all the paraffin has *just melted.* Do not overheat the paraffin.

6. Remove the test tube containing the melted wax from the hot water using a test-tube holder. Allow the wax to cool until the first sign of cloudiness is apparent (Figure E-87). This cloudiness indicates that the wax is just beginning to solidify. While waiting for this cloudiness to appear, measure and record the temperature of the cold water bath (the water in the first beaker).

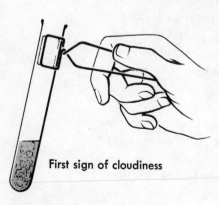

First sign of cloudiness

Figure E-87. *Cooling wax until solidification begins.*

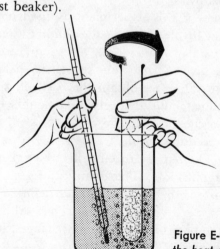

Figure E-88. *Determining the heat of solidification.*

7. As soon as the wax appears cloudy, quickly place this test tube into the cold water bath (our calorimeter). Stir the water gently with the test tube. At the same time hold the thermometer in the water bath half-way between the test tube and the wall of the beaker (Figure E-88). Observe the temperature continually and record the *maximum* temperature that the water reaches.

Data Table

Mass of test tube + wax	g
Mass of empty test tube	g
Mass of beaker + water	g
Mass of empty beaker	g
Temperature of water before solidification	°C
Temperature of water after solidification	°C

Calculations

1. Calculate the total quantity of heat absorbed by the water. Ignore the heat absorbed by the beaker.

2. Calculate the mass of paraffin wax used in this determination.

3. Assuming that the water absorbs all the heat given off by the paraffin during the solidification process, calculate the quantity of heat evolved per gram of paraffin wax in the test tube. This value is the heat of solidification of paraffin.

Part II Heat of Combustion

The burning candle in this procedure is undergoing a chemical change. As the paraffin candle burns, energy is liberated as heat and light are used to warm the water in a metal can. The amount of paraffin that undergoes combustion during this reaction is calculated by determining the mass of the candle before and after the reaction. Before the laboratory period prepare a data table similar in form to the one used in Part I of this experiment. Your teacher will provide information concerning the equipment required for this experiment.

1. Stick a candle to the lid of a tin can and determine the mass of the lid plus candle.

2. Determine the mass of the smaller can.

3. Set up the apparatus as shown in Figure E-89. The iron ring should be adjusted so that the flame of the candle, once the candle is lit, (don't light it yet) *almost* touches the bottom of the can. The larger can, open at both ends, forms a chimney that directs the heat evolved towards the upper can.

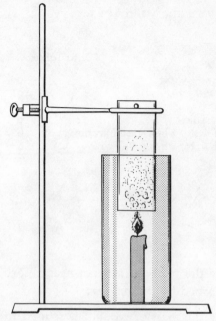

Figure E-89. *Apparatus for determining the heat of combustion.*

4. Fill the smaller can, whose mass is already known, ⅔ full with cold tap water. The temperature of this water must be at least 10 centigrade degrees below room temperature. If it is not, add ice until the temperature of the water is sufficiently low, then remove any excess ice before continuing with the procedure. (Why?)

5. Accurately measure the temperature of the water. Light the candle and stir the water gently as the candle heats it. Continue heating until the temperature of the water is as much above room temperature as it was below room temperature when the heating was started.

6. Blow out the candle flame carefully without spattering the chimney or smaller can with wax. Continue stirring the water and watch the thermometer until the highest temperature is reached. Record this temperature accurately.

7. Again determine the mass of the lid plus candle. If any wax has dripped from the candle, make sure that it is on the lid during the determination of the mass.

8. Determine the mass of the smaller can plus the water.

Calculations

1. Calculate the total quantity of heat absorbed by the water. Ignore the heat absorbed by the can itself.

2. Calculate the mass of paraffin wax that underwent combustion.

3. Assuming that the water absorbed all of the heat from the burning candle, calculate the quantity of heat evolved per gram of paraffin that underwent combustion. This is the heat of combustion of paraffin.

Questions For Thought and Discussion

1. Compare the value obtained for the heat of solidification of paraffin with that obtained for the heat of combustion. Do other members of the class have a similar result?

2. If these results are typical of any physical versus chemical changes, what generalization can be made?

3. Explain precisely why there is such a difference in these two values. Apply your knowledge of bonding to answer this question.

4. Using the symbols $\triangle H_s$ to represent the enthalpy change during solidification and $\triangle H_c$ to represent the enthalpy change during combustion, express the values obtained in Parts I and II as changes in enthalpy. Be careful to use the correct sign convention and units.

5. Usually any changes in enthalpy are expressed per mole of reactant involved. Is it possible to do so in this case? Explain your answer.

6. In Part I, procedure 7, why is the position of the thermometer critical?

7. In Part II, procedure 5, why is the temperature of the water allowed to rise until it is the same number of centigrade degrees above room temperature as it was below room temperature initially?

8. In Part II, procedures 6 and 7, specific instructions are given concerning paraffin that has dripped or spattered from the candle. Why is it important to observe these precautions?

9. Discuss the sources of error in this experiment that stem from the simplified apparatus or the simplifying assumptions made during the calculations. How would the sources of error you have discussed affect the values obtained in Parts I and II?

EXPERIMENT 15-3

Enthalpy Changes: An Application of
The Law of Additivity of Reaction Heats

For many chemical reactions it is difficult to measure directly the change in enthalpy, $\triangle H$. However, the value of $\triangle H$ for a given reaction is independent of the series of steps involved in getting from reactants to products. Furthermore, whenever a reaction can be expressed as the algebraic sum of a series of two or more simpler reactions, the heat of reaction is the algebraic sum of the heats of these simpler reactions. Thus $\triangle H$ for a given reaction is often determined by breaking the reaction down into a series of steps and determining the $\triangle H$ value for each step either experimentally or from standard tables of enthalpy changes.

Magnesium metal combines very rapidly with oxygen gas (recall Experiment 15-1). The equation for this reaction is

$$Mg(s) + \tfrac{1}{2}O_2(g) \rightarrow MgO(s) \qquad (4)$$

Although much energy is evolved in the form of heat and light, it is difficult to measure this energy directly. But this same equation is obtained when the following three equations are combined algebraically.

$$
\begin{array}{ll}
MgO(s) + 2HCl(soln) \rightarrow MgCl_2(soln) + H_2O(l) & (1) \\
Mg(s) + 2HCl(soln) \rightarrow MgCl_2(soln) + H_2(g) & (2) \\
H_2(g) + \tfrac{1}{2}O_2(g) \rightarrow H_2O(l) & (3)
\end{array}
$$

In this experiment the values of $\triangle H$ for equations (1) and (2) are determined experimentally. The value for equation (3) is obtained from the table on enthalpies of formation in the appendix. By combining these three equations appropriately, the enthalpy change for the overall reaction (4) can be calculated. A styrofoam cup is used as the calorimeter.

Procedure

Reaction (1)

1. Add 100 ml of 1.00 M HCl solution to a styrofoam cup and measure the temperature of the solution.

2. Measure out accurately about 1 g of magnesium oxide solid, MgO(s), and add this to the hydrochloric acid solution. Stir the contents of the cup during this addition and measure the highest temperature that the solution reaches.

Reaction (2)

3. Repeat procedures 1 and 2 but add 0.5 g of magnesium metal, Mg(s), to the acid instead of the magnesium oxide.

Calculations

1. Combine equations (1), (2) and (3) in such a way that their algebraic sum gives the overall equation (4).

2. Assuming that one calorie of energy (heat) is required to change the temperature of one ml of solution one centigrade degree, calculate the energy released in each of reactions (1) and (2). Express these values in kilocalories.

3. Calculate the energy released for reaction (1) in kcal mole^{-1} MgO(s). Express this value using the $\triangle$H notation.

4. Calculate the energy released for reaction (2) in kcal mole^{-1} Mg(s). Express this value using the $\triangle$H notation.

5. Using Appendix IX determine the $\triangle$H value for reaction (3).
6. Calculate the $\triangle$H value for the overall reaction (4). Express the answer in kcal mole^{-1} MgO(s).

Questions for Thought and Discussion

1. When doing the calculations, what assumption is made concerning the energy released and the calorimeter?

2. The value obtained in the experiment can be called the *enthalpy of combustion* of magnesium. Since this reaction involves the formation of magnesium oxide from its elements, this value can also be called the *enthalpy of formation* of magnesium oxide. Look up the enthalpy of formation of magnesium oxide. Compare this value with the value determined in this experiment.

3. Discuss any reasons for there being a difference in the values compared in 2.

EXPERIMENT 16-1

Hydrogen and Oxidation-Reduction (Demonstration)

This experiment is intended to show the action of hydrogen as a reducing agent. The usual laboratory method for the production of hydrogen is employed; the oxidation of zinc with hydrochloric acid. Alternatively, the hydrogen can be supplied from a cylinder of the compressed gas. If desired, the whole experiment can be made simply qualitative.

Procedure

1. Prepare the equipment to be assembled as shown in Figure E-90. Have clamps positioned and ready to receive the test tube, drying tube and flask. Note that a cylinder of compressed hydrogen gas can be used in place of the hydrogen generator (Figure E-91).

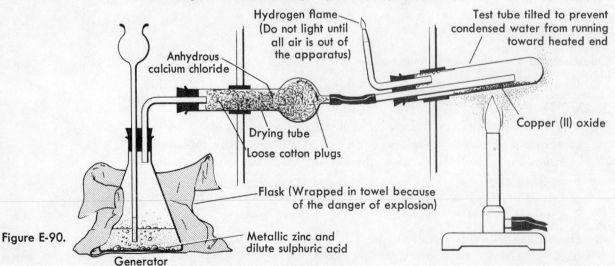

Hydrogen flame (Do not light until all air is out of the apparatus)

Test tube tilted to prevent condensed water from running toward heated end

Anhydrous calcium chloride

Drying tube

Loose cotton plugs

Copper (II) oxide

Flask (Wrapped in towel because of the danger of explosion)

Metallic zinc and dilute sulphuric acid

Generator

Figure E-90.

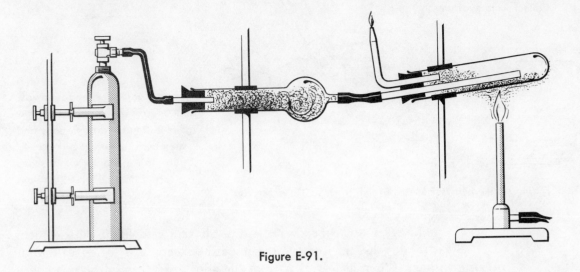

Figure E-91.

2. Dry the hard glass test tube by heating it with the burner, then allow it to cool. Accurately determine the mass of this test tube.

3. Add about 4.0 g of thoroughly dried copper oxide. Accurately determine the mass of the test tube plus the oxide. Stopper the test tube as in Figure E-90 and clamp it to the retort stand.

CAUTION: If a hydrogen generator is used as described below, there is danger of the generator exploding violently. Follow the precautions indicated carefully. Place an explosion shield between the whole apparatus and the class and between you and the apparatus.

---

4. Assemble the hydrogen generator as shown, taking particular care to avoid leaks. Wrap the flask completely with a wet cloth to further safeguard against the explosion hazard.

5. Place about 15 g of mossy zinc in the flask. Through the thistle tube add about 24 ml of dilute hydrochloric acid solution. If necessary, several ml of 0.1 M copper (II) sulphate solution can be added to increase the rate of reaction. As the reaction subsides, continue to add the dilute acid solution in order to maintain a moderate rate of hydrogen production.

6. Connect the hydrogen generator, drying tube and test tube as shown.

7. After allowing hydrogen gas to pass through the test tube for several minutes, test for the complete removal of air by carefully following this procedure.

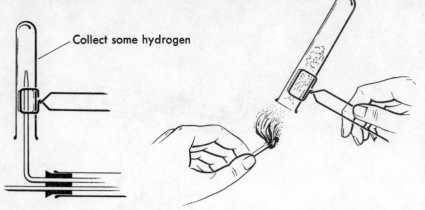

Collect some hydrogen

Carry it at least three feet away from the rest of the apparatus and ignite it. If the hydrogen pops and then burns quietly it is relatively pure. If it explodes with a sharp report it is still mixed with air.

Figure E-92. *Testing for the purity of the hydrogen gas from the generator.*

Invert a test tube over the tapered vent and fill it with effluent gas (Figure E-92). Remove the test tube, keeping it sealed with your thumb. When at least 3 ft from the apparatus, bring a blazing splint to the inverted test-tube mouth after removing the thumb. A sharp pop indicates the presence of air in the hydrogen gas. Continue passing hydrogen through the test tube and repeat the testing until the quiet burning of hydrogen gas at the test-tube mouth indicates purity. Use *this flame* to ignite the hydrogen from the vent.

8. Using the burner, heat the oxide to a moderate temperature. Maintain a steady passage of hydrogen gas through the test tube by adding dilute acid to the generator as required.

9. Continue the passage of this pure hydrogen gas from the gas generator or cylinder of compressed gas for about 5 minutes. During this time, move the burner slightly to warm the upper part of the test tube but not enough to burn or soften the rubber stopper.

10. Put out the burner and allow the test tube, still filled with hydrogen gas, to cool. Do not disconnect the delivery tube.

11. When the test tube is cool, disconnect the test tube and accurately determine the mass of the test tube plus its contents.

12. Examine the contents of the test tube carefully.

Calculations

1. From the masses recorded, calculate the mass of metallic oxide used and the mass of metal remaining.

2. From the mass of oxide used and the mass of metal produced, calculate the per cent by mass of metal and oxygen in the sample.

EXPERIMENT 16-1

3. Determine the simplest formula of this oxide.

4. Name the oxide.

Questions for Thought and Discussion

1. Write equations for the following reactions:
   (a) the oxidation of zinc by hydrochloric acid
   (b) the reduction of the metallic oxide you decided was your sample in the experiment
   (c) the reduction of lead dioxide, PbO_2, with hydrogen
   (d) the reduction of mercury (II) oxide by heat alone.

2. For the following reactions, complete the table under the given headings, wherever they apply.

   (a) $Zn(s) + S(s) \rightarrow ZnS(s)$
   (b) $Br_2(l) + Fe(s) \rightarrow FeBr_2(s)$
   (c) $3Ag(s) + 4HNO_3(conc) \rightarrow AgNO_3(sol'n) + NO(g) + 2H_2O(l)$
   (d) $KClO_4(sol'n) + 4H_3AsO_3(sol'n) \rightarrow KCl(sol'n) + 4H_3AsO_4(sol'n)$

Reaction	Substance Oxidized	Substance Reduced	Oxidizing Agent	Reducing Agent
(a)				
(b)				
(c)				
(d)				

3. From your observations in procedure 5 would you conclude that copper (II) sulphate is a catalyst for this reaction? Explain.

EXPERIMENT 16-2

The Activity Series and Oxidation-Reduction

In this experiment you will be given an opportunity to note the relative activity of several metals with respect to hydrogen. In these reactions, hydrogen may displace or be displaced by the metals. The more elements a metal can displace, the more active it is. Because this activity is a measure of reducing ability, the relative strengths of metals as reducing agents can be established. At the same time, since the elements being displaced are acting as oxidizing agents, their relative strengths as oxidizing agents can also be established. Included in the list of reactions are some substances containing nonmetallic elements. The relative displacement ability and consequently the relative oxidizing and reducing abilities of these non-metallic elements can also be compared.

Recall that for our purposes, oxidation is an increase in positive oxidation state and reduction is a decrease in positive oxidation state where the oxidation states are assigned according to rules to which you have already been introduced.

Prepare a data table as outlined below (Table 2) for Part I of the experiment and complete this table as the experiment proceeds.

Procedure

Part I Activity Series

In Table 1 are listed 21 different reactions involving a metal and a solution (or just water). Reactions 20 and 21 will be demonstrated by your teacher.

Reaction	Metal	Solution or Water
1	Na	H_2O
2	Ca	H_2O
3	Ca	HCl
4	Mg	H_2O (boiling)
5	Mg	HCl
6	Al	HCl
7	Al	$CuCl_2$
8	Zn	HCl
9	Zn	$CuCl_2$
10	Fe	HCl
11	Fe	$AlCl_3$
12	Fe	$CuCl_2$
13	Pb	HCl
14	Pb	$AlCl_3$
15	Pb	$CuCl_2$
16	Hg	HCl
17	Cu	HCl
18	Cu	$AlCl_3$
19	Cu	$AgNO_3$
20	Hg	$CuCl_2$ (Demonstration*)
21	Hg	$AgNO_3$ (Demonstration*)

*CAUTION: Observe the normal precautions when handling mercury.

1. Obtain samples of the above metals. Just before use clean the surfaces of all metals except sodium with emery paper. Be very careful to keep track of which metal is which.

CAUTION: A freshly cut piece of sodium metal about the size of the point of a pencil will be supplied. Do not touch the sodium but handle it as directed by your teacher. Keep face and hands back from the mouth of the test tube as the sodium reacts with the water.

2. As each metal is to be tested, add 5 ml of the solution (or water) designated for that reaction to a clean test tube.

3. Place the cleaned metal into this solution. Look for any evidence of a displacement reaction and test any gas produced with a burning splint.

4. Complete the data table below for any reactions you have carried out. If different reactions have been investigated by different members of the class, add your results to the class tabulation of results.

DATA TABLE PART I

| Reaction Number | Before | | Evidence of Displacement | After | | Element Oxidized | Oxidizing Agent | Element Reduced | Reducing Agent | More Active Element | Stronger Agent |
	Oxidation State of Free Element	Oxidation State of Combined Element		Oxidation State of Combined Element	Oxidation State of Free Element						Oxidizing or Reducing

Part II Thermite Reaction Demonstration

1. Thoroughly mix 15 g of iron (III) oxide, Fe_2O_3, or ferroso-ferric oxide, Fe_3O_4, with 6 g of powdered aluminum.

2. In an iron crucible place about 20 cc of the mixture and cover it with a *thin, loosely packed* layer of potassium chlorate. Insert several four-inch lengths of magnesium ribbon deep into the mixture.

3. Place the crucible in a clay triangle supported by an iron ring. Clamp the ring above a wide container of sand. Permit no one nearer than ten feet.

4. Carefully and quickly ignite the magnesium ribbon with a burner flame. If there is no reaction, wait two minutes before re-igniting.

5. Following the reaction examine the cooled residue.

Questions for Thought and Discussion

1. What element would you suggest using to reduce sodium from a sodium salt solution?

2. From the equations for the reactions in this experiment, decide which reducing agent produced the greatest volume of hydrogen per unit mass.

3. What mass of zinc would be required to produce 10.0 litre of hydrogen gas at a temperature of 25°C and 740 mm Hg?

4. Would the same mass of aluminum produce more or less hydrogen than the zinc in question 3?

EXPERIMENT 17-1

Aqueous Solutions

While there is far more to the solution process than can be illustrated with one experiment using a single solvent, it will be useful to observe some of those features of aqueous solutions which are most common and, for our purposes, most important.

The model for the solution process assumes that there is interaction between the highly polar water molecules and the species of the solute. Water will be attracted to those species which are polar or charged. If the attraction between water and the solute species is greater than the attraction that the solute species have for each other, the solute species will separate from each other.

In this experiment, some of the factors affecting the rate of solution will also be examined.

Procedure

Part I

1. Place about 3 g of powdered sodium chloride in a test tube. Add water to half-fill the test tube and stopper the tube. Repeat this procedure in other test tubes using powdered potassium chromate and powdered calcium hydroxide. Shake each tube vigorously, allow it to stand for about 2 minutes and examine it by holding it up to the light.

2. To each of the test tubes from 1, add an additional 6 g of the solid previously used. Restopper, shake and allow to stand again.

3. Quarter-fill one test tube with glycerol and another with carbon tetra-chloride. Add water to each to half-fill the test tubes. Stopper, shake vigorously and allow to stand for 2 minutes.

CAUTION: Avoid inhaling carbon tetrachloride vapour. Avoid contact between skin and carbon tetrachloride.

4. To each of the test tubes from 3, add an additional 3 ml of the liquid previously used other than water. Restopper, shake and allow to stand again.

5. Examine ginger ale in a clear, colourless, capped bottle. Pour some into a test tube and re-examine. From your own experience, compare the taste of a freshly poured glassful of ginger ale and one which has been standing for a short time.

Part II

1. Select two pea-size crystals of copper (II) sulphate pentahydrate. Add one to a test tube. Crush the other in a mortar and add it to a second test tube. Half-fill each test tube with water, then stopper and shake them for several minutes. Compare the solutions with respect to colour and amount of undissolved solute.

2. Half-fill two test tubes with water and to each add about 3 g of powdered copper (II) sulphate pentahydrate. Place one test tube aside; stopper and shake the other for a minute or so. Compare the solutions with respect to colour and amount of undissolved solute.

3. To each of two test tubes, add about 3 g of powdered copper (II) sulphate pentahydrate. Half-fill one test tube with cold water and half-fill the other with hot water. Set the first test tube aside; keep the second test tube warm *without boiling the contents* by passing it over a small flame for a minute or so. Allow the second solution to cool. Compare the solutions with respect to colour and amount of undissolved solute.

Part III

Data Table

Solvent		Water	Methanol	Carbon Tetrachloride
Type of solvent				
Solute	Type of solute			
iodine I_2 glycerol $C_3H_5(OH)_3$ potassium permanganate $KMnO_4$				

1. Prepare a set of three test tubes each containing 1 ml of *one* of the solvents listed above. Prepare two other sets, one for each of the other solvents.

2. Using a splint or spatula, add 2 small iodine crystals to a test tube containing water. To a second test tube containing water, add 1 ml of glycerol. To the third test tube containing water, add 2 small crystals of potassium permanganate. Stopper and shake each test tube vigorously for 20 seconds.

3. Repeat procedure 2 using first methanol and finally carbon tetrachloride as the solvent.

4. From the colour of the solution or from the formation of separate layers of liquid, decide which of the terms soluble, slightly soluble, insoluble, miscible or immiscible apply to each solute-solvent combination. Record your decisions in the above table.

Questions for Thought and Discussion

1. Which of the following substances is soluble in water to any appreciable extent?
   sodium chloride, potassium chromate, calcium hydroxide, glycerol, carbon tetrachloride, carbon dioxide, copper (II) sulphate, glass

2. Which solid substance listed above is insoluble? Why do you say so? How could you be sure?

3. Of the soluble solids used in this experiment, which is least soluble? Explain the reason for your choice.

4. Indicate each of the following statements as *True, False* or *Inconclusive* according to the following criteria:
   T   if the statement is justified by evidence from this experiment;
   F   if the statement is refuted by evidence from this experiment;
   I   (inconclusive) if the statement cannot be supported or refuted by evidence from this experiment.
   Be prepared to defend your decisions.
   (a) The solution of sodium chloride in Part I, procedure 2 was saturated.
   (b) Potassium dichromate is more soluble than calcium hydroxide.
   (c) The test tube with calcium hydroxide in it (Part I, procedure 2) contained a mechanical mixture.
   (d) Some saturated salt solutions are clear and coloured, others are clear and colourless.

(e) At room temperature, glycerol is immiscible with water, while carbon tetrachloride is miscible.

(f) All aqueous solutions are clear and colourless.

(g) Ginger ale is an example of a solution consisting of more than two components, one of which is a gas.

(h) Solutions of calcium hydroxide, copper (II) sulphate and potassium chromate are homogeneous.

(i) Comparison of the taste of the first and last glassfuls poured from a large bottle of ginger ale show the ginger ale to be homogeneous.

(j) Three factors which hasten the formation of an aqueous solution of copper (II) sulphate are (i) fine subdivision, (ii) hot solvent, (iii) agitation.

(k) All ionic solids are water soluble and all covalent liquids are water immiscible.

(l) Calcium and hydroxide ions are less easily separated from each other by water than are sodium and chloride ions.

5. Which molecule has the greater polarity:

glycerol	carbon tetrachloride
H₂C — OH	Cl
	|
HC — OH	Cl — C — Cl
	|
H₂C — OH	Cl

$$
\begin{array}{cc}
\text{glycerol} & \text{carbon tetrachloride} \\
H_2C-OH & Cl \\
| & | \\
HC-OH & Cl-C-Cl \\
| & | \\
H_2C-OH & Cl
\end{array}
$$

6. The structural formulas for some of the substances used in Part III are as shown:

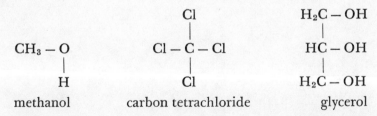

methanol   carbon tetrachloride   glycerol

Complete the columns "type of solvent" and "type of solute" in the data table for Part III as: polar, slightly polar, nonpolar or ionic.

7. From your data table, decide what relationship exists between polarity of solute and solvent and decide which is the better generalization:

(a) like dissolves like,   (b) like dissolves unlike.

8. How would you expect each solute in Part III to behave toward the following solvents?

(a) benzene

$$\begin{array}{c} H \\ | \\ H \diagdown \underset{C}{C} = \underset{|}{C} \diagup H \\ C \diagdown \quad \diagup C \\ H \diagup \underset{C}{C} = \underset{C}{C} \diagdown H \\ | \\ H \end{array}$$

(b) ethylene glycol

$$\begin{array}{c} H_2C - OH \\ | \\ H_2C - OH \end{array}$$

With your teacher's permission, you may care to test your predictions.

EXPERIMENT 17-2

Solubility Curves

Some substances are soluble in water, others are not. Among those solids which are soluble in water there are differences in the extent to which they will dissolve. In addition their solubility changes with changing temperature. In this experiment these differences will be investigated for two substances and the results plotted in the form of solubility curves. The curves can then be used for predicting the results of solution problems.

Procedure

1. Measure 10.0 ml of water from a burette or pipette into a large test tube. Assume that this water has a mass of 10.0 g at all temperatures. Add the amount of the salt assigned for your experimental group to the water. Groups will be assigned the following masses of potassium nitrate and lead nitrate.

Table 1

Concentration: Mass of solute [g] in 10 g of water			
KNO_3		$Pb(NO_3)_2$	
(a)	16	(e)	14
(b)	12	(f)	10
(c)	8	(g)	8
(d)	6	(h)	6

2. Heat the test tube and contents gently, without boiling, until the solid disappears.

3. Place a thermometer in the test tube and allow the test tube and contents to cool. During this cooling stir the contents gently with the thermometer. Note and record the temperature at which crystallization commences. This is the saturation temperature for your experimental concentration. Enter this value in the table of class results.

4. Calculate the mass of solute which would just saturate 100 g of water at the saturation temperature determined in 3. This value is the *solubility* of the salt at the saturation temperature.

5. From the table of class results, calculate the mean saturation temperature for each experimental concentration of each solute. The solubilities calculated in procedure 4 are the solubilities for each salt at the mean saturation temperature.

6. Plot the solubility curves for both salts by plotting solubility as a function of temperature.

7. Empty the test tube into a clean evaporating dish. Place the dish on a wire gauze over an iron ring clamped to a retort stand. Heat the evaporating dish until the liquid is boiling gently and continue evaporation until you estimate the volume has been reduced by 1 to 2 millilitres. Pour the hot concentrated solution back into the test tube and repeat procedure 3.

8. From the solubility curve previously prepared and the saturation temperature, determine the concentration of the solution from the evaporating dish.

9. Express the concentration of this solution as a mass percentage: that is,

$$\frac{\text{mass solute}}{\text{mass solution}} \times 100$$

Questions for Thought and Discussion

1. For which salt does temperature have the greater effect on the solubility?

2. It is said that all nitrates are water soluble. Are all nitrates equally water soluble?

3. Of what significance is the point of intersection of the two solubility curves?

4. A mixture containing 120 g of potassium nitrate and 120 g of lead nitrate is to be separated.

(a) How much water will be required to dissolve the mixture at
   (i) 25°C
   (ii) 60°C
   (iii) 100°C?

(b) Suppose the mixture is dissolved in 100 g of boiling water and allowed to cool.
   (i) At what temperature would the first crystals appear?
   (ii) Which salt would these crystals be?
   (iii) To what temperature could the solution be cooled before the other salt would crystallize?
   (iv) To what volume could the solution be reduced by evaporation to cause the first crystals of the second salt to appear at a temperature 10 C° below the temperature in (i) above?

EXPERIMENT 17-3

Electrical Conductivity of Solids, Liquids and Their Solutions
(Demonstration)

Pure substances have their own individual properties. Our model for the structure of matter accounts for this as differences in the composition of the atoms of the elements and the manner in which these atoms can combine.

One of these characteristic properties of substances is solubility, the ability of substances to enter into solution with each other. In solutions, some of the properties of the individual components seem to be retained. Furthermore, it is relatively easy to reverse the solution process and reform the individual components. How does our model for the structure of matter account for these and other features of solutions? Since our model depends essentially on electrical phenomena, we should examine the electrical properties of solutions.

In this experiment, you will be able to observe the conductivity of different substances and their solutions as a basis for developing a model to explain solution processes. The apparatus has the features shown in the diagram. Two electrodes are connected in series with an electric light bulb

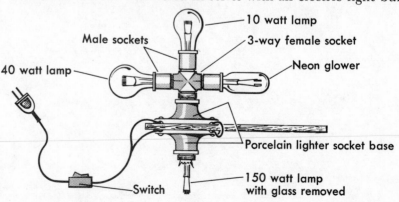

Figure E-93.
Conductivity apparatus.

or bulbs to a source of 110 V AC. While the construction details may vary, the operation of any conductivity apparatus depends upon completion of the circuit across the electrodes. A completed circuit is indicated by the bulb glowing. Using bulbs which respond to the passage of currents of different values, the observations can be compared somewhat quantitatively.

CAUTION: Always turn off the switch or pull the plug while rinsing and drying the electrodes or when changing substances or solutions. This will avoid electric shocks.

Procedure

The conductivity of solids, liquids and solutions can be tested using this conductivity apparatus. When solids are tested, merely touch the solid at two different points with the two different electrodes. When liquids or solutions are tested, use 50 ml of the material in a 2 oz wide mouth bottle for each test. Place the electrodes in the bottle so that both just touch the bottom. This procedure insures covering the electrodes to the same depth each time. Rinse the electrodes with distilled water between each measurement. *Do not touch the electrodes at any time.* The brightness of the light is a measure of the conductivity of the substance or solution tested.

1. Test the conductivity of several pieces of metal or metal wire.

2. Test the conductivity of each of the listed substances in turn. From the intensity of the bulbs which glow, classify each substance as a good, fair or poor conductor, or a non-conductor.

   solvents: distilled water, benzene

   solids: silver nitrate, silver chloride, sucrose, sodium chloride

   liquids: silver nitrate melted in a crucible over a burner
   sucrose melted in a crucible over a burner

   solutions: aqueous solutions of:
   silver nitrate, silver chloride, sucrose
   benzene solution of sucrose

Questions for Thought and Discussion

Choose the best alternative in each of questions 1, 2 and 3.

1. Copper wire and other similar solids conduct electricity because:
   (a) they are metals,
   (b) they have charged particles called electrons,
   (c) they have charged particles called electrons which are free to move.

2. Electricity is also conducted by:
   (a) all liquids, solids and gases,
   (b) some liquids, solids and gases,
   (c) some solutions,
   (d) some crystalline solids,
   (e) only water solutions,
   (f) some solutions and some molten solids,
   (g) only solutions of acids, bases and salts,
   (h) all molten solids.

3. In all cases where electricity is conducted there must be:
   (a) neutral atoms,
   (b) charged particles like electrons,
   (c) charged particles called ions which are free to move,
   (d) hydrogen present.

4. What substances used in the experiment are ionic? Did their aqueous solutions conduct electricity?

5. What effect is common to the melting of ionic solids and the dissolving of ionic solids in water?

6. What substances used in the experiment were covalent? Did any of them conduct? Did all of their solutions conduct? Did their aqueous solutions conduct?

7. Silver chloride is almost insoluble in water. Did the small amount which dissolved affect the conductivity of water?

8. Do all solutions which conduct do so equally as well? What does this suggest regarding the relative numbers of ions present?

EXPERIMENT 17-4

Expressing the Concentrations of Solutions and Pure Substances

Many chemical reactions occur in solutions. These solutions may be gaseous, aqueous or involve solvents other than water. To consider such reactions quantitatively, it is necessary to consider the concentration of solute dissolved in the solvent. The most common concentration units are

(a) percentage by mass,   (b) molarity (moles per litre of solution).

In this experiment you will prepare some solutions, make them more concentrated or more dilute, and become familiar with the concept of solution concentration.

You will also investigate the applicability of the concentration concept to pure substances.

Procedure

Part I   Molarity of a Solution

1. Determine the mass of a dry, empty beaker. Using a pipette or burette, measure accurately about 50 ml of distilled water into the beaker. Determine the mass of this water as accurately as possible.

2. Add about 2 g of calcium chloride to the water in the beaker. Accurately record the mass of calcium chloride added. Stir until the solute has dissolved, then measure the volume of the solution using a graduated cylinder.

3. Place the solution in a beaker or evaporating dish. Heat strongly for several minutes but avoid spattering. Cool the solution to room temperature and re-measure the volume.

4. To the solution in the graduate add about 25 ml of water and re-measure the volume.

5. Pour out of the graduate all but about 5 ml of the solution. Measure the volume of this remaining aliquot.

6. Add water to the aliquot in the graduate to bring the volume up to about 50 ml. Measure this volume.

Calculations

1. Calculate the molecular weight of water.

2. Calculate the number of moles of water present in the sample in procedure 1.

3. From the number of moles of water and the volume of the sample, calculate the number of moles of water which would be present in one litre of water at this temperature. Express this as molarity, M.

4. From the masses of the solute and solvent used in procedure 2, calculate the percentage composition of the solution by mass.

5. Calculate the formula weight of calcium chloride.

6. Calculate the number of moles of calcium chloride added to the water.

7. From the number of moles of calcium chloride and the volume of the solution, calculate the number of moles of calcium chloride which would be present in one litre of the solution at this temperature. Express this as molarity, M.

8. From the number of moles of calcium chloride and the volume of the solution after evaporation, calculate the molarity of the concentrated solution.

9. Calculate the molarity of the solution after the addition of water.

10. From the number of moles of solute remaining in the aliquot and the volume of the diluted solution, calculate the molarity of the final diluted solution.

11. Calculate and compare the following values:

    (a) the ratio: $\dfrac{\text{molarity of final solution}}{\text{molarity of aliquot}}$,

    (b) the ratio: $\dfrac{\text{volume of aliquot}}{\text{volume of final solution}}$.

Procedure

Part II *Molarity of a Solid*

Determine the masses and volumes of a small and a large piece of copper (or some other element that is a metal).

Calculations

Calculate the molarities of the small and large pieces of metal.

Part III *Molarity of a Gas (Calculations Only)*

1. Recalling that the molar volume for gases is 22.4 litre at 0°C and 1 standard atmosphere pressure, calculate the molar volume for any gas at the laboratory temperature and pressure.

2. Calculate the molarity of any gas at laboratory temperature and pressure.

3. Calculate the molarity of any gas under all possible variations of the following conditions:
   (a) laboratory temperature plus and minus 20 C°,
   (b) laboratory pressure plus and minus 200 mm Hg.

Questions for Thought and Discussion

1. How would the change in density of water with temperature affect the molarity of pure water?

2. What species are present in the beaker after the solution of calcium chloride has formed? Write the net equation for the change.

3. Is the volume of a solution always equal to the sum of the volumes of solute and solvent?

4. A solution of potassium hydroxide has a density of 1.344 g ml^{-1} and is 35% solute by mass.
   (a) Calculate the mass of solute per 100 g of solvent.
   (b) Calculate the number of moles of solute per 100 g of solvent.
   (c) Calculate the molarity of the solution.

5. What is the effect on the molarity and percentage composition by mass of (a) concentrating the solution, (b) diluting the solution?

6. How can solutions be (a) concentrated, (b) diluted?

7. From the relationship between the ratios calculated in Part I, calculation 11, which of the following formulas properly expresses the dilution calculations? M is molarity, V is volume in litres, subscript$_1$ is initial solution or aliquot and subscript$_2$ is final solution)

(a) $\dfrac{M_1}{V_1} = \dfrac{M_2}{V_2}$,   (b) $M_1 M_2 = V_1 V_2$,   (c) $\dfrac{M_1}{V_1} = \dfrac{V_2}{M_2}$,

(d) $M_1 V_1 = M_2 V_2$,   (e) $\dfrac{V_2}{V_1} = \dfrac{M_2}{M_1}$.

8. What volume of the final solution in Part I of the experiment would contain 0.002 mole?

9. How would you prepare 200 ml of a 1 M solution of sodium hydroxide?

10. How would you prepare 2 litre of 0.02 M sodium hydroxide solution from the solution prepared in question 9?

11. What assumption can you make regarding the concentrations of pure solids and liquids, such as water and copper, during changes of temperature, pressure, mass and volume?

12. What generalization can you make regarding the concentration of a gaseous pure substance with respect to changes in temperature and pressure?

EXPERIMENT 18-1

Some Further Studies of Electrical Conductivity (Demonstration)

In a previous experiment it was noted that the conductivity of a substance depends on the presence of charged particles which are free to move. In a metal, these particles are electrons of the electron cloud; in molten ionic solids, they are the ions of the melt; in solutions of ionic solids the particles are charged, solvated ions. In water solutions these ions are known as *aqueous ions*. It was also noted that the aqueous solutions of some covalent substances, such as sucrose, were non-conducting.

In this experiment, aqueous solutions of some other covalent substances will be studied together with the effect of solute concentration on conductivity.

Procedure

Part I

1. Using the conductivity apparatus and procedure described in Experiment 17-3, test the conductivity of the following substances. Record the observations in chart form. Indicate the substances as having a high, moderate or low conductivity or as non-conductors.

   solvents: distilled water, alcohol, benzene

   solids: oxalic acid, benzoic acid, sodium hydroxide

   liquids: glacial acetic acid

   gases: dry hydrogen chloride, ammonia

   aqueous solutions of the same concentration:
   > oxalic acid, benzoic acid, sodium hydroxide, acetic acid, hydrochloric acid and ammonia

   alcoholic solution of: acetic acid

   benzene solutions of: hydrogen chloride
   > > hydrogen chloride with water added

Part II

1. Bend the electrodes until they are about 2 cm apart. Immerse them to a depth of 2 cm in 100 ml of distilled water and fix their position. Observe the conductivity.

2. Add 5 drops of 0.1 M NaCl solution (0.25 ml) and observe.

3. Continue to add the sodium chloride solution, 5 drops at a time, until no further change occurs with the largest bulb connected in the circuit.

Part III

1. With the electrodes about 2 cm apart, immerse them in 100 ml of glacial acetic acid in a 250 ml beaker. Insert the electrodes to a depth of 2 cm. If possible a neon glow lamp, in one socket of the conductivity apparatus, should be used for the glacial acetic acid and the first 4 or 5 dilutions.

2. Add one drop of distilled water.

3. Add additional 1-drop portions of distilled water until 20 drops have been added. Note the intensity of the lamp after each addition.

4. Now add a 5 ml portion of distilled water.

CAUTION: Pour the water slowly down the side of the beaker and stir continuously.

---

5. Continue to add 5 ml portions of distilled water until 100 ml of water have been added. During these and subsequent additions of distilled water, keep the electrodes 2 cm below the surface of the liquid when conductivity comparisons are being made.

6. Transfer the solution to a 500 ml beaker. Now continue to add water in 50 ml portions until the beaker is full.

Questions for Thought and Discussion

1. Recognizing the limited basis for drawing general conclusions from the information provided in the two conductivity experiments, answer the following questions.
   (a) Do solids, other than metals, appear to conduct electricity?
   (b) Do liquids, other than molten ionic solids, appear to conduct electricity?
   (c) Do any gases appear to conduct electricity?

(d) Are covalent substances the only type that conduct electricity when in solution?

(e) Do all covalent substances in aqueous solution conduct electricity?

(f) Do those covalent substances which conduct electricity in aqueous solution do so in all solvents?

(g) What kinds of particles must be present for a solution to conduct electricity?

(h) What classes of substances appear to conduct electricity in aqueous solution?

(i) What aqueous ions would you expect to find in aqueous solutions of sodium chloride and sodium hydroxide?

(j) What aqueous ions would you expect to find in aqueous solutions of hydrogen chloride and hydrogen acetate?

(k) Are there ions present in the alcohol or benzene solutions?

2. What evidence do you have that all aqueous solutions which conduct do so in varying degrees?

3. Suggest an explanation to account for the differences in solution conductivities (concentration fixed).

4. Account for the observed differences in conductivity with the different concentrations of (a) sodium chloride solution, (b) hydrogen acetate solution.

5. Draw a generalized qualitative curve on the following axes to show how conductivity changes with solution concentration.

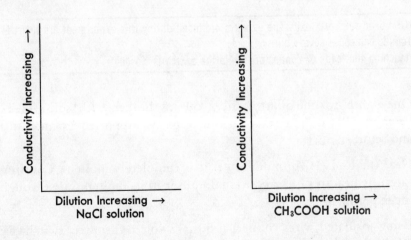

EXPERIMENT 18-2

Conductivity of Molten Lead (II) Bromide
(Demonstration)

In this experiment the conductivity of a crystalline salt is examined after the salt has been melted or fused. This particular salt, lead (II) bromide, has been selected because of its low melting point, but its behaviour may be considered typical of any crystalline salt. Be careful to note any changes that occur around the electrodes.

Procedure

CAUTION: Lead salts are toxic. The vapours produced during this experiment are toxic. Molten lead bromide can cause severe burns.
Avoid touching the leads or connectors while the switch is closed.

---

1. One-eighth to one-quarter fill a 50 ml beaker with solid lead (II) bromide. Place the beaker on a wire gauze supported by an iron ring and retort stand.

2. Heat the lead (II) bromide until it is completely molten. Continue to carefully heat, if necessary, to maintain it in its molten state throughout the experiment.

3. Using insulated wires connect a 6 to 12 volt DC source, switch, 6 volt DC bulb and two carbon electrodes in series, as shown in Figure E-94. Carefully place the electrodes in the melt and close the switch. Record all observations.

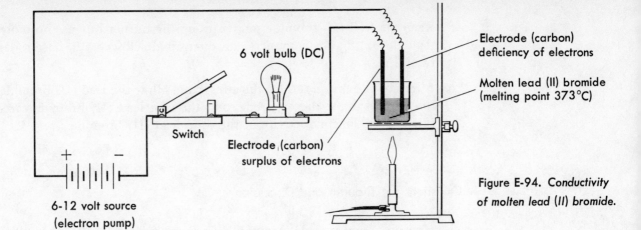

Figure E-94. *Conductivity of molten lead (II) bromide.*

4. At the end of the experiment leave the electrodes in the melt with the current on and allow it to solidify. Note any changes in conductivity that occur.

Alternate Procedure

1. Add lead (II) bromide to a large test tube to a depth of 3 cm. Heat the test tube with a burner until the lead (II) bromide melts.

2. Connect two carbon electrodes and a 6-volt DC bulb in series with a 6-volt DC source. The carbon electrodes must be arranged to fit into the large test tube (Figure E-95).

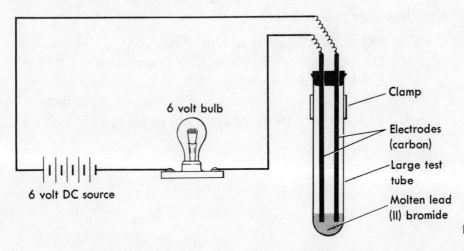

Figure E-95. *Alternate procedure for E-94.*

3. Lower the electrodes into the molten lead (II) bromide.

4. After observing the action of the bulb in procedure 3, remove the bulb from the circuit, close the circuit and again lower the electrodes into the melt.

5. Keep the lead (II) bromide molten using the burner but use no more than the minimum amount of heat required. Observe the electrodes carefully.

6. After about 5 minutes open the circuit and allow the lead (II) bromide to cool. Examine the electrodes and the cool lead (II) bromide carefully. Test the conductivity of the solid lead (II) bromide.

Questions for Thought and Discussion

1. How does solid lead (II) bromide differ from molten lead (II) bromide?

2. Does this change on melting account for the difference in the conductivity observed?

3. Knowing the polarity of the electrodes, how can the directions various ions travel in the melt be predicted? Explain.

4. (a) Describe what was observed at each electrode.
   (b) How can these changes be explained?
   (c) Write equations to explain the changes at each electrode.
   (d) Write an equation for the overall reaction that occurs.

5. Based upon your observations, explain electrical conduction in melts and in aqueous solutions. (Refer to Experiment 17-3).

6. Why is molten lead (II) bromide an electrolyte and solid lead (II) bromide a non-electrolyte?

7. (a) Define an oxidation-reduction reaction.
   (b) Do the reactions that occur at the electrodes constitute an oxidation-reduction reaction? Explain.
   (c) If so, at which electrode does (i) oxidation, (ii) reduction occur?
   (d) If so, name the oxidizing agent and reducing agent in the reaction.

EXPERIMENT 18-3

Electrolytes and Electrolysis: The Chemical Changes Produced by the Passage of an Electric Current Through Aqueous Solutions Containing Ions

Dramatic changes result when an electric current passes through solutions containing ions. This experiment affords an opportunity to examine the effects of an electric current on eight different combinations of electrodes and aqueous solutions. The procedure to be followed is roughly the same for all solutions and is described in the general procedure given below. A description of the apparatus is given in Figures E-96 and E-97. Either of these arrangements can be used, the former being more suitable for class experiments. As different solutions are introduced, the only change that must be made in either apparatus is in the electrodes. Instructions as to the appropriate electrodes are also given in the procedure.

Procedure

1. Set up the electrolytic cell as shown in Figure E-96 or Figure E-97. Use platinum electrodes for each solution listed in procedure 2 except where the electrodes are specifically indicated.

2. Fill the cell with each of the following solutions in turn:
   (a) 1M hydrochloric acid (use carbon electrodes),
   (b) 1M copper (II) sulphate (use carbon electrodes),
   (c) 1M copper (II) sulphate (use a carbon cathode and a copper anode),
   (d) 1M copper (II) sulphate (use copper electrodes),
   (e) 1M sulphuric acid,

(f) 1M sodium hydroxide,

(g) 0.1M sodium chloride containing a few millilitres of either neutral litmus solution or neutral bromthymol blue solution,

(h) 6M sodium chloride containing a few millilitres of either neutral litmus solution or neutral bromthymol blue solution

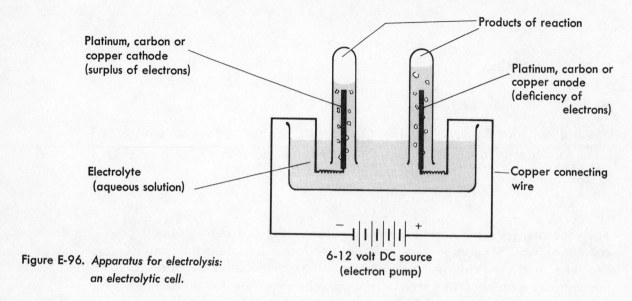

Figure E-96. *Apparatus for electrolysis: an electrolytic cell.*

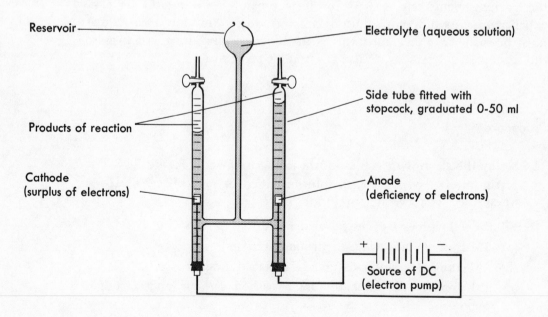

Figure E-97. *Hoffman apparatus for electrolysis.*

3. For each solution turn on the current and observe all of the changes that take place over a period of 5 to 10 minutes.

4. Where gaseous products are formed, make a mark on both tubes to show the level of the gas collected.

5. Test all gaseous products for a characteristic odour.

6. Test all gaseous products with a glowing and/or a burning splint.

7. Measure the volume of each gas collected by filling each gas receiver with water to the mark and pouring the water into a 25 ml graduated cylinder. If using the Hoffmann apparatus, read the volumes of gaseous products directly from the scales provided on the side tubes.

Questions for Thought and Discussion

1M Hydrochloric Acid (a)

1. What ions and molecules are present in this solution?

2. (a) What ions and/or molecules are discharged at the electrodes?
   (b) Why are these ions and/or molecules discharged in preference to the others in the solution?

3. (a) What are the products of the reaction?
   (b) How were the products identified?

4. Write equations for the changes that occur at each electrode.

5. Write an equation for the overall electrochemical reaction.

6. Are the constituents of the solute, solvent or both involved in this reaction?

1M Copper (II) Sulphate (b, c and d)

1. What ions and molecules are present in this solution?

2. (a) What ions and/or molecules are discharged in this process when a carbon cathode and a platinum anode are used?
   (b) Why are these ions and/or molecules discharged in preference to the others in the solution in this process?

3. (a) What are the products of this reaction?
   (b) How were the products identified?

4. (a) Is there any difference in the products of this reaction when (i) a copper anode and a carbon cathode are used, and (ii) copper plates are used as electrodes?

(b) If so, what are the differences? Account for the reactions in each case.

5. Write equations for the changes that occur at each electrode in each of the processes.

6. Write an equation for the overall electrochemical reaction in each of these processes.

7. Are the constituents of solute, solvent or both involved in these processes?

1M Sulphuric Acid (e)

The questions applicable here are the same as questions 1 to 6 under the heading 1M Hydrochloric Acid (a).

1M Sodium Hydroxide (f)

The questions applicable here are the same as questions to 1 to 6 under the heading 1M Hydrochloric Acid (a).

0.1M Sodium Chloride (g)

Again, questions 1 to 6 under the heading 1M Hydrochloric Acid (a) are applicable. In addition, answer the following:

7. Does the solution in the vicinity of the (a) cathode, (b) anode become acidic, basic or remain neutral in this reaction? Explain.

8. (a) How do the products of the electrochemical reactions involving solutions of 1M sulphuric acid, 1M sodium hydroxide, and 0.1M sodium chloride compare?

   (b) What substances undergo chemical changes in these processes?

   (c) What name might be given to each of these processes?

6M Sodium Chloride (h)

1. What ions and molecules are present in this solution?

2. (a) What ions and/or molecules are discharged at the electrodes?

   (b) Why are these ions and/or molecules discharged in preference to the others in the solution?

3. (a) What are the products of the reaction?

   (b) How were the products identified?

4. (a) Does the solution in the vicinity of the (a) cathode, (b) anode become acidic, basic or remain neutral in this reaction? Explain.

   (b) Would you expect the overall solution when the reaction is stopped to be acidic, basic or neutral? Explain.

5. Does any change in colour of the indicator, other than that suggested in question 4, take place in the vicinity of either electrode? If so, suggest an explanation for the change.

6. Oxygen is sometimes produced as a product of this reaction. How can its formation be explained?

7. Write equations for the changes that occur at each electrode.

8. Write an equation for the overall electrochemical reaction.

9. Are the constituents of solute, solvent or both involved in this reaction?

10. (a) How do the products of the electrochemical reactions involving 0.1M and 6M solutions of sodium chloride compare?

   (b) What substances undergo chemical changes in these processes?

Overall Experiment

1. (a) Define, in general terms, the electrochemical reactions studied in this experiment.

   (b) What name is given to all such electrochemical reactions?

2. All of these reactions are redox reactions.

   (a) Using each of the reactions studied, show that this statement is true.

   (b) Name the oxidizing agent and the reducing agent in each case.

EXPERIMENT 18-4

Acids, Bases and Salts

Some of the characteristics of acids, bases and salts are illustrated in this experiment. All data should be recorded in tabular form as the experiment proceeds. Prepare the data tables before the laboratory period using the format provided (Tables 1 and 2).

Procedure

Obtain a 25 ml sample of each of the four solutions of acid and four solutions of base provided. Use these 25 ml portions to supply the acids and bases required in the following procedures.

Effect on Indicators

1. Using a clean, dry stirring rod *each time,* transfer one drop of each of the above solutions to a dry spot on (i) a piece of red and (ii) a piece of blue litmus paper.

2. Place a drop of each of the solutions in turn on a drop of (a) neutral bromthymol blue solution, (b) methyl orange solution and (c) phenolphthalein solution on a watch glass or spot plate.

Effect on Metals

1. (a) In each of eight test tubes, place a piece of magnesium ribbon about 2 cm long.
   (b) To each tube add 1 ml of a different acid or base.
   (c) If no reaction appears at first, warm each test tube.
   (d) Bring a burning splint to the mouth of each tube as the reaction occurs.

2. Repeat procedure 1 using iron, a metal less active than magnesium.

Effect on Oxides and Carbonates

1. (a) In each of 5 test tubes place a small sample of copper (II) oxide.

   (b) Add distilled water to the first tube and stir the contents. Examine the tube for the presence of a blue solution, which is evidence that a soluble copper compound has been formed.

2. (a) To the other 4 tubes add, in turn, 2 ml of the four acid solutions.

   (b) Warm the tubes if no reaction is evident at first. Note any cases where the presence of a blue colour is evident.

3. (a) Repeat procedures 1 and 2, omitting the distilled water, and using a sample of sodium hydrogen carbonate with each of the four acid solutions. Place a one-hole rubber stopper fitted with a glass tube and a 12-inch piece of rubber tubing (Figure E-98) in the mouth of each test tube immediately after the acid is added. The other end of the rubber tubing must be dipped into a solution of lime-water (calcium hydroxide) in another test tube before mixing the reactants. Note all changes that occur.

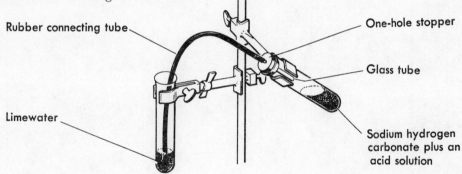

Figure E-98. *Reaction of carbonates with an acid.*

   (b) Repeat procedure 2, using a sample of magnesium hydroxide with each of the four acid solutions.

Interaction of Acids and Bases

1. Combine all of the remaining acid solutions into one test tube. Measure the temperature of this solution.

2. Combine all of the remaining sodium and potassium hydroxide solutions into another test tube. Measure the temperature of this solution.

3. Keep the thermometer in the solution of bases and add the solution of acids. Stir the mixture gently with the thermometer and record the highest or the lowest temperature reached by the mixture.

DATA TABLE: ACIDS AND BASES

Table 1

Property / Solution	sulphuric acid	hydrochloric acid	phosphoric acid	nitric acid	sodium hydroxide	potassium hydroxide	calcium hydroxide	aqueous ammonia
Formula								
Effect on Indicators litmus bromthymol blue methyl orange phenolphthalein								
Effect on Metals magnesium iron								
Effect on Oxides and Carbonates copper (II) oxide sodium hydrogen carbonate								
Effect of Acids on Bases magnesium hydroxide solid								
Interaction of Acids with Bases								

DATA TABLE: SALT SOLUTIONS

Table 2

Property / Salt solution	sodium chloride	sodium carbonate	sodium hydrogen carbonate	sodium nitrate	potassium bromide	iron (III) chloride	copper (II) sulphate	potassium phosphate
Effect on Indicators litmus bromthymol blue								

Solutions of Salts in Water

1. In each of eight test tubes, place 1 ml of a solution of each salt listed in Table 2.

2. Using a clean, dry stirring rod *each time*, transfer one drop of each solution to a dry spot on (i) a piece of red and (ii) a piece of blue litmus paper.

3. Place one drop of each salt solution in turn on a drop of neutral bromthymol blue solution on a watch glass or spot plate.

4. Complete Table 2.

Questions for Thought and Discussion

1. Based upon the observations made in this experiment:
   (a) List the properties common to acids.
   (b) List the properties common to bases.
   (c) Classify the salt solutions studied as acidic, basic or neutral.

2. What is the effect of interaction between acid and base?

3. Write balanced chemical equations and ionic equations to explain the chemical changes observed in this experiment.

EXPERIMENT 18-5

Hydrogen-ion Concentration and pH

Indicators are coloured dyes that change colour as the pH of an aqueous solution changes. Since these colour changes occur over a very narrow range of pH values, indicators can be used to establish the pH of aqueous solutions. The universal indicator used in this experiment contains a mixture of coloured dyes. The dyes selected for this indicator respond to pH changes over a wide range of pH values.

Two distinct ideas are examined in this experiment. In Part I, the pH values are determined for a series of solutions of acids, bases and salts. All of *these solutions have the same molar concentration.* In Part II, three of the solutions from Part I are subjected to a series of dilutions. After each dilution the pH is determined for the new concentration. In this way the effect of dilution on the pH of acids and bases is examined. Prepare Data Tables 1 and 2 before coming to the laboratory period and complete these tables as the experiment proceeds. The columns marked "Concentration" and "Calculated pH" can be filled in before the experimental results are obtained.

Procedure

Part I   The pH of Various Solutions of the Same Molar Concentration

1. Add 3 drops of the universal indicator to 5 ml of each of the solutions being tested. The complete list of solutions to be tested is given in Table 1.

2. Determine the numerical value for the pH of each solution by comparing the colour of the solution with the standard colour chart.

Solutions (0.1M)	Indicator Colour	Numerical pH	Strength as Acid or Base
hydrochloric acid			
acetic acid			
phosphoric acid			
sodium hydroxide			
aqueous ammonia			
sodium chloride			
sodium carbonate			
sodium hydrogen carbonate			
ammonium acetate			

Part II   The Effect of Dilution on pH

1. Start with 5 ml of 0.1M HCl solution and dilute the solution *to* 50 ml. Save 5 ml of this diluted solution in a properly labelled test tube.

2. Take a second 5 ml portion of the diluted solution in procedure 1 and dilute *to* 50 ml. Save 5 ml of this diluted solution in a properly labelled test tube.

3. Repeat this dilution process two more times with the same solution. Retain 5 ml of the solutions from each successive dilution and label them appropriately.

4. Test each 5 ml portion of the diluted acid with universal indicator as in Part I.

5. Repeat procedures 1 to 4 using 0.1M NaOH solution and 0.1M CH_3COOH solution. Record these results in tabular form (Table 2).

Data Table   Table 2

Concentration of Hydrochloric Acid	Calculated pH	Indicator Colour	Observed pH (colour chart)
Concentration of Sodium Hydroxide	Calculated pH	Indicator Colour	Observed pH (colour chart)
Concentration of Acetic Acid	Indicator Colour		Observed pH (colour chart)

Questions for Thought and Discussion

1. Which of the definitely acidic substances is (a) the strongest acid, (b) the weakest acid?

2. Why is a 0.1M solution of sodium hydroxide a much stronger base than a 0.1M solution of aqueous ammonia?

3. What effect does dilution have on the pH of (a) an acid, (b) a base?

4. (a) Is there any relationship between the concentration and strength of a solution of an acid or base?
   (b) Distinguish between these two terms.

EXPERIMENT 18-6

The Reaction of an Acid with a Base

The single reaction investigated in this procedure can be considered typical of the reactions that occur between *any* acid and *any* base.

Procedure

1. Place 2 or 3 drops of phenolphthalein indicator solution in an evaporating dish containing 10 ml of 0.1M sodium hydroxide solution.

2. Take the temperature of this solution.

3. Take the temperature of the 0.1M hydrochloric acid solution.

4. Using a 10 ml measuring (graduated) pipette, add 0.1M hydrochloric acid solution to the basic solution drop by drop, with stirring, ūntil the indicator just changes colour (Figure E-99).

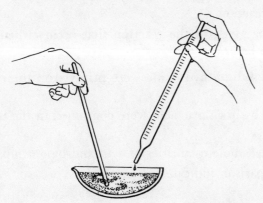

Figure E-99.

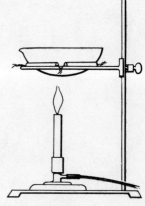

Figure E-100.

5. Take the temperature of the resulting solution as soon as the indicator changes colour.

6. Place the evaporating dish, containing about 5 ml of the solution, on a clay triangle supported by an iron ring and retort stand. Heat the evaporating dish gently to evaporate the solution to dryness (Figure E-100).

7. Allow the evaporating dish to cool. Under your teacher's direction, dip a moist finger tip into the residue in the dish and cautiously taste it.

8. Make a careful record of all observations.

CAUTION: Never taste chemicals unless specifically directed to do so by your teacher.

Questions for Thought and Discussion

1. (a) What is the product of the evaporation procedure?
   (b) Write a balanced chemical equation to explain the changes observed when this acid and base react.
   (c) What are the apparent products of this reaction?
   (d) Write a balanced equation for the evaporation reaction.

2. (a) Write an *ionic equation* to explain the changes observed in this reaction involving an acid and a base.
   (b) What reacting species are involved in this reaction?
   (c) Would you expect this to be the case in all reactions between acid and base? Justify your answer.

3. (a) Is this reaction exothermic or endothermic?
   (b) Would you expect the energy relationships in all such acid-base reactions to be the same? Why?

4. (a) Define this type of reaction.
   (b) What name could be given to the reaction that occurs when an acid is mixed with a base?

5. (a) How many moles of sodium hydroxide were involved in the reaction?
   (b) How many moles of hydrochloric acid were consumed in the reaction?
   (c) How do the calculated mole quantities of acid and base compare?
   (d) What does this comparison indicate?

EXPERIMENT 18-7

A Quantitative Study of the Reaction of an Acid with a Base

Acids react with bases to form a salt and water. This process, neutralization, was examined in Experiment 18-6. Although this determination was to some extent quantitative, it is possible to determine far more precisely the quantities of acid and base involved in a neutralization reaction.

The procedure outlined in this experiment is called a *titration*. Any titration involves the addition of some solution, a drop at a time, to a second solution until the end point of the reaction is reached. One solution is said to be *titrated* with the other. The end point of any titration is usually indicated by a sharp colour change. In the case of neutralization reactions, this colour change is provided by the addition of a few drops of an indicator solution, such as phenolphthalein or bromthymol blue. Both solutions involved in any titration are drawn from some device capable of measuring, rather precisely, the volume of the solution added. Burettes are often used for both solutions, although in many determinations, an accurate transfer pipette will replace one of the burettes.

It is important to remember throughout the experiment that this is a rather precise quantitative procedure if it is executed carefully. Follow the instructions for handling the burettes with great care, if you are interested in an accurate result.

Procedure

1. Clean two burettes with a synthetic detergent and warm (*not hot*) water using a long-handled wire brush. Rinse each burette at least ten times with tap water followed by one rinse using 10 ml of distilled water. Finally, rinse each burette with 5 ml of *the solution to be used in it*. Discharge this solution through the jet end of the burette.

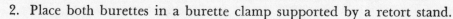
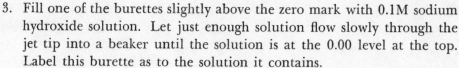

Test tube

Base   Acid

Piece of white paper

Figure E-101. *Titration apparatus.*

2. Place both burettes in a burette clamp supported by a retort stand.

3. Fill one of the burettes slightly above the zero mark with 0.1M sodium hydroxide solution. Let just enough solution flow slowly through the jet tip into a beaker until the solution is at the 0.00 level at the top. Label this burette as to the solution it contains.

   Use the straight edge of a piece of paper to help read the level of the liquid in the burette. Keep the line of sight tangent to the bottom of the meniscus of the liquid, and read the scale where it intersects with the line of sight. If the starting measurement is more than 0.00 ml, record this level and continue (see Figures I-12 to I-16).

4. Repeat procedure 3 using the second burette and the hydrochloric acid solution of unknown concentration.

5. Place a test tube over each burette as indicated in Figure E-101. This will avoid evaporation and contamination of the solutions.*

6. Run about 25 ml of 0.1M sodium hydroxide solution from the burette into an Erlenmeyer flask.

7. Add two or three drops of phenolphthalein indicator solution to the sodium hydroxide.

8. Place a piece of white paper under the Erlenmeyer flask to serve as a background against which the colour change can be observed. Slowly add hydrochloric acid solution to the flask, swirling the flask to ensure mixing. Continue until one drop of acid makes the colour just disappear.

9. Add sodium hydroxide solution to the flask, *one drop at a time*, until the first sign of colour reappears.

10. Once again add hydrochloric acid solution, one drop at a time, until the colour just disappears.

    If you pass this so-called "end point", repeat procedures 9 and 10 until the solution is neutral to the indicator, that is, until one drop of either solution produces a change in colour.

11. Read the final level of the solution in each burette.

12. Calculate the total volume of each solution that was used in the reaction.

13. Repeat procedures 6 to 12 two more times.

---

*Solutions should not be left in burettes for prolonged periods of time. Burettes should be drained, cleaned and put away after being used. Solutions should be stored in stock bottles.

Calculations

1. Calculate the number of moles of sodium hydroxide used in this reaction. Make this calculation for each titration you carried out.

2. Write the balanced chemical equation for the reaction.

3. Using the equation above, calculate the number of moles of hydrochloric acid that must have reacted with the number of moles of sodium hydroxide calculated in 1. Make this calculation for each titration.

4. Calculate the concentration of the hydrochloric acid solution. Express the answer as (a) molarity (b) grams of solute per litre of solution. Calculate the average value of the three experimental results in each case.

Questions For Thought and Discussion

1. Why is it preferable to use an Erlenmeyer flask in this operation instead of a beaker and a stirring rod?

2. The results of an experiment indicate that 25 ml of the hydrochloric acid solution used in this experiment are required to completely react with 30 ml of a solution of sodium carbonate.
   (a) Write the balanced chemical equation for the reaction.
   (b) Calculate the molarity of the sodium carbonate solution.

EXPERIMENT 18-8

Reactions Involving Ions in Aqueous Solutions

Procedure

1. (a) Place 5 ml of each of the following solutions in separate test tubes: 6M copper (II) chloride, 0.1M copper (II) chloride, 0.1M potassium permanganate and 0.1M potassium chloride. Compare the colours of these solutions.

   (b) Add concentrated hydrochloric acid to the 6M copper (II) chloride solution and note any change that occurs.

2. (a) To six different large test tubes add, in turn, 0 ml, 1 ml, 2 ml, 3 ml, 4 ml and 5 ml of water. Add 5 g of mossy zinc to each test tube.

   (b) Carefully add 5 ml of concentrated sulphuric acid to the contents of each test tube. Pour this acid very slowly down the side of each tube and shake the tube periodically.

3. (a) Add 5 ml of 0.1M silver nitrate solution to 5 ml of solutions of potassium chloride and calcium chloride.

   (b) Add a few drops of carbon tetrachloride to a test tube one-third filled with distilled water. Add 5 ml of 0.1M silver nitrate solution and shake the contents of the tube to mix thoroughly.

4. In four separate test tubes place a strip of magnesium, a strip of zinc, a strip of copper and a piece of iron wire. Add 5 ml of 0.1M hydrochloric acid solution to each test tube. Test any gaseous products that are liberated with a burning splint.

5. (a) Place 5 ml of 0.1M magnesium nitrate solution in each of five small test tubes and 10 ml of 0.1M magnesium nitrate in a 150 ml beaker.

   (b) Add to the five test tubes and the beaker, respectively, (i) a strip of magnesium, (ii) a piece of zinc, (iii) a piece of iron wire, (iv) a strip of lead, (v) a strip of copper, (vi) a silver coin. Wait for a short time then note any changes.

6. Repeat procedure 5, replacing the magnesium nitrate solution with (i) 0.1M zinc nitrate solution, (ii) 0.1M iron (II) nitrate solution, (iii) 0.1M lead (II) nitrate solution, (iv) 0.1M copper (II) nitrate solution, (v) 0.1M silver nitrate solution. Record all the results in tabular form.

7. (a) Place 5 ml of distilled water in each of two test tubes. Add 5 ml of 1M hydrochloric acid solution to one of these test tubes.

   (b) Add a small piece of iron (II) sulphide to each test tube. Shake the test tubes and note any changes that occur.

8. Repeat procedure 7 but add a small piece of calcium carbonate instead of the iron (II) sulphide to each test tube.

9. Place 5 ml of 0.1M barium nitrate solution in a test tube. Add 5 ml of 0.1M sulphuric acid solution and note any changes.

10. Place 5 ml of 0.1M copper (II) nitrate solution in a test tube. Add 5 ml of 0.1M sodium sulphide solution and note any changes.

11. (a) Place 5 ml of distilled water in a test tube. Add one drop of 0.5M potassium iodide solution and five drops of 0.5M lead (II) nitrate solution. Stopper the test tube and shake it well.

    (b) After the precipitate completely settles out to the bottom of the tube, add one drop of 0.1M silver nitrate solution to the solution above the precipitate.

Questions for Thought and Discussion

The questions below are numbered to correspond with the steps in the procedure.

1. Based upon your observations from procedure 1:
   (a) What is the colour of each ion in the solutions?
   (b) Account for the colour of the concentrated copper (II) chloride solution after the addition of the concentrated hydrochloric acid solution.

2. (a) Explain the changes observed in procedure 2.

   (b) Write an ionic equation for the reaction.

3. Based upon your observations in procedure 3:

   (a) Explain what happens in each case.

   (b) Write ionic equations for any chemical changes that occur.

4. (a) Write ionic equations to account for any chemical changes observed when a metal is placed in a dilute acid.

   (b) Compare the rates of the reactions that occur.

   (c) List the metals in descending order of activity in reaction with dilute acids.

   (d) Are these reactions oxidation-reduction reactions?

   (e) For each of the reactions that you would classify as a redox reaction name: (i) the reduced substance, (ii) the reducing agent, (iii) the oxidized substance, (iv) the oxidizing agent.

5. & 6. (a) Write ionic equations to account for any chemical changes observed when the metals magnesium, zinc, iron, lead, copper and silver are added in turn to solutions of magnesium nitrate, zinc nitrate, iron (II) nitrate, lead (II) nitrate, copper (II) nitrate and silver nitrate.

   (b) Compare the rates of the reactions that occur.

   (c) List the metals in descending order of activity in reaction with solutions of their compounds.

   (d) Are these reactions oxidation-reduction reactions?

   (e) For each of the reactions that you classify as a redox reaction, name: (i) the reduced substance, (ii) the reducing agent, (iii) the oxidized substance, (iv) the oxidizing agent.

   (f) Arrange the metals studied in descending order of their ability to displace other metals from solutions of their compounds, that is, in descending order of their ability to reduce other metallic ions in solution.

   (g) Where would hydrogen gas be positioned in this list of metals?

   (h) Arrange the metal ions studied in descending order of the ease with which they are reduced to metal from aqueous solution.

   (i) Where would the hydrogen ion be positioned in this list of ions?

   (j) Which of the metals studied is the strongest reducing agent and which of the metallic ions is the strongest oxidizing agent?

   (k) How does the order of the metals and metallic ions in these lists compare with the order of the metals in the activity series developed in Chapter 16?

7. (a) Write a balanced chemical equation for the reaction that occurs between iron (II) sulphide and hydrochloric acid.

   (b) Write an ionic equation for the reaction.

   (c) What factors are responsible for the reaction occurring in acid solution?

   (d) What are the products of the reaction?

   (e) Would you expect this reaction to go to completion? Explain.

   (f) Is this a redox reaction? Explain.

8. Answer 7(a) to 7(f) above as they apply to the reaction that occurs between calcium carbonate and hydrochloric acid.

9. (a) Write an ionic equation for the reaction that occurs between barium nitrate and sulphuric acid solutions.

   (b) What is the product of this reaction?

   (c) Would you expect that this reaction would go to completion? Explain.

10. Answer 9(a) to 9(c) above as they apply to the reaction between copper (II) nitrate and sodium sulphide solutions.

11. (a) Write an ionic equation for the reaction that occurs between lead (II) nitrate and potassium iodide solutions.

    (b) What is the product of this reaction?

    (c) Which reactant is used in excess in this reaction?

    (d) Would you expect that all of the iodide would be precipitated in this reaction?

    (e) Write an ionic equation to explain the reaction that occurs when silver nitrate solution is added to the clear solution above the precipitate.

    (f) What is the product of this reaction?

    (g) Does this reaction go to completion?

    (h) On the basis of your observations, would you expect that precipitation reactions go to completion? Justify your answer.

    (i) Compare the solubilities of the products of the two reactions studied.

    (j) Are precipitation reactions redox reactions?

EXPERIMENT 18-9

Enthalpy Changes and Neutralization

In this experiment the change in enthalpy is measured for three different reactions. Although each determination involves a different reaction, the three reactions are closely related. The algebraic sum of the first two reactions is equivalent to the third reaction. If the procedure is carried out carefully, it should be possible to verify experimentally the law of additivity of reaction heats.

A 250 ml flask serves as a simple calorimeter. In all calculations assume that the heat evolved during the reactions is absorbed by the solution and the glass flask. The solutions can be considered to have a specific heat of 1.0, the specific heat of water. Thus the temperature of 1 g of solution rises 1 centigrade degree when 1 calorie of heat is absorbed. On the other hand, it takes approximately 0.2 calorie to change the temperature of 1 g of glass in the flask 1 centigrade degree. You will notice that the mass of the water or solution used in each procedure is not determined. This will necessitate still another assumption when making the calculations.

This experiment combines a number of ideas from various parts of the course. You would be wise to review the ideas already covered on aggregates, enthalpy changes, ions in solution and neutralization before coming to the laboratory period.

Procedure

CAUTION: Don't touch the sodium hydroxide pellets with your hands. Use a glass stirring rod to slide them off the paper if necessary.

Reaction 1

1. Accurately determine the mass of an empty 250 ml flask. Be sure the flask is clean and dry.

2. Using a 100 ml graduate add 200 ml of cool water to the flask. Stir this water slowly, using the thermometer, until the temperature remains constant. Record this temperature as accurately as possible.

3. Add a mass of 2 g of solid sodium hydroxide, NaOH(s), (pellets) to a piece of smooth paper. (20 pellets of sodium hydroxide should be about 2 g). Accurately determine the mass of this sodium hydroxide.

4. Pour this sodium hydroxide into the water in the flask. Swirl the flask until all the solid has dissolved. As the last of the solid dissolves, put a thermometer in the flask and record the highest or lowest temperature reached.

Reaction 2

Use the same flask as in reaction 1 but rinse the flask thoroughly before proceeding.

5. Add 100 ml of 0.5M HCl solution to the 250 ml flask using a 100 ml graduate.

6. Add 100 ml of 0.5M NaOH solution to a clean, dry 250 ml beaker. Be sure that the graduate used does not contain any of the acid solution.

7. Both of these solutions should be at room temperature or slightly below room temperature. Check this with the thermometer but be careful not to mix the solutions in the process.

8. Place the thermometer in the flask, then add the sodium hydroxide solution to the acid in the flask. Mix the solutions *quickly* by briefly swirling the flask, then immediately watch for and record the highest or lowest temperature reached.

Reaction 3

Use the same flask again after thorough rinsing.

9. Follow procedures 2 to 4 as in reaction 1 making *one change* only. Instead of adding water to the flask in procedure 2 add 200 ml of 0.25M HCl solution.

Calculations

Reaction 1

1. Write the ionic equation for the reaction that occurs when sodium hydroxide solid is added to water.

2. Calculate the heat absorbed by the solution during reaction 1.

3. Calculate the heat absorbed by the flask during reaction 1.

4. Calculate the total heat absorbed during the reaction.

5. Calculate the number of moles of sodium hydroxide involved in this reaction.

6. Calculate the total amount of heat evolved in this reaction for every mole of NaOH(s) that was used. Express this value as $\triangle H_1$.

Reaction 2

7. Write an ionic equation for the second reaction. Include all the ions present as the reaction occurs.

8. Calculate the heat absorbed by the solution during reaction 2.

9. Calculate the heat absorbed by the flask during reaction 2.

10. Calculate the total heat absorbed during reaction 2.

11. From the concentration and volume of the sodium hydroxide solution used, calculate the number of moles of sodium hydroxide involved in this reaction.

12. Calculate the total amount of heat evolved in this reaction for every mole of sodium hydroxide that reacted. Express this value as $\triangle H_2$.

Reaction 3

The process that occurs in this reaction involves solid sodium hydroxide, NaOH(s), and an aqueous solution of hydrochloric acid. It can be summarized by:

$$NaOH(s) + H^+(aq) + Cl^-(aq) \rightarrow H_2O(l) + Na^+(aq) + Cl^-(aq)$$

Repeat steps 2 to 6 in the calculations using the data obtained from reaction 3. Express the final value as $\triangle H_3$.

Questions for Thought and Discussion

1. What type of process occurs in reaction 1? Why is heat evolved?

2. What type of process occurs in reaction 2?

3. By combining the equations for reactions 1 and 2 algebraically, show that reaction 3 is just a combination of these two reactions.

4. In your own words, describe why reaction 3 is just a combination of reactions 1 and 2.

5. Compare $\triangle H_1 + \triangle H_2$ with $\triangle H_3$. Assuming some experimental error, what appears to be the relationship between these quantities?

6. What law is verified by this relationship? State this law.

EXPERIMENT 18-10

The Enthalpy of Formation of Solid Ammonium Chloride

The *enthalpy of formation* of any substance is defined as the change in enthalpy that occurs when 1 mole of any substance is produced from its component elements, the component elements being in the standard state. The standard state is usually defined as 1 atmosphere of pressure and 25°C. It is customary to list the enthalpies of formation of many substances in a standard table. From this table the enthalpy changes for many other chemical reactions can be calculated by applying the law of additivity of reaction heats (Hess's law). Because it is not always possible to determine the enthalpy of formation by direct measurement with a calorimeter, it is sometimes necessary to combine direct experimental results with enthalpies of formation given in the standard tables.

The purpose of this experiment is to determine the enthalpy of formation of the solid ammonium chloride, $NH_4Cl(s)$. The overall equation for the formation of 1 mole of ammonium chloride from its component elements is given below.

$$\tfrac{1}{2}N_2(g) + 2H_2(g) + \tfrac{1}{2}Cl_2(g) \rightarrow NH_4Cl(s)$$

Determining the enthalpy of formation for this reaction would appear to be a simple matter; bring the three elements together and measure the heat evolved or absorbed when they react. But this particular reaction is not easily investigated in the laboratory. Instead, it is necessary to conduct the reaction as a series of steps, culminating in the product $NH_4Cl(s)$. You will recall from Chapter 15 that the amount of heat absorbed or evolved during a chemical reaction is independent of the sequence of reactions followed to arrive at the final products. Thus, it should be possible to determine the enthalpy change for each reaction step and add these algebraically to calculate the enthalpy change for the overall reaction.

In the procedure outlined below, two of the enthalpy changes are determined experimentally and the remainder must be determined by consulting appropriate reference texts. It will be assumed that the temperature and pressure at which the experimental portions are carried out are 25°C and 1 atmosphere pressure respectively. Procedures 1, 2, 3 and 8 can be carried out before the laboratory period.

Procedure

Six steps are involved in the formation of ammonium chloride solid from its component elements.

  (i) the formation of ammonia gas from hydrogen gas and nitrogen gas

 (ii) the addition of ammonia gas to water to form ammonium ions and hydroxyl ions (an aqueous ammonia solution)

(iii) the formation of hydrogen chloride gas from hydrogen gas and chlorine gas

 (iv) the addition of hydrogen chloride gas to water to form hydrogen ions and chloride ions (a hydrochloric acid solution)

  (v) the reaction between the ammonia solution of (ii) and the hydrochloric acid solution of (iv)

 (vi) the formation of solid ammonium chloride from the ammonium and chloride ions in (v).

1. Write a balanced chemical equation for each of the steps described above. In each case write the equation showing no more than one mole of each product. Check these equations to see that they are all balanced.

2. Add all the equations in 1 together. If these equations have been written correctly their algebraic sum will be the same as the overall equation given previously.

3. Using information given in this text and other reference texts, find the enthalpy changes associated with equations (i) to (iv) inclusive. This information for equations (i) and (iii) will be found in tables under the heading "enthalpy of formation". For equations (ii) and (v) the information will be found in tables headed "heats of solution" or "enthalpies of solution". Express these values beside each equation using the $\triangle H$ notation. Be careful to observe the correct sign convention and be consistent with the units. The enthalpy changes associated with equations (v) and (vi) will be determined experimentally as outlined below.

4. Construct a simple calorimeter by placing a 250 ml beaker within a 400 ml beaker and lining the space between beakers with rolled newspaper, wood shavings or some other insulating material.

5. Using a graduated cylinder, add 100.0 ml of 1.5M aqueous ammonia solution to the inner beaker of the calorimeter. Record the temperature of this solution.

6. Stirring gently but continuously, pour 100.0 ml of 1.5M hydrochloric acid solution into the same beaker. Record the maximum or minimum temperature that the solution reaches.

7. Repeat procedures 5 and 6 until consistent results are obtained.

8. The reaction conducted in procedures 5 and 6 was written as (v) above. If all the water were evaporated from the inner vessel of the calorimeter after this reaction, a white crystalline salt, ammonium chloride, would remain. Calculate the mass of ammonium chloride that could be prepared from this 200 ml of solution.

9. Pour out the solution in the calorimeter. After rinsing the container, add 200 ml of distilled water.

10. Determine the temperature of this distilled water.

11. Add the mass of ammonium chloride calculated in procedure 8 to the distilled water in the calorimeter. Stir gently but continuously and record the maximum or minimum temperature that the solution reaches.

12. Repeat procedures 9, 10 and 11 until consistent results are obtained.

Calculations

In all these calculations assume that the specific heat of any of the solutions is 1.0. (That is, assume that 1 calorie is the heat absorbed when 1 gram of solution increases 1 centigrade degree in temperature.)

1. For the reaction between aqueous ammonia and hydrochloric acid, calculate the number of calories of heat absorbed by the solution. Ignore any heat absorbed by the glass of the beaker.

2. Calculate the enthalpy of reaction of aqueous ammonia and hydrochloric acid. Observing the sign convention, express this value in kcal mole $^{-1}$ beside equation (v).

3. Following a similar procedure, calculate the enthalpy of solution for ammonium chloride.

4. From this data, obtained both experimentally and from the literature, calculate the enthalpy of formation for solid ammonium chloride.

Questions for Thought and Discussion

1. For determining the temperature change when the ammonia and hydrochloric acid solutions are mixed, what assumption is made concerning the initial temperature of the hydrochloric acid solution? Is this assumption valid?

2. Compare the value you obtained for the enthalpy of formation of solid ammonium chloride with the value given in a standard reference text.

3. Examine the procedure with a view to discovering sources of error in the experiment. In what way would these sources of error affect your result? If these sources of error were eliminated, would they bring your result any closer to the accepted value from the reference text?

4. For purposes of enthalpy changes the temperature of the standard state is usually defined as $25\,^\circ$C. Why is this temperature chosen?

III Guide to the Laboratory Sessions

Equipment and Chemicals

EXPERIMENT 1-2

Apparatus Required (per pair of students or per student)

   laboratory balance
   50 ml volumetric burette
   100 ml Erlenmeyer flask (or 100 ml beaker)
   100 ml graduated cylinder

Chemicals Required

Part I

   sugar solution
   sodium chloride solution
   ethyl alcohol   any one of or any combination of
   glycerol
   ethylene glycol

EXPERIMENT 2-1

Apparatus Required (per pair of students or per student)

   capillary tube 5 to 7 cm long
   thermometer ($-10°C$ to $100°C$)
   rubber tubing
   cut rubber stopper (one-hole—no. 4 or no. 6)
   250 ml beaker
   iron ring
   wire gauze
   retort stand
   burner

Chemicals Required

naphthalene (m.p. 80.22°C)

Other solids with melting points below 100°C may be used. If the m.p. is much below 80°C the water should not be heated rapidly to 60°C but to some lower temperature.

Capillary tubes (melting point tubes) are available commercially or can be prepared from glass tubing.

EXPERIMENT 2-2

Apparatus Required (per pair of students or per student)

4 test tubes (18 × 150 mm)
bar magnet
hand lens
porcelain crucible
clay triangle
iron ring
retort stand
burner
glass stirring rod

Chemicals Required

powdered iron
powdered sulphur
dilute hydrochloric acid solution

EXPERIMENT 2-3

Apparatus Required (per pair of students or per student)

test-tube rack
test tubes (18 × 150 mm)
straight pins
emery paper (or steel wool)
burner
splints
3 gas bottles (and solid stoppers)
deflagrating spoon

glass plate
asbestos pad
glass stirring rod

Chemicals Required

potassium metal
sodium metal
calcium metal (granular)
magnesium metal (ribbon)
water
litmus paper (blue and red)
sodium chloride
manganese dioxide
sodium bromide

sodium iodide
concentrated sulphuric acid
source of chlorine gas and
  bromine gas
iodine crystals
yellow phosphorus
shredded asbestos
copper foil

EXPERIMENT 2-4

Apparatus Required (per pair of students or per student)

test tube (18 × 150 mm)
paper (for trough)
scoopula (possibly)
clamp
retort stand
burner
splints
test-tube brush (possibly)

Chemicals Required

mercury (II) oxide
lead dioxide (possibly)

EXPERIMENT 3-1

Apparatus Required (per pair of students or per student)

2 ebonite rods
2 glass rods
retort stand
iron ring
stirrup
thread
small pieces of paper
wool cloth (or flannel)
silk cloth

Apparatus Required (for demonstration purposes)

cathode ray tube (cold cathode)
Crookes tube with fluorescent screen
Crookes tube with Maltese cross
magnet
set of discharge tubes at various stages of evacuation (set of 6)
discharge tube (for evacuation)
vacuum pump
induction coil
test leads

EXPERIMENT 3-2

Apparatus Required

1-litre flask
2-hole stopper
rubber tubing (heavy walled)
2 elbow tubes
2 clamps
retort stand
vacuum pump
light source
cloud chamber

Chemicals Required

alcohol
dry ice
radioactive source

EXPERIMENT 3-3

Apparatus Required

ebonite rod and wool
glass rod and silk
electroscope
radioactive sources
lead (metal) object

photographic film or plate enclosed in light protective wrapper
Geiger-Müller tube
radiation counter   Geiger counter
sheet of paper
book
3 sheets of aluminum
3 sheets of lead
brick
watch with luminous dial
slotted board to support sheets

EXPERIMENT 3-4

Apparatus Required (per pair of students or per student)

induction coil and appropriate DC source
100 ml beakers (maximum 8)
spectrum kit (student spectroscope from this kit)
demonstration spectroscope(s)
Plücker-Geissler tubes of: hydrogen, neon, helium, nitrogen, oxygen and mercury vapour
10 strips of asbestos (approximately 5 cm. $\times$ 15 cm.)
burner
retort stand
clamp

Chemicals Required

a lithium salt
a sodium salt
a potassium salt
a calcium salt   saturated or at least very concentrated
a barium salt   solutions of each
a strontium salt
a copper salt

EXPERIMENT 5-2

Apparatus Required (per pair of students or per student)

electrical conductivity apparatus (1 only, demonstration)

safety glasses for every student
forceps (tweezers)
knife (1 only)
test tubes (18 × 150 mm)
burner
spatula
flint lighter
rubber tubing

Chemicals Required

lithium metal
sodium metal   pre cut to pieces smaller than a pea
potassium metal
wooden splints
phenolphthalein indicator solution
litmus paper (blue and red)
hydrochloric acid (dilute solution)
lithium oxide (or lithium peroxide)
sodium peroxide
potassium peroxide

EXPERIMENT 5-3

Apparatus Required (per pair of students or per student)

conductivity apparatus (as in experiment 5-2)
emery paper
test tubes (18 × 150 mm)
wooden splints
burner
test tube (larger than above)
1-hole stopper to fit large test tube
elbow tube
rubber tubing
solid rubber stoppers to fit 18 × 150 mm test tubes
file
spatulas
pneumatic trough (or beaker)
funnel
filter paper (11 cm)

Note: *Source of oxides and peroxides of the alkali metals: K and K Laboratories Inc., 121 Express St., Engineer's Hill, Plainview, New York, 11803.*

Chemicals Required

calcium (turnings)

magnesium ribbon (or turnings)

litmus paper (red and blue)

phenolphthalein

distilled water

hydrochloric acid (dilute)

calcium oxide or hydroxide

magnesium oxide or hydroxide

barium oxide or hydroxide

magnesium sulphate

calcium sulphate

barium sulphate

asbestos sheet (or platinum wires) for flame tests

sodium carbonate

magnesium chloride

calcium chloride solutions

barium chloride

Reaction of Magnesium with Steam

This part of the experiment should be done as a *demonstration*.

Procedure

1. Place magnesium turnings in a 25 × 200 mm pyrex test tube. Use only enough to cover the bottom (rounded portion) of the tube.

2. Heat the magnesium turnings almost to the melting point. Do not heat the turnings so strongly that they ignite in air.

3. Pass steam from a generator over the *hot* magnesium turnings.

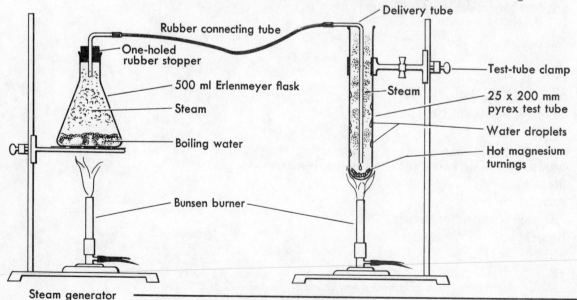

Delivery tube

Rubber connecting tube

One-holed rubber stopper

500 ml Erlenmeyer flask

Steam

Boiling water

Bunsen burner

Steam generator

Test-tube clamp

Steam

25 x 200 mm pyrex test tube

Water droplets

Hot magnesium turnings

CAUTION: Once the reaction starts, immediately turn off the burner under the magnesium turnings for safety. This reaction results in the liberation of hydrogen gas.

4. When the reaction ceases allow the tube to cool and observe the residue.

This reaction is strongly exothermic. The heat evolved is usually sufficient to soften and deform the test tube. The tube almost always cracks on heating or on cooling but it does not break or shatter. The tube should be discarded after the experiment.

*The test tube may be supported by a test-tube holder rather than the retort stand and clamp as shown in the diagram. The set up shown is safer and thus more desirable.

EXPERIMENT 5-4

Apparatus Required (per pair of students or per student)

(any apparatus marked D is for demonstration purposes only)

gas bottles (14)
test tubes (13 × 100 mm)
          (18 × 150 mm)
solid rubber stoppers to fit
   bottles and test tubes
deflagrating spoons D
burner

flint lighter
rubber tubing
tongs
scoopula (spatula)
asbestos gauze D

Chemicals Required

chlorine (lecture bottle)
bromine (lecture bottle or
   vials, or set up a generator)
iodine crystals
sodium
potassium
copper foil
antimony powder
red phosphorus
yellow phosphorus
asbestos (shredded)

chlorine water
bromine water
iodine water (iodine in
    potassium iodide solution)
potassium chloride solution
potassium bromide solution
potassium iodide solution
carbon tetrachloride
red and blue litmus paper

EXPERIMENT 5-5

Apparatus Required (per pair of students or per student)

conductivity apparatus

spatula

test tubes (18 × 150 mm)

(demonstration) large pyrex
test tube (25 × 200 mm)

burner

flint lighter

rubber tubing

safety glasses

32 one-inch styrofoam spheres

55 two-inch styrofoam spheres

pipe cleaners

tongs

250 ml beakers

deflagrating spoons

gas bottles (or beakers)

cover glasses (glass plates)

test-tube clamp

plastic sheets (acetate)

scotch tape

Chemicals Required

sodium

magnesium (turnings and
ribbon)

aluminum

silicon

phosphorus

sulphur

chlorine

argon

universal indicator or
hydrion paper

dilute (2M or 3M)
hydrochloric acid

red and blue litmus paper

aluminum nitrate (0.1M)

ammonia-water solution (6M)

sodium hydroxide solution
(6M)

hydrochloric acid (6M)

hydrous silicon dioxide

red phosphorus

asbestos paper (or fibres)

0.5M perchloric acid solution

dilute sulphuric acid (6M)

sodium chloride

iron (II) sulphide and
ammonium chloride

EXPERIMENTS 6-1 and 7-1

Apparatus Required (per pair of students or per student)

No.   Description

4   6-pronged connectors   —this gives an extra one of each

3	5-pronged connectors	—in Prentice-Hall kit these are coloured
3	4-pronged connectors	differently for quick identification
2	5½″ length pipe stem cleaner—red	
2	5½″ length pipe stem cleaner—blue	
26	4¾″ length plastic tubing to fit connectors—black	
8	4¾″ length plastic tubing to fit connectors—red	
8	3⅛″ length plastic tubing to fit connectors—white	
8	3⅛″ length plastic tubing to fit connectors—blue	
1	2¾″ length plastic tubing to fit connectors—green	
1	2″ length plastic tubing to fit connectors—green	
2	3″ diameter styrofoam or polystyrene spheres—white	
38	tear-shaped lobes (about 2″ max. diam.) and about 2¾″ length	

> —all must be drilled
> —most must be coloured (see below)
> —2 (two) have ends cut off

lobes are coloured as follows:

> 20 yellow
> 4 blue
> 4 red
> 4 white (whole)
> 2 white (ends cut)
> 4 black

Base—block of wood
> 8″ × 5″ × ¾″
—5 holes drilled in wood at appropriate positions

*Connectors and plastic tubes are available separately in packages of 100 from Prentice-Hall Inc., 520 Ellesmere Road, Scarborough, Ontario.

Expanded polystyrene spheres (4″ diameter), teardrop lobes (66 mm × 51 mm), and a colour kit are available from Plasteel Corporation, 26970 Princeton Avenue, Inkster, Michigan 48141, U.S.A.

EXPERIMENT 8-1

Apparatus Required

beakers, 250 ml	glass rod
burettes	pith ball, suspended by a
ebonite rod	thread from a metal stand
funnels	test-tube clamps
cat's fur	retort stand(s)
silk	

Chemicals Required

carbon disulphide
carbon tetrachloride
water

EXPERIMENT 8-2

Apparatus Required (per pair of students or per student)

Any available molecular model set, for example, the Sargent Set or Johns Glass set.

EXPERIMENT 8-3

Apparatus Required (per pair of students or per student)

5 coloured styrofoam spheres (2″)
upholstery tacks (white and black)

The five spheres represent elements from groups IIA, IIIA, IVA, VA and VIA.

EXPERIMENT 8-4

Apparatus Required (per pair of students or per student)

filter paper	funnel	filter paper
litmus paper, red and blue	graduated cylinder	funnel support
	iron ring	
burner and tubing	retort stand	
clamp	Pyrex test tubes	
test tubes	test-tube rack	
evaporating dish	wire gauze	
dropping bottles		

Chemicals Required

dilute aqueous ammonia solution

dilute hydrochloric acid (1:3)

chromium (III) sulphate solution (0.1 mole l^{-1})

hydrogen peroxide solution (3%)

dilute nitric acid (1:4)

potassium nitrate (solid)

sodium hydroxide (pellets)

dilute sulphuric acid (1:6)

sodium hydroxide of solution
   (6 mole 1^{-1})

potassium iodide solution
   (0.2 mole 1^{-1})

potassium permanganate solution
   (0.1 mole 1^{-1})

starch suspension

iron (II) sulphate (solid)

potassium ferricyanide solution
   (0.1 mole 1^{-1})

potassium thiocyanate solution
   (0.2 mole 1^{-1})

iron (III) chloride (solid)

powdered iron

iron (III) oxide (solid)

chlorine water, Cl_2(soln)

dilute iron (III) chloride solution
   (0.1 mole 1^{-1})

dilute tin (II) chloride solution
   (0.1 mole 1^{-1})

zinc (powdered)

dilute sodium hydroxide solution (0.1 mole 1^{-1})

dilute iron (II) ammonium sulphate solution

dilute iron (II) sulphate solution (freshly prepared)   either (0.1 mole 1^{-1})

dilute iron (II) chloride solution (freshly prepared, 0.1 mole 1^{-1})

Note: *In some cases solutions may be prepared before the laboratory period or left for students to prepare as they go along.*

Procedure 5

Part I   Chromium, Cr

This procedure to convert chromium (III) to chromium (II) does not produce positive results. Chromium (II), Cr^{2+}, is a very strong reducing agent. It is rapidly oxidized in air and will slowly liberate hydrogen from water. It is recommended that this part of the experiment be performed, even though it does not produce positive results. The question can be left with the student as to why. Hopefully, this will emphasize the instability of the chromium (II) oxidation state.

An Alternate Procedure

This procedure is somewhat more complicated but will, if carefully carried out, produce positive results.

The steps in the procedure are as follows:

1. Weigh out 1 g of potassium dichromate ($K_2Cr_2O_7$) and 5 g of granulated zinc on a triple-beam balance.

2. Place these chemicals in an Erlenmeyer flask with 10 ml of water. Shake the flask to dissolve the dichromate.

3. Also place 10 g of sodium acetate in a 150 ml beaker.

4. Prepare a funnel, for use in the filtration process to follow, by placing a small plug of glass wool in it.

5. To the dichromate-zinc mixture, carefully add in small portions, 20 ml of concentrated hydrochloric acid. Shake between each addition.

6. Carefully observe all colour changes that occur.

7. When the solution becomes pale blue in colour, filter it immediately through the glass wool into the beaker containing the sodium acetate.

8. Stir the contents of the beaker for a few minutes to complete the precipitation of chromium (II) acetate.

9. Filter off the precipitate and wash with a little dilute hydrochloric acid.

10. Leave the precipitate exposed to air for a period of time and carefully observe any colour changes that occur.

EXPERIMENT 9-1

Apparatus Required (per pair of students or per student)

Number 00 porcelain crucible
clay triangle
tongs
wire gauze
tripod or retort stand with iron ring
centigram balance
burner
flint lighter

Chemicals Required

lead foil
powdered sulphur

EXPERIMENT 10-1

Apparatus Required (per pair of students or per student)

For Parts I and II

styrofoam spheres: 36 × 2-inch
13 × 1-inch (coloured)
13 × ¾-inch (coloured)
Toothpicks or pipestem cleaners (short lengths)

For Part III

styrofoam spheres: 40 × ¾-inch (black)
connectors:

72 long

toothpicks or pipestem cleaners

72 short

EXPERIMENT 10-2

Apparatus Required (per pair of students or per student)

asbestos square
platform balance
250 ml beaker
burner and tubing
test-tube clamp
evaporating dish
funnel
filter paper

graduated cylinder
hand lens or binocular microscope
mortar and pestle
iron ring
retort stand
Pyrex test tube
glass rod

Chemicals Required

carbon disulphide
flowers of sulphur

roll sulphur
zinc dust

Suggestion

To avoid getting hot sulphur spilled on the laboratory desk top, a large square of asbestos paper may be used to cover it temporarily. Any burning sulphur that may drop on the paper can be extinguished by pouring a little cold water on it.

Due to the difficulty involved in cleaning test tubes containing sulphur, it is best to exchange clean test tubes for the ones used in this experiment and save the sulphur-coated ones for use with other classes and with classes the following year.

EXPERIMENT 10-3

Apparatus Required (per pair of students or per student)

evaporating dish
burner
wire gauze
graduated cylinder
test tubes

medicine dropper
beaker
electrical conductivity apparatus (demonstration only)

Chemicals Required

potassium iodide	sodium
paradichlorobenzene	calcium all of or one of
silicon dioxide	aluminum
iron (II) sulphate	
dilute sulphuric acid solution (2M)	
potassium permanganate solution (0.05M)	
oxalic acid	
benzene	

Suggestions

1. Have the first class that does the experiment put paradichlorobenzene crystals in clean test tubes for procedure 3 of Part I. After completing the procedure, make no attempt to clean out the paradichlorobenzene but use these same test tubes in subsequent classes. The same paradichlorobenzene and test tubes can be stored in a closed container for use the following year.

2. A convenient method to avoid the hazards of pouring benzene and, at the same time, cut down on the fumes in the laboratory, is to supply the student with stoppered test tubes containing benzene. One test tube containing about 2 ml of benzene should be supplied to each student for each material whose solubility is to be tested (procedure 5 of Part I). Adequate instructions should be given as to disposing of the benzene after the procedure.

3. Specific instructions must be given for disposal of some of the substances used in this experiment (for example, those in Part I, procedure 3).

4. The electrodes of the conductivity apparatus must be hot when dipped into molten potassium iodide. If this precaution is not taken, the potassium iodide will solidify on the electrodes and prevent the conduction of current.

EXPERIMENT 10-4

Apparatus Required (per pair of students or per student)

styrofoam (or polystyrene) spheres:
    27 1-inch spheres
    14 2-inch spheres
toothpicks (or short lengths of pipestem cleaners)

EXPERIMENT 11-1

Apparatus Required (per pair of students or per student)

    Boyle's law apparatus
    masses (700 to 900 g) or similar textbooks

EXPERIMENT 11-2

Apparatus Required (per pair of students or per student)

    Charles' law apparatus (including metric scale)
    2-litre beaker (something deep enough to immerse the apparatus)
    thermometers ($-10°C$ to $110°C$)
    burner or hot plate (hot plate preferable)
    stirring rods (glass)

Chemicals Required

    ice

EXPERIMENT 11-3

Apparatus Required (per pair of students or per student)

    Metal sphere with attached pressure gauge to examine the
        P-T relationship
    bicycle pump (1 only for class)
    thermometer ($-10°C$ to $110°C$)
    alcohol thermometer ($-80°C$ to $10°C$)
    hot plate (or burner)
    3 2-litre beaker (or pail)
    stirring rod (glass)
    dewar flask (possibly)

Chemicals Required

    ice
    dry ice, $CO_2(s)$
    alcohol (denatured ethyl or methyl hydrate)

EXPERIMENT 11-4

Apparatus Required (per pair of students or per student)

Exelo gas syringe apparatus including: 3-way stopcock
   2 syringes
   connecting tubing

large test tube and 1-hole stopper to fit
drying tube and 1-hole stopper to fit
"T" valve (2)
rubber tubing
burner
250 ml Erlenmeyer flask
#6 stopper, 2-hole
clamp
retort stand
thistle tube

Chemicals Required

concentrated aqueous ammonia solution
calcium chloride
concentrated sulphuric acid
sodium chloride
(Cylinders of the compressed gases hydrogen chloride and ammonia can
be used instead of the generators described in the experiment.)

EXPERIMENT 11-5

Apparatus Required (per pair of students or per student)

Exelo apparatus as in Experiment 11-4 with silica tube
inserted between syringes.
large test tube and 1-hole stopper to fit
drying tube and 1-hole stopper to fit
"T" valve
rubber tubing
burner (with wing top)
damp cloth

Chemicals Required

steel wool
concentrated aqueous ammonia solution

calcium chloride
cylinder of compressed nitrogen gas (possibly)
(A cylinder of compressed ammonia can be used as the source of ammonia gas).
copper (II) oxide

EXPERIMENT 11-6

Apparatus Required (per pair of students or per student)

eudiometer tube
hydrometer jar
small rubber pad
clamps lined with a flexible material (rubber)
retort stand
induction coil
connectors
switch   or Tesla Coil
3 dry cells
glass plate
splints
burner
rubber tubing

Chemicals Required

cylinder of compressed hydrogen or hydrogen generator
cylinder of compressed oxygen or oxygen generator

EXPERIMENT 11-7

Apparatus Required (per pair of students or per student)

#6 stopper, 1-hole (with groove cut in it)
plastic sandwich bag
rubber band
medicine dropper
cloth
balance (± 0.01g.) or more accurate if available
rubber tubing

beaker

thermometer (−10°C to 110°C)

barometer

large bottle (small mouth) with capacity greater than
  the volume of the plastic sandwich bag

glass plate

pneumatic trough or facsimile (sink)

graduated cylinder

Chemicals Required

cylinder of compressed oxygen

cylinder of compressed carbon dioxide

cylinder of compressed nitrogen

     helium possibly

EXPERIMENT 11-8

Apparatus Required (per pair of students or per student)

gas syringe and pinhole tube for nozzle

clamp

retort stand

rubber tubing

timer (stopwatch or sweep second hand of wrist watch)

Chemicals Required

cylinder of compressed nitrogen

cylinder of compressed hydrogen

cylinder of carbon dioxide

cylinder of oxygen

natural gas or methane

Note: *For Part II, natural gas, oxygen, or any convenient gas with a molecular weight less than 44 can be used.*

EXPERIMENT 11-9

Apparatus Required (per pair of students or per student)

glass tubing (length 30 cm, diameter 1.5 cm)

medicine droppers (2)

absorbent cotton (or combustion boats)
solid stoppers (2) to fit glass tubing
forceps
timer (stopwatch or sweep second hand on wristwatch)
metre stick

Chemicals Required

concentrated aqueous ammonia solution
concentrated hydrochloric acid

EXPERIMENT 12-1

Apparatus Required (per pair of students or per student)

400 ml beaker (2)
thermometer $-10°$ C to $110°$C (2)
burner
test tubes
clamp, test tube to retort stand
retort stand
stopwatch
iron ring
wire gauze
stirring rod

Chemicals Required

paradichlorobenzene

Note: *Rather than cleaning out the test tubes containing paradichlorobenzene, leave the material in the test tubes, store the test tubes in a
sealed container and use them from year to year. Add more paradichlorobenzene as required.*

EXPERIMENT 12-2

Apparatus Required (Demonstration Experiment)

barometer tubes (3)
cistern (large mortar)

clamp
retort stand
metre stick
thermometer ($-10°C$ to $110°C$)
condenser
rubber stoppers (2)
rubber tubing
medicine dropper (3)
funnel (possibly)

Chemicals Required

mercury
benzene
diethyl ether
source of hot and cold water

EXPERIMENT 12-3

One method:

Add two different liquids to the same barometer tube using the medicine droppers. Measure the height of the column of mercury after each liquid is added.

EXPERIMENT 13-1

Apparatus Required (per pair of students or per student)

50 ml gas measuring burette (or 50 ml volumetric burette)
rubber stopper (1-hole) to fit bottom of burette
rubber stopper (1-hole) to fit test tube (18×150 mm)
rubber tubing
glass tubing
levelling bulb
open-ended iron ring
retort stand
test tube (18×150 mm)
clamp, asbestos lined (2 or 3), test tube to retort stand,
burette to retort stand

burner
sheet of asbestos (or asbestos mat)
balance (as precise as possible)
barometer
thermometer ($-10°C$ to $110°C$)

Chemicals Required

potassium chlorate (reagent grade)

Note: *The mass of the potassium chlorate before and after heating should be determined with as accurate a balance as is available.*

The experiment can be performed using a 100 ml graduated cylinder instead of the gas measuring burette. The mass of potassium chlorate used should be adjusted to correspond to the size of the graduated cylinder. The graduated cylinder must be filled with water and inverted into a reservoir (cistern) large enough that the water levels can be adjusted appropriately when volume readings are taken.

EXPERIMENT 13-2

Apparatus Required (per pair of students or per student)

emery paper
balance
400 ml beaker
large glass cylinder
50 ml gas measuring tube
10 ml graduated cylinder
rubber stopper (1-hole) to fit gas measuring tube
clamp (rubber lined), gas measuring tube to retort stand

retort stand
barometer
thermometer ($-10°C$ to $110°C$)

Chemicals Required

magnesium ribbon
fine copper wire
hydrochloric acid solution (6M)

Note: *Alternatively, clean a length of magnesium ribbon and accurately cut this length into strips 4.5 cm long. Determine the total mass of 20 such strips then divide and determine the mass of one strip. Have all students use this same mass. This procedure saves time, and because of the uniformity of the magnesium ribbon, gives a fairly accurate mass.*

The 400 ml beaker can be eliminated from the procedure and the gas measuring tube placed directly in the large glass cylinder and clamped. However, this extra step illustrates a useful general procedure. Whenever it is impossible to adjust the water levels, the container in which a gas has been collected can be stoppered and switched to a larger reservoir (cistern).

A graduated cylinder can be substituted for the gas measuring tube. If a 50 ml cylinder is used, the quantities of magnesium and hydrochloric acid solution used remain unchanged. If a 100 ml graduated cylinder is used, these quantities should be doubled.

CAUTION: Under no circumstances should the hydrogen gas collected in this experiment be ignited.

EXPERIMENT 13-3

Apparatus Required (per pair of students or per student)

container of compressed gas (several different gases may
    be used for Part I)
Tygon tubing
balance
400 ml beaker
50 ml gas measuring tube or 100 ml graduated cylinder
rubber stopper, 1-hole, to fit gas measuring tube or 100 ml
    graduated cylinder
clamp, rubber lined (2), gas measuring tube or graduated cylinder
    to retort stand
retort stand
gas-collecting tip   barometer
large glass cylinder   thermometer ($-10°C$ to $110°C$)

Chemicals Required

container of compressed gas (several different gases may be used)

Note: *The small containers of compressed gas used to fill butane lighters are suitable for this experiment. There is considerable variation in the purity of the "butane" in these containers. This has no bearing on Part I of this experiment since the purpose is to demonstrate a method by which molecular weights of gases can be determined. However, the purity of this butane has considerable bearing on Part II of the experiment. The percentages given ideally refer to butane. It is wise to check the molecular weight of the compressed gas before assigning Part II.*

Again, if gas measuring tubes are not available, a 100 ml graduated cylinder works well for this experiment.

EXPERIMENT 13-4

Apparatus Required (per pair of students or per student)

retort stand
iron ring
crucible
clay triangle
balance
burner
desiccator and desiccant (possibly)
crucible tongs

Chemicals Required

Any of the following hydrates:

barium chloride dihydrate	$BaCl_2 \cdot 2H_2O$
copper (II) sulphate pentahydrate	$CuSO_4 \cdot 5H_2O$
magnesium sulphate heptahydrate	$MgSO_4 \cdot 7H_2O$
manganese (II) sulphate monohydrate	$MnSO_4 \cdot H_2O$
sodium carbonate monohydrate	$Na_2CO_3 \cdot H_2O$

EXPERIMENT 14-1

Apparatus Required (per pair of students or per student)

test tubes
balance (± 0.01 g minimum)
vial (to hold 3 to 5 g of silver nitrate)
beaker, 250 ml (2)
glass stirring rod
watch glass
wash bottle (for distilled water)
drying facilities (heatlamps, drying oven or sand bath)

Chemicals Required

(distilled water must be used in this experiment)
silver nitrate solid
silver nitrate solution (0.2M $AgNO_3$)
copper strip (each strip 0.5 cm $\times$ 5 cm)
copper wire, #16, bare (30 cm per pair of students or per student)

EXPERIMENT 14-2

This experiment is most effective when students work individually rather than in pairs.

Apparatus Required (for each student)

filter paper (preferably quantitative grade)
balance (± 0.01 g)
100 ml beaker
25 or 50 ml graduated cylinder
hot plate
stirring rod
funnel
250 ml beaker
funnel holder   or 400 ml beaker and clay triangle
wash bottle for distilled water
facilities for drying the precipitate would be an advantage but are
    probably not essential
grease pencils

Chemicals Required

distilled water
lead (II) nitrate (reagent grade)
sodium iodide (reagent grade)

EXPERIMENT 15-1

Apparatus Required (per pair of students or per student)

test tubes (large and small)
splints
burner
barometer
thermometer ($-10°C$ to
    $110°C$)
funnel
funnel support
filter paper
drying oven (possibly)
spatula
balance

retort stand
thistle tube
250 ml Erlenmeyer flask
clamp, flask to retort stand
rubber stopper, 2-hole to fit
    250 ml flask
250 ml beaker
25 ml graduated cylinder
pneumatic trough
250 ml wide-mouth bottle (5)
(that is gas collecting bottle)
glass plate (5)

rubber stopper, 1-hole to fit
   large test tube
glass tubing
rubber tubing
clamp, test tube to retort stand

gas-collecting tip
emery paper
crucible tongs
deflagrating spoon (2)

Chemicals Required

potassium chlorate
manganese dioxide
hot water
potassium nitrate
5% hydrogen peroxide
   solution
sodium peroxide
distilled water

magnesium ribbon
wood charcoal
red phosphorus
asbestos fibres
roll sulphur
boron trioxide
bromthymol blue
steel wool

Procedure

Part II   Section 2

The teacher should either test the purity of the manganese dioxide in this mixture himself or have his students test it prior to using it in the preparation of oxygen (as described in steps three and four of this procedure).

The purity of the manganese dioxide may be tested by heating a small quantity of the mixture in an open test tube or evaporating dish. Any evidence of sparking, at temperatures below the melting point of potassium chlorate and prior to any local melting and sparking that may occur in the mixture due to the exothermic nature of this reaction, is indicative of the presence of reducing impurities in the manganese dioxide.

Such mixtures should be discarded. Manganese dioxide containing powdered carbon or some other reducing agent as an impurity usually explodes violently on heating with potassium chlorate. Many serious accidents (some fatal) have been caused in this way. Powdered carbon should never be stored close to manganese dioxide in the chemical laboratory.

EXPERIMENT 15-2

Apparatus Required (per pair of students or per student)

test tube (18 × 150 mm) (2)
balance
250 ml beaker (2)

small tin can, open at one end, two
holes punched in sides (Figure
E-89)

thermometer (−10°C to
110°C)
burner
test-tube holder
stirring rod (2)

large tin can, open at both ends
lid of tin can
iron ring
retort stand
wire gauze

Note: students supply

1) *large fruit juice can, both ends removed, openings for air around base*

2) *smaller can (10 to 17 oz), open at one end, two holes opposite one another at open end just below the rim.*

Chemicals Required

paraffin wax
candle

matches, to ignite candle
ice (possibly)

Note: Instead of using the tare described in Part I, procedure 2, a set of test tubes can be numbered and the mass of each determined and recorded. The 10 g of paraffin can now be added to each test tube and left there from class to class. Given the mass of the empty test tube from this record, students can calculate the mass of paraffin involved in the solidification process.

EXPERIMENT 15-3

Apparatus Required (per pair of students or per student)

styrofoam cup (calorimeter)
thermometer (−10°C to
110°C)

250 ml beaker
balance
glass stirring rod

Chemicals Required

hydrochloric acid solution (1.00 M)
magnesium oxide
magnesium metal

EXPERIMENT 16-1

Apparatus Required (per pair of students or per student)

pyrex test tube, 18×150 mm (2)
rubber stopper, 2-hole, to fit
test tube

250 ml Erlenmeyer flask
clamp, Erlenmeyer flask to retort
stand

glass tubing
clamp, test tube to retort stand
retort stand(s)
burner
rubber connecting tubing
drying tube
stopper, 1-hole, to fit drying
   tube
clamp, drying tube to retort
   stand

thistle tube
rubber stopper, 2-hole, to fit
   Erlenmeyer flask
cloth
test-tube holder
splints
balance
explosion shield (2)

Chemicals Required

metal oxide such as copper
   (II) oxide
zinc (mossy)
dilute hydrochloric acid
   solution

calcium chloride (anhydrous),
   for drying tube
cylinder of compressed hydrogen
   gas (alternate)
copper (II) sulphate solution, 0.1M

EXPERIMENT 16-2

Apparatus Required (per pair of students or per student)

test tubes
burner
test-tube rack
balance
iron crucible

triangle
iron ring
retort stand
large container of sand

Chemicals Required

distilled water
Solutions
hydrochloric acid
copper (II) chloride
aluminum (III) chloride
silver nitrate

steel wool
wooden splints

―――――――

Metal Samples
sodium
calcium
magnesium
aluminum
zinc
iron
lead
mercury (liquid)
copper

iron (III) oxide
ferroso-ferric oxide   alternatives
aluminum, powdered
potassium chlorate
magnesium ribbon

EXPERIMENT 17-1

Apparatus Required (per pair of students or per student)

test-tubes, 18 × 150 mm   mortar and pestle
   (several)   burner
solid stoppers, to fit test tubes spatula or splint (2)
test tube rack

Chemicals Required

sodium chloride (powder)   copper (II) sulphate pentahydrate
potassium chromate (powder)   distilled water
calcium hyroxide (powder)   methanol
glycerol   iodine
carbon tetrachloride   potassium permanganate
ginger ale (colourless bottle)

EXPERIMENT 17-2

Apparatus Required (per pair of students or per student)

10 ml transfer pipette   test-tube holder
   (or burette)   test-tube rack
large test tube   evaporating dish
balance   wire gauze
burner   iron ring
thermometer (− 10°C to   retort stand
   110°C)

Chemicals Required

distilled water
potassium nitrate
lead (II) nitrate

EXPERIMENT 17-3

Apparatus Required (per pair of students or per student)

conductivity apparatus, see description with experiment
2 oz wide mouth bottles
crucible (2)
wire gauze
iron ring
retort stand
burner

Chemicals Required

copper wire, or any metal wire
strips of copper or other metals
(alternative to wire)
distilled water
benzene
silver nitrate
silver chloride

sucrose
sodium chloride
silver nitrate solution, aqueous
silver chloride solution, aqueous
sucrose solution, aqueous
solution of benzene and sucrose

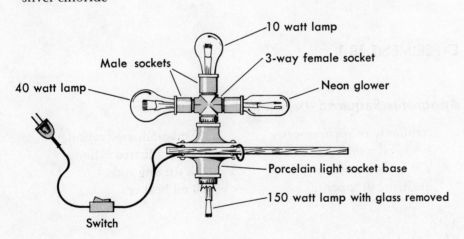

The demonstration apparatus shown permits testing a wide range of conductivities. Two porcelain receptacles are mounted back to back on a piece of plywood (shaped like a ping pong paddle) to permit the apparatus to be mounted on a ring stand or held by hand. The conducting wires are those which held the filament in a broken 150-250 W lamp. The wiring is done as shown in the diagram.

CAUTION: To avoid an electric shock, always turn off the switch or pull the plug while rinsing the electrodes or changing the solutions.

EXPERIMENT 17-4

Apparatus Required (per pair of students or per student)

balance
250 ml beaker (or 100 ml beaker)
pipette, 25 ml
burette, 50 ml   alternatives
stirring rod
graduated cylinder, 100 ml
graduated cylinder, 50 ml

evaporating dish
burner
iron ring
wire gauze
retort stand
barometer
thermometer ($-10°C$ to $110°C$)

Chemicals Required

distilled water
calcium chloride
large and small pieces of copper metal (or some other metal)

EXPERIMENT 18-1

Apparatus Required (Demonstration Experiment)

conductivity apparatus (see Experiment 17-3)
250 ml beaker (many)
medicine dropper (2)

100 ml graduated cylinder
10 ml graduated cylinder
glass stirring rod
500 ml beaker

Chemicals Required

glacial acetic acid
distilled water
alcohol
benzene
oxalic acid
benzoic acid   solids
sodium hydroxide
dry hydrogen chloride
ammonia   gases

oxalic acid
benzoic acid
sodium hydroxide
acetic acid
hydrochloric acid
ammonia
    solutions of the same concentration
sodium chloride solution (0.1 M)

EXPERIMENT 18-2

Apparatus Required (Demonstration Experiment)

50 ml beaker, *Pyrex*
burner, asbestos pad beneath it
wire gauze
iron ring
retort stand
insulated connecting wires

6 to 12 volt DC source
switch
6-volt DC bulb and socket
2 carbon rods (electrodes)
flint lighter

Chemicals Required

lead (II) bromide

Apparatus Required for Alternate Procedure
(Demonstration Experiment)

test tube (25 × 150 mm), *Pyrex*
burner
clamp, test tube to retort stand
retort stand

carbon electrodes (2) and support,
    possibly a cork or stopper
6-volt bulb and holder
6-volt DC source
wire connectors

Chemicals Required (same as above)

Note: The lead (II) bromide used in this experiment must be of a high quality. If it is not, a large amount of bromine will be given off when the solid is melted. The lead (II) bromide must not contain nitrate.

Although the lead (II) bromide is expensive, only a small amount is required for the experiment and this can be re-used many times.

Lead (II) iodide can also be used for this experiment but is more expensive.

Source of lead (II) bromide: K & K Laboratories Inc.

        121 Express St., Engineer's Hill
        Plainview, New York, 11803.

EXPERIMENT 18-3

Apparatus Required (per pair of students or per student)

electrolysis apparatus consisting of:
    container for solution
    platinum electrodes (2)
    carbon electrodes (2), pencil lead will work   alternatives
    copper electrodes (2)
    test tubes, into which electrodes can be fitted (2)

insulated connecting wires
DC source, dry cells, storage battery or power supply
glass marking pencil (grease pencil)
25 ml graduated cylinder

OR

Hoffman apparatus with appropriate electrodes and 2 test tubes
250 ml beaker
burner
flint lighter
retort stand
clamp, test tube to retort stand (2)
wooden splints

Chemicals Required

distilled water
1M hydrochloric acid solution
1M copper (II) sulphate solution
1M sulphuric acid solution
1M sodium hydroxide solution
0.1M sodium chloride solution
6M sodium chloride solution
neutral bromthymol blue or neutral litmus solution
litmus paper, red and blue

EXPERIMENT 18-4

Apparatus Required (per pair of students or per student)

test tubes: 15 × 180mm	test-tube holder
13 × 100mm	thermometer (−10°C to 110°C)
glass stirring rods	rubber stopper, 1-hole, to fit test
watch glasses or spot plates	tube
burner	glass tubing
flint lighter	rubber tubing

Chemicals Required

litmus paper, red and blue	hydrochloric acid solution
neutral bromthymol blue solution	phosphoric acid solution
	nitric acid solution
methyl orange solution	sodium hydroxide solution

phenolphthalein solution
distilled water
magnesium metal (ribbon)
iron metal
copper (II) oxide
sodium hydrogen carbonate
magnesium hydroxide
calcium hydroxide solution
sulphuric acid solution

potassium hydroxide solution
aqueous ammonia solution
sodium chloride solution
sodium carbonate solution
sodium nitrate solution
potassium bromide solution
iron (III) chloride solution
copper (II) sulphate solution
potassium phosphate solution

EXPERIMENT 18-5

Apparatus Required (per pair of students or per student)

250 ml beaker
colour chart (for universal
   indicator)
glass stirring rods

10 ml graduated cylinder
50 ml graduated cylinder
test tubes, 13×100 mm (10)
test-tube rack

Chemicals Required

universal indicator
hydrochloric acid solution,
   0.1M
acetic acid solution, 0.1M
phosphoric acid solution, 0.1M
sodium hydroxide solution,
   0.1M
aqueous ammonia solution,
   0.1M

sodium chloride solution, 0.1M
sodium carbonate solution, 0.1M
sodium hydrogen carbonate
   solution, 0.1M
ammonium acetate solution, 0.1M
distilled water for dilution and for
   all solutions

EXPERIMENT 18-6

Apparatus Required (per pair of students or per student)

evaporating dish
thermometer ($-10°C$ to $110°C$)
10 ml graduated pipette
glass stirring rod
clay triangle

retort stand
burner
flint lighter
iron ring

Chemicals Required

phenolphthalein indicator solution
sodium hydroxide solution, 0.1M
hydrochloric acid solution, 0.1M

EXPERIMENT 18-7

Apparatus Required (for each student). Have students work individually rather than in pairs.

long-handled wire brush, to clean burettes
burette (2)
burette clamp
retort stand
Erlenmeyer flask
beaker
test tubes
piece of white paper

Chemicals Required

synthetic detergent
distilled water
0.1M sodium hydroxide solution
hydrochloric acid solution of unknown concentration
phenolphthalein indicator solution

EXPERIMENT 18-8

Apparatus Required (per pair of students or per student)

150 ml beakers
13×100 mm test tubes
rubber stoppers, to fit test
   tubes

wooden splints
burner
test tube rack
$8'' \times 1''$ test tubes

Chemicals Required

magnesium metal
zinc metal
iron metal (wire)
lead foil
copper foil
silver foil (a silver coin)
solid iron (II) sulphide

0.5M solutions of
   potassium iodide
   lead nitrate
1M solution of hydrochloric acid
6M solution of copper (II) chloride
12M solution of hydrochloric acid
concentrated (18M) sulphuric acid

solid calcium carbonate

distilled water
carbon tetrachloride

0.1M solutions of

zinc nitrate
lead (II) nitrate
copper (II) nitrate
silver nitrate
barium nitrate
sulphuric acid
sodium sulphide

copper (II) chloride
potassium permanganate
potassium chloride
calcium chloride
magnesium nitrate
iron (II) nitrate
hydrochloric acid

EXPERIMENT 18-9

Apparatus Required (per pair of students or per student)

balance
250 ml Erlenmeyer flask
100 ml graduated cylinder
thermometer ($-10°C$ to $110°C$)

piece of smooth paper
250 ml beaker (2)
glass stirring rod

Chemicals Required

sodium hydroxide (pellets)
hydrochloric acid solution (0.5M)
sodium hydroxide solution (0.5M)
hydrochloric acid solution (0.25M)

EXPERIMENT 18-10

Apparatus Required (per pair of students or per student)

250 ml beaker
400 ml beaker
insulating material (newspaper, woodshaving, etc.)
100 ml graduated cylinder (2)
thermometer ($-10°C$ to $110°C$)

stirring rod
balance

Chemicals Required

1.5M aqueous ammonia solution
1.5M hydrochloric acid solution
distilled water
ammonium chloride (reagent grade)

Note: Another effective way of constructing a simple calorimeter is to set a 250 ml beaker into styrofoam.

Note: *In recent years much concern has been expressed about the use of mercury and its compounds for experimental work because mercury is so toxic. For this reason, you may prefer not to use mercury (II)-oxide in experiment 2-4. Silver oxide, Ag_2O, may be successfully substituted for mercury (II) oxide. The silver oxide is somewhat more expensive but it is much safer to use. Also, the silver oxide can be recovered and used over again from year to year.*

The recovery is carried out as follows:

1. *dissolve the silver in nitric acid*
2. *precipitate the silver as silver hydroxide with 50% by mass, carbonate-free sodium hydroxide*
3. *filter the mixture using either a fritted glass crucible or a Buchner funnel with an asbestos filter mat, filter flask and vacuum*
4. *thoroughly wash the precipitate with distilled water*
5. *transfer the precipitate to a dry watch glass and dry it in an oven at 100°C*
6. *store the dry silver oxide in a tightly stoppered amber glass bottle.*

Bromine may be safely stored and generated in a controlled fashion using "Brom saf". This solid mixture consists of bromine adsorbed on carbon. The bromine is liberated either by the addition of a suitable solvent or thermally. It is available from Fisher Scientific Company of Canada Limited at a cost of approximately $12.00 a pound.

Carbon tetrachloride is an extremely hazardous solvent. Its use should be avoided as far as possible. A suitable substitute for carbon tetrachloride as a solvent is the refrigerent Freon 113(trichlorotri-fluroethane,CCl_3CF_3). This solvent is available from any refrigeration service company at a cost of approximately $1.00 a pound. It has the odour of carbon tetrachloride, very nearly the same specific gravity, and it is non-flammable and non-toxic.

REFERENCES

1. Metcalfe, Williams, Castka, *Laboratory Experiments in Chemistry* (3rd edition), Holt, Rinehart and Winston, Incorporated, 1966.

2. Kolthoff and Sandell, *Textbook of Quantitative Inorganic Analysis* (3rd edition), The MacMillan Company, 1964.

3. Eblin P. E., *Chemistry: A Survey of Laboratory Techniques and Procedures* (1st edition), Harcourt, Brace and World, Incorporated, 1968.

4. Sienko and Plane, *Experimental Chemistry* (3rd edition), McGraw-Hill Book Company, Incorporated, 1966.

5. Neuzil, *Introduction to Modern Chemistry* (1st edition), Harcourt, Brace and World, Incorporated, 1968.

6. *Chemical Bond Approach Project, Investigating Chemical Systems* (1st edition), McGraw-Hill Book Company, Incorporated, 1963.

7. Garrett, Sisler, Bonk, Stonfer, *Semimicro Qualitative Analysis* (3rd edition), Blaisdell Publishing Company, 1966.

8. DeBruyne, Kirk, Beers, *Semimicro Chemistry* (2nd edition), Holt, Rinehart and Winston, Incorporated, 1962.

9. Motherwell and Bullock, *The Essentials of Chemistry in the Laboratory* (Teacher's Edition), Clarke, Irwin and Company Limited, Toronto, 1957.

10. Manufacturing Chemist's Association, Incorporated, *Scientific Experiments in Chemistry* (Student book), Holt, Rinehart and Winston, Incorporated, 1962.

11. Lee and Van Orden, *Laboratory Manual for General Chemistry* (1st edition), W. B. Saunders Company, 1960.

12. Quam, *Safety Practice for Chemical Laboratories* (1st edition), Villanova Press, 1963.

13. Fisher Scientific Company of Canada Limited, *Handbook of Laboratory Safety*, 1969.

14. *Nuffield Chemistry Project*, Longmans Canada Limited, 1967

15. Brownlee, Fuller, Whitsit, *Laboratory Experiments in Chemistry*, Allyn and Bacon.

16. Chemical Educational Material Study, *Chemistry an Experimental Science Laboratory Manual*, W. H. Freeman and Company Cooperating Publishers, 1963

17. Toon and Ellis, *Laboratory Experiments for Foundations of Chemistry*, Holt, Rinehart and Winston, Inc. 1968

18. Franz and Malm, *Essentials of Chemistry in the Laboratory*, W. H. Freeman and Company

19. Greenstone, *Concepts in Chemistry Laboratory Manual*, Harcourt, Brace and World, Incorporated

20. Sisler, Stewart, Lippincott, *A Systematic Laboratory Course in General Chemistry*, The MacMillan Company

21. Teeter and Westwater, *Chemistry a Science Laboratory Manual*, McGraw-Hill Book Company Incorporated, 1966

22. Motherwell and Young, *The Elements of Chemistry in the Laboratory*, Clark Irwin and Company Limited, 1959

23. O'Conner, Davis, Haenisch, MacNab, McClellan, *Experiments and Principles in the Laboratory*, D. C. Heath Company Limited, 1968

24. Lorimer and Willis, *First Year Chemistry Laboratory Manual*, Chemistry Department, University of Western Ontario

25. Freisen, et al., *Chemistry Laboratory Manual (first year)*, Chemistry Department, University of Waterloo

26. Page, Allen, Bonnyman, Talesnick, *Chemistry An Introductory Study*, W. J. Gage Limited, 1967

27. Onyszchuk, *M. Stereochemistry Parts 1 and 2*, Canadian Chemical Education, The Chemical Institute of Canada, April and October 1968.

IV Appendices

APPENDIX I

Conversion Factors

1 metre (m) = 100 centimetre = 1000 millimetre = 39.370 inch
1 centimetre (cm) = 10 millimetre (mm) = 0.39370 inch
1 Ångstrom (Å) = 10^{-8} centimetre
1 micron (μ) = 10^{-3} millimetre
1 kilogram (kg) = 1000 gram = 2.2046 pound
1 gram (g) = 1000 milligram (mg)
1 ounce = 28.350 g
1 pound = 453.59 g
1 atomic mass unit (a.m.u.) = 1.6604 $\times$ 10^{-24} g
1 ml = 1.000027 cubic centimetre (cc)
1 litre (l) = 1000 millilitre (ml) = 1.0567 quart
1 gallon (gal) = 3.7854 litre
1 cubic inch (in³) = 16.387 ml
1 cubic foot (ft³) = 28,317 ml
1 electron volt (ev) = 1.6021 $\times$ 10^{-12} erg = 23.061 kcal mole^{-1}
1 calorie (cal) = 4.1840 $\times$ 10^7 erg
1 joule = 10^7 erg
1 litre-atmosphere = 24.217 calorie   Avogadro's number = 6.0235 $\times$ 10^{23}
°C = $\frac{5}{9}$ (°F — 32)
°K = °C + 273
1 mm Hg(torr) = 0.019337 lb in^{-2}
1 lb in^{-2} = 51.715 mm Hg
1 standard atmosphere (atm) = 760 mm Hg = 13.5 $\times$ 760 mm H_2O

APPENDIX II

Solubility of Gases in Water

Volume of gas (reduced to STP) that can be dissolved in 1 volume of water

Gas	0°C	10°C	20°C
air	0.0292	0.0228	0.0187
ammonia	1298.9	910.4	710.6
carbon dioxide	1.713	1.194	0.878
chlorine	4.54	3.148	2.299
hydrogen	0.0215	0.0196	0.0182
hydrogen chloride	506.7	473.9	442.0
hydrogen sulphide	4.670	3.399	2.582
nitrogen	0.0235	0.0186	0.0155
oxygen	0.0489	0.0380	0.0310
sulphur dioxide	79.79	56.65	39.37

APPENDIX III

Common Ions and Their Charges

Name	Symbol	Charge	Name	Symbol	Charge
aluminum	Al^{3+}	3+	lead(II)	Pb^{2+}	2+
ammonium	NH_4^+	1+	magnesium	Mg^{2+}	2+
barium	Ba^{2+}	2+	mercury(I)	Hg_2^{++}	1+
calcium	Ca^{2+}	2+	mercury(II)	Hg^{2+}	2+
chromium(III)	Cr^{3+}	3+	nickel(II)	Ni^{2+}	2+
cobalt(II)	Co^{2+}	2+	potassium	K^+	1+
copper(I)	Cu^+	1+	silver	Ag^+	1+
copper(II)	Cu^{2+}	2+	sodium	Na^+	1+
hydronium	H_3O^+	1+	tin(II)	Sn^{2+}	2+
iron(II)	Fe^{2+}	2+	tin(IV)	Sn^{4+}	4+
iron(III)	Fe^{3+}	3+	zinc	Zn^{2+}	2+
acetate	$C_2H_3O_2^-$	1−	hydroxide	OH^-	1−
bromide	Br^-	1−	hypochlorite	ClO^-	1−
carbonate	CO_3^{2-}	2−	iodide	I^-	1−
chlorate	ClO_3^-	1−	nitrate	NO_3^-	1−
chloride	Cl^-	1−	nitrite	NO_2^-	1−
chromate	CrO_4^{2-}	2−	oxide	O^{2-}	2−
fluoride	F^-	1−	permanganate	MnO_4^-	1−
hexacyanoferrate(II)	$Fe(CN)_6^{4-}$	4−	peroxide	O_2^{2-}	2−
hexacyanoferrate(III)	$Fe(CN)_6^{3-}$	3−	phosphate	PO_4^{3-}	3−
hydride	H^-	1−	sulphate	SO_4^{2-}	2−
hydrogen carbonate	HCO_3^-	1−	sulphide	S^{2-}	2−
hydrogen sulphate	HSO_4^-	1−	sulphite	SO_3^{2-}	2−

APPENDIX IV

Density and Specific Gravity of Gases

Gas	Density (g litre^{-1} at STP)	Specific Gravity (Air Standard)	Gas	Density (g litre^{-1} at STP)	Specific Gravity (Air Standard)
ammonia	0.771	0.597	hydrogen chloride	1.636	1.268
carbon dioxide	1.977	1.529	hydrogen sulphide	1.539	1.190
carbon monoxide	1.250	0.968	methane	0.714	0.554
chlorine	3.214	2.486	nitrogen	1.251	0.964
dinitrogen monoxide	1.977	1.530	nitrogen monoxide	1.340	1.037
ethyne (acetylene)	1.169	0.906	oxygen	1.429	1.105
hydrogen	0.0899	0.0695	sulphur dioxide	2.927	2.264

Principal Quantum Number	1	2		3			4				5				6				7
Orbitals	1s	2s	2p	3s	3p	3d	4s	4p	4d	4f	5s	5p	5d	5f	6s	6p	6d	6f	7s
1 hydrogen	1																		
2 helium	2																		
3 lithium	2	1																	
4 beryllium	2	2																	
5 boron	2	2	1																
6 carbon	2	2	2																
7 nitrogen	2	2	3																
8 oxygen	2	2	4																
9 fluorine	2	2	5																
10 neon	2	2	6																
11 sodium	2	2	6	1															
12 magnesium	2	2	6	2															
13 aluminum	2	2	6	2	1														
14 silicon	2	2	6	2	2														
15 phosphorus	2	2	6	2	3														
16 sulphur	2	2	6	2	4														
17 chlorine	2	2	6	2	5														
18 argon	2	2	6	2	6														
19 potassium	2	2	6	2	6		1												
20 calcium	2	2	6	2	6		2												
21 scandium	2	2	6	2	6	1	2												
22 titanium	2	2	6	2	6	2	2												
23 vanadium	2	2	6	2	6	3	2												
24 chromium	2	2	6	2	6	5	1												
25 manganese	2	2	6	2	6	5	2												
26 iron	2	2	6	2	6	6	2												
27 cobalt	2	2	6	2	6	7	2												
28 nickel	2	2	6	2	6	8	2												
29 copper	2	2	6	2	6	10	1												
30 zinc	2	2	6	2	6	10	2												
31 gallium	2	2	6	2	6	10	2	1											
32 germanium	2	2	6	2	6	10	2	2											
33 arsenic	2	2	6	2	6	10	2	3											
34 selenium	2	2	6	2	6	10	2	4											
35 bromine	2	2	6	2	6	10	2	5											
36 krypton	2	2	6	2	6	10	2	6											
37 rubidium	2	2	6	2	6	10	2	6			1								
38 strontium	2	2	6	2	6	10	2	6			2								
39 yttrium	2	2	6	2	6	10	2	6	1		2								
40 zirconium	2	2	6	2	6	10	2	6	2		2								
41 niobium	2	2	6	2	6	10	2	6	4		1								
42 molybdenum	2	2	6	2	6	10	2	6	5		1								
43 technetium	2	2	6	2	6	10	2	6	6		1								
43 ruthenium	2	2	6	2	6	10	2	6	7		1								
45 rhodium	2	2	6	2	6	10	2	6	8		1								
46 palladium	2	2	6	2	6	10	2	6	10										
47 silver	2	2	6	2	6	10	2	6	10		1								
48 cadmium	2	2	6	2	6	10	2	6	10		2								
49 indium	2	2	6	2	6	10	2	6	10		1	2							
50 tin	2	2	6	2	6	10	2	6	10		2	2							
51 antimony	2	2	6	2	6	10	2	6	10		2	3							
52 tellurium	2	2	6	2	6	10	2	6	10		2	4							

Electronic Configurations of the Elements (cont'd)

Principal Quantum Number	1	2		3			4				5				6				7
Orbitals	1s	2s	2p	3s	3p	3d	4s	4p	4d	4f	5s	5p	5d	5f	6s	6p	6d	6f	7s
53 iodine	2	2	6	2	6	10	2	6	10		2	5							
54 xenon	2	2	6	2	6	10	2	6	10		2	6							
55 cesium	2	2	6	2	6	10	2	6	10		2	6			1				
56 barium	2	2	6	2	6	10	2	6	10		2	6			2				
57 lanthanum	2	2	6	2	6	10	2	6	10		2	6	1		2				
58 cerium	2	2	6	2	6	10	2	6	10	2	2	6			2				
59 praseodymium	2	2	6	2	6	10	2	6	10	3	2	6			2				
60 neodymium	2	2	6	2	6	10	2	6	10	4	2	6			2				
61 promethium	2	2	6	2	6	10	2	6	10	5	2	6			2				
62 samarium	2	2	6	2	6	10	2	6	10	6	2	6			2				
63 europium	2	2	6	2	6	10	2	6	10	7	2	6			2				
64 gadolinium	2	2	6	2	6	10	2	6	10	7	2	6	1		2				
65 terbium	2	2	6	2	6	10	2	6	10	9	2	6			2				
66 dysprosium	2	2	6	2	6	10	2	6	10	10	2	6			2				
67 holmium	2	2	6	2	6	10	2	6	10	11	2	6			2				
68 erbium	2	2	6	2	6	10	2	6	10	12	2	6			2				
69 thulium	2	2	6	2	6	10	2	6	10	13	2	6			2				
70 ytterbium	2	2	6	2	6	10	2	6	10	14	2	6			2				
71 lutetium	2	2	6	2	6	10	2	6	10	14	2	6	1		2				
72 hafnium	2	2	6	2	6	10	2	6	10	14	2	6	2		2				
73 tantalum	2	2	6	2	6	10	2	6	10	14	2	6	3		2				
74 tungsten	2	2	6	2	6	10	2	6	10	14	2	6	4		2				
75 rhenium	2	2	6	2	6	10	2	6	10	14	2	6	5		2				
76 osmium	2	2	6	2	6	10	2	6	10	14	2	6	6		2				
77 iridium	2	2	6	2	6	10	2	6	10	14	2	6	9						
78 platinum	2	2	6	2	6	10	2	6	10	14	2	6	9		1				
79 gold	2	2	6	2	6	10	2	6	10	14	2	6	10		1				
80 mercury	2	2	6	2	6	10	2	6	10	14	2	6	10		2				
81 thallium	2	2	6	2	6	10	2	6	10	14	2	6	10		2	1			
82 lead	2	2	6	2	6	10	2	6	10	14	2	6	10		2	2			
83 bismuth	2	2	6	2	6	10	2	6	10	14	2	6	10		2	3			
84 polonium	2	2	6	2	6	10	2	6	10	14	2	6	10		2	4			
85 astatine	2	2	6	2	6	10	2	6	10	14	2	6	10		2	5			
86 radon	2	2	6	2	6	10	2	6	10	14	2	6	10		2	6			
87 francium	2	2	6	2	6	10	2	6	10	14	2	6	10		2	6			1
88 radium	2	2	6	2	6	10	2	6	10	14	2	6	10		2	6			2
89 actinium	2	2	6	2	6	10	2	6	10	14	2	6	10		2	6	1		2
90 thorium	2	2	6	2	6	10	2	6	10	14	2	6	10		2	6	2		2
91 protactinium	2	2	6	2	6	10	2	6	10	14	2	6	10	2	2	6	1		2
92 uranium	2	2	6	2	6	10	2	6	10	14	2	6	10	3	2	6	1		2
93 neptunium	2	2	6	2	6	10	2	6	10	14	2	6	10	5	2	6			2
94 plutonium	2	2	6	2	6	10	2	6	10	14	2	6	10	6	2	6			2
95 americium	2	2	6	2	6	10	2	6	10	14	2	6	10	7	2	6			2
96 curium	2	2	6	2	6	10	2	6	10	14	2	6	10	7	2	6	1		2
97 berkelium	2	2	6	2	6	10	2	6	10	14	2	6	10	8	2	6	1		2
98 californium	2	2	6	2	6	10	2	6	10	14	2	6	10	10	2	6			2
99 einsteinium	2	2	6	2	6	10	2	6	10	14	2	6	10	10	2	6	1		2
100 fermium	2	2	6	2	6	10	2	6	10	14	2	6	10	11	2	6	1		2
101 mendelevium	2	2	6	2	6	10	2	6	10	14	2	6	10	12	2	6	1		2
102 nobelium	2	2	6	2	6	10	2	6	10	14	2	6	10	13	2	6	1		2
103 lawrencium	2	2	6	2	6	10	2	6	10	14	2	6	10	14	2	6	1		2

APPENDIX VI

Properties of Important Elements

Name	Specific Gravity		Melting point (°C)	Boiling point (°C)	Common Oxidation Numbers
	Water Std.	Air Std.			
aluminum	2.70		660	2057	3+
antimony	6.68		631	1380	3+, 5+
arsenic	5.73		(sublimes)	(sublimes)	3+, 5+
barium	3.78		850	1140	2+
bismuth	9.75		271.3	1560	3+
boron	2.34		2300	2550 (sublimes)	3+
bromine	3.12		−7.2	58.8	1−, 5+
calcium	1.55		842	1240	2+
carbon	1.7-3.5		(sublimes above 3500° C)	4200	2+, 4+
chlorine		2.486	−101.6	−34.6	1−, 5+, 7+
chromium	7.14		1890	2482	2+, 3+, 6+
cobalt	8.90		1495	2900	2+, 3+
copper	8.9		1083	2336	1+, 2+
fluorine		1.312	−223	−187	1−
gold	19.3		1063	2600	0, 3+
hydrogen		0.0695	−259	−253	1−, 1+
iodine	4.93		113.5	184.4	1−, 5+
iron	7.86		1535	3000	2+, 3+
lead	11.34		327.5	1750	2+, 4+
magnesium	1.74		651	1107	2+
manganese	7.3		1244	2097	2+, 4+, 7+
mercury	13.55		−38.9	356.6	1+, 2+
nickel	8.90		1455	2900	2+
nitrogen		0.964	−209.9	−195.8	3−, 3+, 5+
oxygen		1.105	−218	−183	2−
phosphorus	1.8-2.3		44.1	280	3+, 5+
platinum	21.45		1769.3	3825	2+, 4+
potassium	0.86		62.3	760	1+
radium	5(?)		700	1140	2+
silicon	2.42		1420	2355	4+
silver	10.5		960.8	1950	1+
sodium	0.97		97.5	880	1+
strontium	2.54		800	1150	2+
sulphur	2.0		114.5	444.6	2−, 4+, 6+
tin	7.31		231.9	2270	2+, 4+
titanium	4.5		1677	3277(?)	3+, 4+
tungsten	19.3		3410	5927	6+
zinc	7.14		419.5	907	2+

APPENDIX VII

Vapour Pressure of Water

Temperature (°C)	Pressure (mm Hg)	
−90	0.00007	(7×10^{-5})
−80	0.0004	(4×10^{-4})
−70	0.0019	(1.9×10^{-3})
−60	0.0081	(8.1×10^{-3})
−50	0.0296	(2.96×10^{-2})
−40	0.0966	(9.66×10^{-2})
−30	0.286	(2.86×10^{-1})
−20	0.766	(7.66×10^{-1})
−10	1.95	
0	4.579	(normal melting point)
5	6.54	
10	9.21	
15	12.79	
20	17.54	
25	23.76	
30	31.82	
35	42.18	
40	55.32	
45	71.88	
50	92.51	
55	118.04	
60	149.38	
65	187.54	
70	233.7	
75	289.1	
80	355.1	
85	433.6	
90	525.76	
95	633.90	
100	760.00	(normal boiling point and definition of one atmosphere)
110	1074.6	
120	1489.1	
130	2026.2	
140	2710.9	

APPENDIX VIII

Electrochemical Series of the Metals

1. lithium $Li \rightleftharpoons Li^+ + e^-$
2. potassium $K \rightleftharpoons K^+ + e^-$
3. calcium $Ca \rightleftharpoons Ca^{2+} + 2e^-$
4. sodium $Na \rightleftharpoons Na^+ + e^-$
5. magnesium $Mg \rightleftharpoons Mg^{2+} + 2e^-$
6. aluminum $Al \rightleftharpoons Al^{3+} + 3e^-$
7. manganese $Mn \rightleftharpoons Mn^{2+} + 2e^-$
8. zinc $Zn \rightleftharpoons Zn^{2+} + 2e^-$
9. chromium $Cr \rightleftharpoons Cr^{3+} + 3e^-$
10. iron $Fe \rightleftharpoons Fe^{2+} + 2e^-$
11. cadmium $Cd \rightleftharpoons Cd^{2+} + 2e^-$
12. cobalt $Co \rightleftharpoons Co^{2+} + 2e^-$
13. nickel $Ni \rightleftharpoons Ni^{2+} + 2e^-$
14. tin $Sn \rightleftharpoons Sn^{2+} + 2e^-$
15. lead $Pb \rightleftharpoons Pb^{2+} + 2e^-$
16. hydrogen $H_2(g) \rightleftharpoons 2H^+ + 2e^-$
17. copper $Cu \rightleftharpoons Cu^{2+} + 2e^-$
18. mercury $Hg(1) \rightleftharpoons Hg^{2+} + 2e^-$
19. silver $Ag \rightleftharpoons Ag^+ + e^-$
20. platinum $Pt \rightleftharpoons Pt^{2+} + 2e^-$
21. gold $Au \rightleftharpoons Au^{3+} + 3e^-$

APPENDIX IX

Enthalpy of Formation

$\triangle H_f$ = heat of formation of the given substance from its elements. All values of $\triangle H_f$ are expressed as kcal mole^{-1} at 25° C. Negative values of $\triangle H_f$ indicate exothermic reactions. State of substance: s = solid, l = liquid, g = gaseous.

Substance	State	$\triangle H_f$	Substance	State	$\triangle H_f$
aluminum oxide	s	−399.09	iron(II, III) oxide	s	−267.0
ammonia	g	−11.04	iron(III) oxide	s	−196.5
barium sulphate	s	−350.2	lead(II) oxide	s	−52.07
benzene	g	+19.82	lead(II) nitrate	s	−107.35
benzene	l	+11.72	lead(II) sulphide	s	−22.54
calcium chloride	s	−190.0	magnesium chloride	s	−153.40
calcium hydroxide	s	−235.80	magnesium oxide	s	−143.84
calcium oxide	s	−151.9	mercury(II) chloride	s	−55.0
carbon (diamond)	s	+0.45	mercury(II) fulminate	s	+64
carbon (graphite)	s	0.00	mercury(II) nitrate	s	−93.0
carbon dioxide	g	−94.05	mercury(II) oxide	s	−21.68
carbon disulphide	g	+27.55	methane	g	−17.89
carbon disulphide	l	+21.0	nitrogen dioxide	g	+8.09
carbon monoxide	g	−26.42	nitrogen monoxide	g	+21.60
carbon tetrachloride	g	−25.5	oxygen (O$_2$)	g	0.00
carbon tetrachloride	l	−33.3	ozone (O$_3$)	g	+34.00
copper(II) nitrate	s	−73.4	potassium bromide	s	−93.73
copper(II) oxide	s	−37.1	potassium chloride	s	−104.18
copper(II) sulphate	s	−184.00	potassium hydroxide	s	−101.78
dinitrogen monoxide	g	+19.49	potassium nitrate	s	−117.76
dinitrogen pentoxide	g	+3.6	potassium sulphate	s	−342.66
dinitrogen pentoxide	s	−10.0	silver chloride	s	−30.36
dinitrogen tetroxide	g	+2.31	silver nitrate	s	−29.43
diphosphorus pentoxide	s	−360.0	silver sulphide	s	−7.60
ethyne (acetylene)	g	+54.19	sodium bromide	s	−86.03
hydrogen (H$_2$)	g	0.00	sodium chloride	s	−98.23
hydrogen bromide	g	−8.66	sodium hydroxide	s	−101.99
hydrogen chloride	g	−22.06	sodium nitrate	s	−101.54
hydrogen fluoride	g	−64.2	sodium sulphate	s	−330.90
hydrogen iodide	g	+6.20	sulphur dioxide	g	−70.96
hydrogen oxide (water)	g	−57.80	sulphur trioxide	g	−94.45
hydrogen oxide (water)	l	−68.32	tin(IV) chloride	l	−130.3
hydrogen peroxide	g	−31.83	zinc nitrate	s	−115.12
hydrogen peroxide	l	−44.84	zinc oxide	s	−83.17
hydrogen sulphide	g	−4.82	zinc sulphate	s	−233.88
iron(II) sulphate	s	−220.5	zinc sulphide	s	−14.0

APPENDIX X

Solubility and Temperature

Solubilities given in grams of anhydrous compound that can be dissolved in 100 grams of water at the indicated temperatures.

Compound	0°C	20°C	60°C	100°C
ammonium chloride	29.4	37.2	55.2	77.3
ammonium nitrate	118.3	192	421.0	871.0
barium hydroxide	1.67	3.89	20.94	101.40$^{80°}$
calcium hydroxide	0.19	0.17	0.12	0.08
calcium sulphate (gypsum)	0.18	0.19	0.20	0.16
cerium sulphate	17.35	9.16	3.73	
copper(II) sulphate	14.3	20.7	40.0	75.4
lead(II) chloride	0.67	0.99	1.98	3.34
lead(II) nitrate	38.8	56.5	95	138.8
mercury(II) chloride	3.5	6.1	14	38
potassium bromide	53.5	65.2	85.5	104.0
potassium chlorate	3.3	7.4	24.5	57.0
potassium chloride	27.6	34.0	45.5	56.7
potassium iodide	127.5	144	176	208
potassium nitrate	13.3	31.6	110.0	246.0
potassium sulphate	7.4	11.1	18.2	24.1
silver nitrate	122	222	525	952
sodium acetate	119	123.5	139.5	170
sodium chloride	35.7	36.0	37.3	39.8
sodium nitrate	73.0	88.0	124.0	180.0
sugar (sucrose)	179.2	203.9	287.3	487.2

APPENDIX XI

Enthalpy of Combustion

$\triangle H_c$ = heat of combustion of the given substance. All values of $\triangle H_c$ are expressed as kcal mole^{-1} of substance oxidized to $H_2O(l)$ and/or $CO_2(g)$ at constant pressure and 25° C. State of substance: s = solid, l = liquid, g = gaseous.

Substance	Formula	State	$\triangle H_c$
hydrogen	H_2	g	−68.52
graphite	C	s	−94.05
carbon monoxide	CO	g	−67.64
methane	CH_4	g	−212.80
ethane	C_2H_6	g	−372.82
propane	C_3H_8	g	−530.60
butane	C_4H_{10}	g	−687.98
pentane	C_5H_{12}	g	−845.16
hexane	C_6H_{14}	l	−995.01
heptane	C_7H_{16}	l	−1151.27
octane	C_8H_{18}	l	−1307.53
ethene (ethylene)	C_2H_4	g	−337.23
propene (propylene)	C_3H_6	g	−491.99
ethyne (acetylene)	C_2H_2	g	−310.62
benzene	C_6H_6	l	−780.98
toluene	C_7H_8	l	−934.50

APPENDIX XII

Solubilities

S, soluble in water. A, soluble in acids, insoluble in water. P, partially soluble in water, soluble in dilute acids. I, insoluble in dilute acids and in water. a, slightly soluble in acids, insoluble in water. d, decomposes in water.

	acetate	bromide	carbonate	chlorate	chloride	chromate	hydroxide	iodide	nitrate	oxide	phosphate	silicate	sulphate	sulphide
aluminum	S	S	—	S	S	—	A	S	S	a	A	I	S	d
ammonium	S	S	S	S	S	S	—	S	S	—	A	I	S	d
barium	S	S	P	S	S	A	S	S	S	—	A	I	a	d
calcium	S	S	P	S	S	S	S	S	S	S	P	A	a	d
copper(II)	S	S	—	S	S	—	A	—	S	A	A	A	S	P
iron(II)	S	S	P	S	S	—	A	S	S	A	A	A	S	A
iron(III)	S	S	—	S	S	A	A	S	S	A	P	—	P	d
lead(II)	S	S	A	S	S	A	P	P	S	A	A	A	P	d
magnesium	S	S	P	S	S	—	A	S	S	A	A	A	S	d
manganese(II)	S	S	P	S	S	—	A	S	S	A	A	I	S	A
mercury(I)	P	A	A	S	a	P	—	A	S	A	A	A	P	I
mercury(II)	S	S	—	S	S	P	A	P	S	A	A	—	d	I
potassium	S	S	S	S	S	S	S	S	S	S	S	—	S	S
silver	P	a	A	S	a	P	—	I	S	S	P	S	P	I
sodium	S	S	S	S	S	S	S	S	S	S	S	—	S	S
strontium	S	S	P	S	S	P	S	S	S	S	A	A	P	S
tin(II)	d	S	—	S	S	A	A	S	d	A	—	S	S	A
tin(IV)	S	S	—	—	S	S	P	d	—	A	—	—	S	A
zinc	S	S	P	S	S	P	A	S	S	A	A	A	S	A

APPENDIX XIII

Acid-Base Indicators

pH Range	Indicator	Colour Change
0.4–1.8	methyl violet	yellow-blue violet
1.2–2.8	thymol blue	red-yellow
1.2–3.8	benzopurpurin 4B	violet-red
3.1–4.9	congo red	blue-red
3.0–4.6	bromphenol blue	yellow-blue violet
3.1–4.4	methyl orange	red-yellow
4.0–5.6	bromcresol green	yellow-blue
4.4–6.2	methyl red	red-yellow
5–7	litmus	red-blue
5.2–6.8	bromcresol purple	yellow-violet
6.2–7.6	bromthymol blue	yellow-blue
6.4–8.0	phenol red	yellow-red
7.2–8.8	cresol red	yellow-red
7.4–9.0	metacresol purple	yellow-violet
8.0–9.6	thymol blue	yellow-blue
8.2–10.0	phenolphthalein	colourless-red
9.4–10.6	thymolphthalein	colourless-blue
10.0–12.0	alizarin yellow	yellow-violet
11.4–13.0	sodium indigosulphonate	blue-yellow
12.0–14.0	1, 3, 5-trinitrobenzene	colourless-orange

V INDEX